Any book which you borrow remains your responsibility until the loan slip
is cancelled

DATE DUE FOR RETURN

THE EPITOME OF
ANDREAS
VESALIUS

THE EPITOME OF
ANDREAS VESALIUS

TRANSLATED
FROM THE LATIN WITH
PREFACE AND INTRODUCTION BY
L. R. LIND

WITH ANATOMICAL NOTES BY
C. W. ASLING

FOREWORD BY
LOGAN CLENDENING

THE M.I.T. PRESS
MASSACHUSETTS INSTITUTE OF TECHNOLOGY
CAMBRIDGE, MASSACHUSETTS, AND LONDON, ENGLAND

TABLE OF CONTENTS

FOREWORD

WHEN Dr. L. R. Lind, Dr. H. C. Tracy, and Dr. C. W. Asling first came to us in the Department of the History of Medicine at the University of Kansas with the proposal to translate Vesalius into English, we were happy to be able to put our material at their service.

After careful discussion, it was generally agreed among us that the most practical plan would be to select the *Epitome* for complete translation. The *Fabrica* * by its bulk alone condemns itself, except for the hardiest and most curious scholars. What is true and sound in it has long since been incorporated in common anatomical knowledge.

Most of the mistakes have been discussed and are familiar to all who have undertaken more than a superficial review of Vesalius' place in the progress of science.

What would be useful, we all agreed, would be to place in the hands of the modern student a brief summary of what Vesalius said he was trying to do, what he found, and what he meant. Vesalius himself did this for us perfectly in the *Epitome*. Here, as Professor Lind says in the introduction, is a masterpiece of condensation. Here are the very words of the master himself, freed from controversial arguments long since outmoded. Here, indeed, is the *Epitome* of one of the greatest works on science ever to be written, one of the foundations of modern civilization.

The Department of Medical History is very proud to have had the privilege of sharing in the production of this work.

LOGAN CLENDENING
Professor of the History of Medicine

University of Kansas
November, 1944

* The *Fabrica* is now being translated by Professor J. B. deC. M. Saunders and Charles D. O'Malley.

ix

TRANSLATOR'S PREFACE

THE year 1943 marked the four-hundredth anniversary of the publication at the press of Johannes Oporinus in Basel, Switzerland, of both the *De Humani Corporis Fabrica Libri Septem* and the *Epitome* of that work. The *Epitome,* intended by Vesalius as a very brief descriptive anatomy and actually a remarkable condensation of the larger book, is here presented for the first time in a complete English translation; it has thus far been translated into no other modern tongues except German and Dutch.

The translation was begun at the suggestion of Professor H. C. Tracy, former head of the Department of Anatomy at the University of Kansas, who has served as a genial godfather to the undertaking. Doctor C. W. Asling, formerly of the Department of Anatomy, University of Kansas, has contributed the anatomical notes. I am greatly indebted to him for his patient and inspiring collaboration. It is a pleasure to acknowledge in this place the importance of his influence upon the entire book. His acute scrutiny has removed a number of errors from the translation; his concise, scholarly notes will make the text far more valuable to the medical student and historian than it might otherwise have been.

The late Logan Clendening made this translation possible by lending me his personal copy of the *Epitome* (1543); he showed a warm and generous interest in the progress of the work and was kind enough to write a Foreword for it. I deeply regret that he did not live to see the book in print. It is a great pleasure to express my appreciation to Mrs. Logan Clendening, who in pursuance of her husband's interest in the history of medicine made the publication of this book possible.

Doctor W. W. Francis, librarian of the Osler Library, McGill University, Montreal, Canada, has made several judicious suggestions from which I have profited and for which I thank him. I am indebted likewise to the kindness of Dr. Max H. Fisch, professor of philosophy at the University of

Illinois, Urbana, Illinois, for reading the manuscript and making a number of corrections.

The book has been read also by Professor J. B. deC. M. Saunders, chairman of the Divisions of Anatomy and of Medical History and Bibliography, University of California, San Francisco, California, who has helped me to avoid certain inaccuracies; for his assistance, so freely given, I am exceedingly grateful. His deep knowledge of the intricate history of sixteenth century anatomical terminology has been invaluable in setting me aright in many instances. Both he and Dr. Asling have persuaded me to use a more modern and technical phraseology throughout the translation, one more in keeping with the language now in use by the medical profession, rather than the somewhat picturesque English which Vesalius' Latin had at first tempted me to use. The difficulties involved in translating Vesalius are clearly represented by these words of Dr. Saunders in one of his letters to me. It should be remembered that they proceed from a scholar whose translations of the *Fabrica* and the *Venesection* and *China Root Epistles* of Vesalius are now eagerly awaited:

> I have never found Vesalius's style easy to handle but then neither did his contemporaries. Fabricius regarded it as difficult and Amatus Lusitanus calls it, with some justice, harsh. I seldom find a grammatical error but his Ciceronian periodic style is at times a trial and can be on occasions very obscure. This is particularly the case as he is attempting to use a technical language which is in the state of flux. I put in a long apprenticeship in developing a vocabulary of 16th century terms in medicine and have found the comparison of the Latin with the contemporary English translation of the works of Ambrose Paré most useful.

The translation has been completely rewritten in order to avoid the literalness to which both Dr. Francis and Dr. Fisch had also objected. I wish to thank Professor Henry E. Sigerist for his comments on the first sentence of Chapter I and for several encouraging letters.

Through the generous co-operation of Mr. A. Colish, and especially of Mr. Henry Schuman, to whom I am obliged for his unfailing concern and helpfulness in bringing the book to completion, I have been supplied with a photostatic copy of the contemporary (1543) German translation by Albanus Torinus, with which I have collated my translation throughout. Although I found Torinus sometimes in what I take to be error, his work cleared up several points for me—a fair exchange across four hundred years.

Dr. John F. Fulton, of the Historical Library, Yale Medical Library, has done me a signal honor in sponsoring this book as one of the Monograph Series published by the Historical Library. His constant and careful interest in the final stages of publication lays me under a debt difficult to repay.

I wish to thank both Mrs. Alta H. Lonnecker, secretary to the director of libraries, and Mrs. David D. Robb, formerly reference librarian, University of Kansas, for obtaining photostats, microfilm, and interlibrary loan books used in making the translation. To my wife, as often before, I am grateful for her capable assistance with the typing of the manuscript and the reading of the proofs.

L. R. LIND

Lawrence, Kansas
September, 1948

TRANSLATOR'S INTRODUCTION

THE LIFE AND WORK OF ANDREAS VESALIUS

I

THE echoes of the absurd quarrel between the sciences and the humanities in education still reverberate in certain quarters; but that quarrel has never had the slightest justification when the respective claims of each are considered from a historical point of view. Although Thomas Henry Huxley and Charles W. Eliot, each in his own land, fought hard to bring the sciences into the curriculum on a more equal footing with Greek and Latin, neither man wished to exclude the classical humanities in turn. They knew that in origin both forms of knowledge were embraced in the conception of the seven liberal arts; and they must have known that, in view of the basic unity of all knowledge, to speak of a "College of Liberal Arts and Sciences" was a tautological blunder.

Our age of specialization, with its urgent emphasis upon what is immediate, practical, and expedient, has been tempted in a fury of extremism to discard the classical humanities. Furthermore, while they are on the whole far more friendly to the Classics than their colleagues in certain other fields, some scientists, content to regard a moderate knowledge of French and German as exclusively sufficient for the linguistic training of their students, ignore the fact that the terminology of their sciences is predominantly Greek or Latin or both in its content. But those very scientists would be the first to recognize that an adequate understanding of the history of science is impossible without either a knowledge of Latin and Greek or the use of translations of the great books of any science written before the eighteenth century.

The best scientists of the Renaissance since Leonardo present an instructive contrast in this respect as well as in others to their modern brethren.

The former were not content to place limitations upon their own opportunities for wider knowledge with the simple excuse that there was not time for everything in a "crowded curriculum"; nor did they believe that one or two special talents, interests, studies, or languages were enough for their purposes. The scientist of that day was often an artist, a philologist, a philosopher, and a man of letters as well as a scientist. In fact, in Renaissance science, so little known to us as yet since many of its chief works, written in Latin, remain untranslated, the genuine rebirth of the ideals of classical civilization may be perceived sometimes even more clearly than in the more purely literary aspect of Renaissance culture. The Renaissance implies not only the rediscovery of Cicero but the revival of the Greek spirit of scientific inquiry in Europe. That rebirth of learning is typified in the persons of Leonardo da Vinci, Copernicus, Vesalius, and Galileo no less than in those of Petrarch and Erasmus; it has required the often neglected but patient and persistent efforts of the historian of science in our own day to bring this truth home to the modern humanist. These men of the Renaissance were profound enough to profit from, wise enough not to reject, and possessed of enough genius to build upon, the science, art, and literature of the ancient Greeks and Romans. Theirs was that marvelous unity of art, learning, and literature which has been lost in the narrow specialization of modern science; the bond which linked their common endeavors was a common understanding and respect for the tradition of ancient knowledge.

The year 1943 was the quadricentennial anniversary of two very important events in the history of science: the publication by Nikolaus Copernicus of his book *On the Motions of the Heavenly Bodies* and the publication by Andreas Vesalius of his work *On the Fabric of the Human Body*. That these two works, so far apart in subject, so close together in method and purpose, should have appeared simultaneously is not, perhaps, entirely a coincidence. Copernicus laid the foundations of modern astronomy and arrived at the true conception of the universe or the macrocosm; Vesalius, in his turn, founded modern anatomy upon a true conception of the physical microcosm, which is man. These ideas—the macrocosm and the microcosm—are among the most widely discussed in Renaissance thought; and it is no small part of the greater achievements of these scientists that they brought these ideas at last out of the vague shadow of Platonic and Aristotelian dogmatism into the clear light of scientific reality. The dignity of man, that favorite theme of Renaissance philosophers, gained further stature from the detailed scientific discoveries of the age.

Andreas Vesalius of Brussels—anatomist, surgeon, teacher, philologist, artist, philosopher, and poet—was a man worthy to be known as "un uomo universale," in the soaring Renaissance meaning of the phrase. His achievements have been heralded from his day to ours in the highest terms, although his books have been more often praised than read. He is the "founder of human anatomy"; he "has left his name on the whole fabric of the human body"; he is "the first modern anatomist to place his study on a firm foundation of observation"; his book (*De Humani Corporis Fabrica*) is "not only the foundation of modern Medicine as a science but the first positive achievement of Science itself in modern times." Sir William Osler, indeed, regarded the *Fabrica* as the greatest medical book ever written.

Vesalius was born of a long line of medical men at Brussels on December 31, 1514. His family came originally from Wesel in Cleves and preserved on its coat of arms the memory of that town by way of a pun in the shape of three weasels; these appear also in the title pages of the *Fabrica* and the *Epitome*. Vesalius' father was the personal apothecary of Charles V and followed that monarch on the latter's campaigns until his own death in 1546. After a youthful education at Brussels during which, as a sixteenth century biographer writes, he dissected mice, moles, dormice, dogs, and cats, Vesalius studied first at the University of Louvain and then at Paris from 1533 to the autumn of 1536 under Jacobus Sylvius and Johannes Guinterius, both strict Galenists in doctrine and method. Leaving a reputation for brilliance behind him in Paris, he returned to Louvain in 1536. The next year found him again in Brussels, but he soon left for Italy.

His departure from the North can probably be accounted for by the relatively greater liberality of the intellectual atmosphere in the South. Certainly in Padua he found for his pioneering efforts the sort of encouragement which was soon to spur him on to the publication of his masterpiece, the *Fabrica*. At Padua he was appointed to the chair of anatomy and surgery in the university, a post he held until 1543. He passed his doctoral examination December 6, 1537, and assumed his teaching duties the next day when not yet twenty-three years old. At Padua he freed anatomical pedagogy from much of its antiquated apparatus by dissecting in person and dispensing with the ignorant barber-surgeon and the *ostensor,* the servant whose duty was to point out the parts of the cadaver while the lecturer, at a safe distance, explained them. In his courses in anatomy he cleared away many of the errors of Galenic anatomy. At Padua the greatest period in his productive life unfolded; here at the age of twenty-eight he completed the *Fabrica,* upon which he had been working for almost five years.

After visits to Venice and Ferrara, Vesalius journeyed to Basel, where the *Fabrica* and the *Epitome* were published by Johannes Oporinus, the famous humanist printer. At Basel, while visiting friends and seeing his books through the press, he found time to prepare a skeleton which he gave to the university; it can be seen there today. In September, 1544, he had married, at Brussels, Anna van Hamme, who bore him a daughter also named Anna. Vesalius took service as a court physician with Charles V from 1544 until he became physician (1556) to Philip II, to whom Charles had turned over the throne of Spain. Vesalius remained in Spain until 1564, practicing medicine at court and preparing a work on pathological anatomy which has not survived. His stay at the Spanish court is not well described for us in the sparse biographical details we have; he seems to have been despondent and to have lost interest in his science. In 1561 he wrote his last published book, a critique of Fallopius' *Observationes Anatomicae.*

After 1561 we begin to lose sight of Vesalius. His last writing is a diagnosis and prescription, one of a number which have been preserved, written at Christmas, 1562. In the spring of 1564 he appeared at Venice on his way to the Holy Land. Three separate traditions, all untrustworthy, profess to give the reasons for this pilgrimage; the only certainties are that he embarked upon it and on his return fell ill with plague or fever and died at Zante, in Greece, where he was buried by a Venetian goldsmith who had befriended him in his last days. Moritz Roth, in his meticulously documented biography, the best single book on Vesalius, briefly records the various tales, and their sources, concerning the end of his life. Charles Kingsley has summed up the matter in a few paragraphs of an essay on Vesalius:

After eight years of court life, he resolved early in the year 1564 to go on pilgrimage to Jerusalem.

The reasons for so strange a determination are wrapped in mystery and contradiction. The common story was that he had opened a corpse to ascertain the cause of death, and that, to the horror of the bystanders, the heart was still seen to beat; that his enemies accused him to the Inquisition, and that he was condemned to death, a sentence which was commuted to that of going on pilgrimage. But here, at the very outset, accounts differ. One says that the victim was a nobleman, name not given; another that it was a lady's maid, name not given. It is most improbable, if not impossible, that Vesalius, of all men, should have mistaken a living body for a dead one; while it is most probable, on the other hand, that his medical enemies would gladly raise such a calumny against him, when he was no longer in Spain to contradict it. Meanwhile Llorente, the historian of the Inquisition, makes no mention of Vesalius having been brought before its tribunal, while he does mention Vesalius' residence at Madrid. Another story is that he went abroad to escape the bad temper of his wife; another that he wanted to enrich himself. Another story—and that not an unlikely one—is that he was jealous of the rising reputation of his pupil Fallopius, then professor of anatomy at Venice. This distinguished surgeon, as I said before, had written a book, in which he had added to Vesalius' discoveries, and corrected certain errors of his. Vesalius had answered him hastily and angrily, quoting his anatomy from memory; for, as he himself complained, he could not in Spain obtain a subject for dissection; not even, he said, a single skull. He had sent his book to Venice to be published, and he had heard, seemingly, nothing of it. He may have felt that he was falling behind in the race of science, and that it was impossible for him to carry on his studies in Madrid; and so, angry with his own laziness and luxury, he may have felt the old sacred fire flash up in him, and have determined to go to Italy and become a student and a worker once more.

This is not the proper place in which to give more than a brief summary of the achievements of Vesalius, nor will medical readers need to be reminded of their importance. Roth's treatment of this subject is practically exhaustive. The writings of Vesalius, from the early revision of Rhazes to the examination of Fallopius, are characterized by a rigorous subjection of all medical and anatomical investigation to the evidence of observation, not to the authority of books or predecessors. The establishment of human anatomy upon a scientific basis is only one of his contributions to knowledge; he wrote also, as almost the first, upon pathological and comparative anatomy and on anthropology. Anatomical instruction was completely revolutionized by Vesalius; and his use of careful illustrations is a feature in it which modern teaching owes largely to him. The numerous discoveries he made in the "fabric" (or "working": the word has functional implications as well) of the human body are not distinguished as are those of other anatomists by the attachment of his name to any specific part of the body; but his revision of anatomy included more than two hundred corrections of Galen, as he states in the preface to the *Fabrica*.

The artistic activity of Vesalius is illustrated by the *Tabulae Anatomicae* of 1538, designed by himself, as were the illustrations of the *Fabrica* and *Epitome,* but executed by his countryman, Jan Stephan van Calcar. The illustrations of his books reveal a Renaissance feeling for symbolism carried out in the smallest details. The Classical influence appears in the cupids of the wood block—illustrated initials of the chapters, the children of the Asclepiad physicians of whom he speaks in his prefaces. The plates showing the external parts of the human body follow closely the classical statues of the Venus de' Medici and the Antinoüs. The frontispiece common to both *Fabrica* and *Epitome* represents a public anatomy conducted by Vesalius. Such public dissections were often gala affairs in the Renaissance, crowded with curious spectators and sometimes attended by the great. Certainly Vesalius seems to have been in his element performing before an admiring audience.

The philosophic bent of Vesalius was chiefly Platonic as is demonstrated by frequent references to Plato and by an unusual passage of Platonic doctrine in the *Fabrica* VII, 6, at the end of his description of the human brain. His pedagogical genius is apparent on every page of his books: the clear organization of material; the style of direct address to the student; the explicit, patient, and concise description—all indicate the gifts of a great teacher. The philological scholarship of Vesalius was exercised throughout his working life by his acute criticisms of ancient and contemporary anatomical doctrine, by his revision of Rhazes, and by his critical editorial work upon the Giunta edition of Galen, where the phrase in the heading of one of the pieces he revised—*aliquot in locis recognitus*—gives only a faint idea of the true magnitude of his contribution. His efforts in poetry may be gauged by the epigram "Ad Candidum Lectorem" in the *Epistola* of· 1539 (Venesection Epistle), a competent but not inspired piece of humanist verse. His distich on the number of bones in the human body was plagiarized by several people and finally interpolated as verses 1627 and 1628 into the text of the famous

medical poem, the *Schola Salernitana* (*Regimen Sanitatis Salernitanum*);
see De Renzi, *Collectio Salernitana* V (Naples, 1859), 45:

> Adde quater denis bis centum senaque, habebis
> quam sis multiplici conditus osse, semel.

His motto, which appears beneath the 1542 portrait, was borrowed from the
prose of Celsus: *Ocyus, iucunde et tuto.*

The personality of Vesalius himself remains, in spite of much self-revela-
tion in his writings and biographical material of another nature, still largely
an enigma. His far-ranging and penetrating intellect, his marvelous skill in
controversy, his excellent Latin style, resemble those of Erasmus; indeed,
Olschki calls him "the Erasmus of medicine." The customary and conven-
tional flattery of his dedicatory prefaces does not conceal the real independence of Vesalius; he is one of the men whom the Renaissance princes
delighted to honor for their genius and sought to attach to their courts: but
he was never their vassal.

Anatomy, like astronomy, was a study always a bit suspected among
churchmen. The procurement of cadavers was often a perilous business.
Galen was the anatomical authority accepted by the Church. Yet Vesalius
revolutionized anatomy, dissected cadavers without subterfuge or reti-
cence in his public demonstrations, stole the bodies when necessary, and
showed beyond a doubt that Galen knew anatomy only from the dissection of apes, dogs, and pigs—and did not thoroughly understand even
the anatomy of these animals. The Church, nevertheless, did not lay
hands upon Vesalius. Galileo and Servetus suffered under the Inquisition, but not Vesalius.

His portrait reveals an imperious, passionately energetic and self-willed
character, confident, scornful, utterly fearless. The dark eyes, the short curly
hair and beard, are physical features which recall other Renaissance portraits,
but none perhaps is represented in so arresting an attitude as Vesalius, both
in a large woodcut at the end of the text of the *Epitome* and in the frontispiece of the *Fabrica* and *Epitome*. Here, in probably the only authentic ones
of the twelve different portraits which are preserved, Vesalius is shown as
he demonstrates his art upon a cadaver identical with Figure 24 of the

Fabrica V. All the pride of his accomplishment, the self-assurance of his swiftly won knowledge, stand forth. The motley, eager crowd; the classic dissecting theater; the naked man whom he employed when pointing out the external parts of the body; lastly, the skeleton in the center with all its grim significance—these details are symbolic of his profession and reminders to his reader of the scenes amid which he achieved such signal success in the study of the human body. To this success, modern science owes the very foundation upon which it has erected the theory and practice of present-day anatomy.

THE EPITOME

II

THE *Epitome,* completed two weeks after the *Fabrica* on August 13, 1542, was published in June, 1543, and was followed two months later by the German translation of Albanus Torinus. The Latin *Epitome* which I have used consists of fourteen folio pages measuring twenty-one by sixteen inches. It contains eleven plates made from wood blocks, showing the bones, muscles, external parts, nerves, veins, and arteries; some portions of the plates were intended to be cut out and attached to their proper places upon the drawings of the body or skeleton. These plates show the human figure about 42.5 centimeters in height, thus revealing a proportion of one-fourth natural size if we reckon the average height of men as 165 to 175 centimeters. They were very probably executed by Jan Stephan van Calcar, possibly assisted, as in the pictures for the *Fabrica,* by some unknown artist and closely supervised throughout by Vesalius himself. Van Calcar completed the early *Tabulae Anatomicae Sex* of 1538, printed in Venice; but no artist is mentioned specifically by name by Vesalius in reference to the *Fabrica* and the *Epitome.*

In an age inspired in much of its art by the conception of death, when Holbein's great pictures of the dead and dying reflect the desolation and misery of plagues and massacres, it was only to be expected that Vesalius should present his anatomical figures in the gloomy attitudes of death. One skeleton figure leans like a Roman *genius mortis* upon a pedestal which bears upon it a pair of funereal verses from Silius Italicus (*Punica* XII, 243-44):

> Solvitur omne decus leto, niveosque per artus
> it Stygius color, et formae populatur honores.

The same plate in the *Fabrica* carries the sentiment, "Vivitur ingenio, caetera mortis erunt," instead. This figure "is said to have inspired Shakespeare's concept of Hamlet" (A. Castiglioni, *A History of Medicine,* 1941, p. 423). Although I have found no real evidence for this statement by Castiglioni, English literature plays a small part in the dissemination of Vesalian anatomy through Nicholas Udall, the author of "Ralph Roister Doister."

To the plagiarism in London of the Vesalian plates by Thomas Geminus (*Compendiosa Totius Anatomie Delineatio,* etc., English ed., 1553; 2d ed., 1559) an English text was provided, drawn not from Vesalius' Latin *Epitome* but from a text similar to that used by Thomas Vicary in his *Anatomie of the Body of Man* (1548). Udall seems to have done nothing more for this plagiarism by Geminus than to translate the *characterum indices* of the Vesalian plates and to re-arrange Vicary's text skillfully to conform with the anatomical teaching of Mundinus; he also added a preface. (See Sanford V. Larkey, "The Vesalian Compendium of Geminus and Nicholas Udall's Translation: their Relation to Vesalius, Caius, Vicary and de Mondeville": *Transactions of the Bibliographical Society,* XIII [London, 1933], 367-94; also, H. Cushing, *A Bio-Bibliography of Andreas Vesalius,* 1943, p. 127. Larkey also explains why Udall in the English Geminus abandoned the order of presentation of material in the *Epitome;* see below.)

The *Epitome* is, like the *Fabrica,* at once a descriptive anatomy and an anatomical atlas. Vesalius speaks of it most diffidently as an appendix, index, compendium, and pathway (*semita*) to the *Fabrica.* Clearly Vesalius wished to reach as wide a public as possible by means of the Latin and German texts of his manual, with the hope of forestalling as well as he could the plagiarists whom he knew were inevitable. The latter paid him their sincere compliments by pirating his books in England, France, and Germany.

The order in which the material is arranged in the *Epitome* differs from that of the *Fabrica*. This is apparent from the contents of each book as given below:

Epitome	Fabrica
Book I Bones and Cartilages	I The Skeleton
II Muscles and Ligaments	II Muscles
III Abdominal Viscera	III Vascular System
IV Thoracic Viscera and Vascular System	IV Nervous System
V The Brain and the Nervous System	V Abdominal Viscera and . Organs of Reproduction
VI Organs of Reproduction	VI Thoracic Viscera
	VII The Brain

The style of the *Epitome* is clear and brief. There is no evidence in it that Vesalius wrote bad Latin. Indeed, his style is among the best Latin styles written by the Renaissance thinkers; even the *Fabrica,* which involves an immensely greater amount of detail and is often couched in a conversational Latin natural between teacher and student, still preserves many classical features of Latin prose: the verb at the end of the sentence, the separation of subject and modifier by various forms of the verb, the careful arrangement of clauses, the use of the genitive, the clausula at the sentence-end. His choice of words is quite classical; yet, realizing the great necessity for systematizing the terminology of science (almost as bewildering in its present form as it was in his day), he constantly admits new words and phrases. The *Epistola* of 1539 shows a brilliance of epigrams, anecdotes, analogies, and descriptions which is not surpassed even by the books of his more mature years.

The *Epitome* is a triumph of condensation. Anyone who has examined the vast bulk of the *Fabrica* knows what an immense amount of detail has, in the *Epitome,* been reduced to the lowest possible limits. Written in language which does not merely repeat that of the *Fabrica,* the *Epitome* is a book in its own right, independent in treatment, point of view, and purpose. The book embodies the principles of his educational method in a more striking fashion than does the *Fabrica.* Not the least important of his teaching devices is shown in the plate which calls for the clipping out of certain anatomical features and their superimposition by pasting upon the larger figure of the human body.

The tone of the *Epitome* is sober and impartial; Vesalius never mentions his contemporaries by name and scarcely refers even to Galen, except in the dedicatory epistle. "Professors of dissection" is a term he uses when necessary; the comments in the context where those words appear are usually Vesalius' own views upon controversial points and, by a characteristic ironical implication, he manages to give the impression that the "professors" are wrong. Naturally the students for whom the *Epitome* was intended would not be interested in scholarly controversy; hence Vesalius does not indulge in it. His purpose was pedagogical; the *Epitome* was a guide, a brief manual, an index, as he called it, to the parts of the body; and, master that he was, he never departs for a moment from that purpose. Seldom has so large an amount of scientific knowledge been so skillfully compressed into the narrow limits of a few pages.

The monumental *Bio-Bibliography of Andreas Vesalius,* the result of more than forty years of devoted study by Harvey Cushing (New York: Schuman's, 1943), is the great mine of information to which all readers of this first complete published translation into English of any of the longer works of Vesalius must now be referred for additional facts about the editions and plates of his books as well as for certain biographical material. The bibliography there provided is exhaustive, elaborately detailed, and sumptuously printed. In this brief introduction I have intended to convey merely the chief facts about Vesalius and the *Epitome.* The very short bibliography immediately following contains a selection of the more important works on Vesalius and his writings from which the student of Renaissance medical history and the general reader would be most likely to profit.

The reader's attention is called to the list of marginal notes by Vesalius given at the end of the text of this translation. This is a series of Greek equivalents for the Latin terms used by Vesalius in his text; he did not, as will be seen, make it either exhaustive or carry it out through the six books with the same consistency. These Greek terms, occurring as they do with great frequency in modern anatomical terminology, will help the reader to find his way more easily and provide additional synonyms for the Latin and English terms.

Dr. Asling's general interpretations for each book together furnish a convenient orientation for understanding the anatomical principles discussed in the *Epitome*. They sum up briefly and competently the substance of each book and are particularly recommended to the reader of this translation. Both the general interpretations and serial notes often serve as a condensed paraphrase of the text such as was provided by Albanus Torinus in his German translation of the *Epitome*. (See Henry E. Sigerist, "Albanus Torinus and the German Edition of the *Epitome* of Vesalius"; *Bulletin of the History of Medicine*, XIV [1943], 652-66.) Albanus, faced by the lack of equivalent German scientific terms, was forced to coin words and to resort to paraphrase. Modern English possesses most of the required terms for reproducing the Latin of Vesalius. I have not often therefore resorted to paraphrase in translating the *Epitome* but have attempted to say as clearly and briefly as possible in English what Vesalius said so well in Latin.

L. R. LIND

BIBLIOGRAPHY

THE PRINCIPAL EDITIONS OF VESALIUS

Paraphrasis in nonum librum Rhazae medici Arabis clariss. ad regem Almansorem de singularum corporis partium affectuum curatione, autore Andrea Wesalio Bruxellensi medicinae candidato. Lovanii ex officina Rutgeri Rescii. Mense Februar. 1537.

Ibid., Basileae in officina Roberti Winter. Anno 1537. Mense Martio.

[Tabulae anatomicae.] Imprimebat Venetiis B. Vitalis Venetus sumptibus Joannis Stephani Calcarensis. Prostrant vero in officina D. Bernardi. Anno 1538.

Institutionum anatomicarum secundum Galeni sententiam ad candidatos medicinae Libri quatuor, per Joannem Guinterium Andernacum medicum. Ab Andrea Wesalio Bruxellensi, auctiores et emendatiores redditi. Venetiis in officina D. Bernardini. 1538.

Andreae Wesalii Bruxellensis, scholae medicorum Patavinae professoris publici, Epistola, docens venam axillarem dextri cubiti in dolore laterali secandam: et melancholicum succum ex venae portae ramis ad sedem pertinentibus, purgari. Basileae, in officina Roberti Winter. Mense Aprili. Anno 1539.

Galeni omnia opera nunc primum in unum corpus redacta. Apud haeredes Lucæantonij Juntae Florentini Venetiis. 1541. Vol. II:

Galeni de nervorum dissectione liber ab Antonio Fortolo Joseriensi latinitate donatus, et ab Andrea Wesalio Bruxellensi aliquot in locis recognitus.

Galeni de venarum arteriarumque dissectione liber ab A. F. Joseriensi latinitate donatus, et ab Andrea Wesalio Bruxellensi plerisque in locis recognitus.

Galeni de anatomicis administrationibus libri novem ab Joanne Andernaco latinitate donati, et nuper ab Andrea Wesalio Bruxellensi correcti, ac pene alii facti.

Andreae Vesalii Bruxellensis, scholae medicorum Patavinae professoris, de humani corporis fabrica Libri septem. Basileae, ex officina Joannis Oporini. Anno salutis reparatae 1543. Mense Junio.

Andreae Vesalii Bruxellensis, invictissimi Caroli V. Imperatoris medici, de Humani corporis fabrica Libri septem. Basileae, ex officina Joannis Oporini, Anno salutis per Christum partae 1555. Mense Augusto.

Andreae Vesalii Bruxellensis, scholae medicorum, Patavinae professoris, suorum de humani corporis fabrica librorum Epitome. Basileae, ex officina Joannis Oporini. Anno 1543. Mense Junio.

Von des menschen cörpers Anatomey, ein kurtzer, aber vast nützer ausszug, auss D. Andree Vesalii von Brussel Bücheren, von ihm selbs in Latein beschriben, unnd durch D. Albanum Torinum verdolmetscht. Gedruckt zü Basel, bey Johann Herpst, genant Oporino, unnd vollendet am neünten tag des Augstmonat, nach der geburt Christi imm 1543 Jar.

Andreae Vesalii Bruxellensis, medici Caesarei epistola, rationem modumque propinandi radicis Chynae decocti, quo nuper invictissimus Carolus V. Imperator usus est, pertractans: et praeter alia quaedam, epistolae cuius' dam ad Jacobum Sylvium sententiam recensens, veritatis ac potissimum humanae fabricae studiosis perutilem: quum qui hactenus in illa nimium Galeno creditum sit, facile commonstret. Basileae, ex officina Joannis Oporini, anno salutis humanae 1546. Mense octobri.

Andreae Vesalii, anatomicarum Gabrielis Falloppii observationum Examen. Venetiis, apud Franciscum de Franciscis, Senensem. 1564.

Collected Works:

Andreae Vesalii Invictissimi Caroli V. Imperatoris Medici Opera omnia Anatomica et Chirurgica cura Hermanni Boerhaave. . . . et Bernhardi Siegfried Albini. Lugduni Batavorum, apud Joannem du Vivie, et Joan. et Herm. Verbeek, 1725. 2 vols.

Andreae Vesalii Bruxellensis Icones anatomicae. Ediderunt Academia

Medicinae Nova-Eboracensis et Bibliotheca Universitatis Monacensis, 1934. (Series of plates from original woodcuts of *Fabrica* and *Epitome*.)

BOOKS AND ARTICLES ABOUT VESALIUS

Ball, J. M., Andreas Vesalius, the Reformer of Anatomy. St. Louis: Medical Science Press, 1910.

Boyden, E. A., "The Problem of the Double Ductus Choledochus," etc. [a translation of gall-bladder description from the *Fabrica*], *Anat. Rec., LV* (1932), 74.

Burggraeve, A., Etudes sur André Vésale, précédées d'une notice historique sur sa vie et ses écrits. Gand, Belgium: C. Annoot-Braeckman, 1841.

Castiglioni, A., A History of Medicine. New York: Alfred A. Knopf, Inc., 1941, pp. 76, 418-27, 431, 444, 490.

Choulant, L., History and Bibliography of Anatomic Illustration; tr. with preface by M. Frank. Chicago: University of Chicago Press, 1920.

Clendening, Logan, Source Book of Medical History. New York: Paul B. Hoeber, Inc., 1941, pp. 126-51. Contains translation of the preface to the *Fabrica;* also a translation of "On Dissection of the Living," *Fabrica,* Book VII, xix.

Cushing, Harvey, A Bio-Bibliography of Andreas Vesalius. New York: Henry Schuman, 1943.

Feyfer, F. M. G. de, "Die Schriften des Andreas Vesalius." *Janus, XIX* (1914), 435-507.

Fisch, Max H., "Vesalius in English State Papers." *Bull. Med. Libr. Ass., XXXIII* (1945), 231-53.

Foster, Sir M., Lectures on the History of Physiology. Cambridge: The University Press, 1901.

Kingsley, Charles, "Vesalius, the Anatomist." In his: Health and Education. New York: D. Appleton and Company, 1893, pp. 385-411.

Lambert, S. W., and Goodwin, G. M. Medical Leaders from Hippocrates to Osler. Indianapolis: Bobbs Merrill Co., 1929.

Morley, Henry, "Anatomy in Long Clothes." *Frasers Magazine,* Nov., 1853.

Olschki, Leonardo, Geschichte der neusprachlichen wissenschaftlichen Literatur I (Leipzig, 1919), 265, 284; II (Leipzig, 1922), 16, 24, 34 ff., 39, 81 ff., 95, 98 ff., 178, 330.

Roth, Moritz, Andreas Vesalius Bruxellensis. Berlin: Georg Reimer, 1892.

Saunders, J. B. deC. M., and O'Malley, C. D., The Bloodletting Letter of 1539. In: Studies and Essays in the History of Science and Learning offered to George Sarton, ed. by M. F. Ashley Montagu. New York: Henry Schuman, 1946, pp. 5-74.

———, "A Reading from the De Humani Corporis Fabrica of Andreas Vesalius." *J. Amer. Coll. Dentists,* X (1944), pp. 211-18.

———, "Bernardino Montana de Monserrate, Author of the First Anatomy in the Spanish Language; Its Relationship to De Mondeville, Vicary, Vesalius, the English Geminus, and the History of the Circulation." *J. Hist. Med. Allied Sci.,* I (1946), 87-107.

Singer, Charles, The Evolution of Anatomy. London: Kegan Paul, Trench, Trubner & Co., 1925, pp. 111-35.

Spielmann, M. H., The Iconography of Andreas Vesalius. London: John Bale, Sons and Danielsson, Ltd., 1925.

VESALIUS TO THE READER *

THE compendium of the books on the fabric of the human body which I now publish is divided into two sections, of which the first is comprised of six chapters embracing a most succinct description of all the parts; the second section displays their delineation in a number of plates accompanied by indices of the characters by which they are designated. Therefore, it is a matter of your own choice and dependent upon your desire whether you shall first approach my ordering of the material (which from various considerations of printing and drawing I have selected as the most suitable) from the description of the parts, or their designation and index of their distinctive features starting with the figures showing the nude forms of man and woman, where the names of their external portions, serving as an index to these figures, occur.

The figure printed on the recto of the leaf with the nude male figure offers the complete structure of the bones,† whereas the figures drawn to the same scale as the nude man and labeled as muscle tables show the bones also in the order in which they are reached in dissection, especially the fourth and fifth muscle figures.‡

The delineation of the muscles and ligaments is to be sought first from that figure which we place opposite the one showing all the bones, and it is therefore called the first muscle figure. Next in order comes that which is called the third, then the fourth and fifth.§ The organs by which

---

* From the frontispiece of the *Epitome*. An English translation appears also in H. Cushing, *A Bio-Bibliography of Andreas Vesalius*, New York: Schuman's (1943), pp. 110-11, where an attempt has been made to indicate by symbols the exact references to the plates. Vesalius is not entirely clear in his suggestions for the use of the plates; an error, moreover, exists in the serial enumeration, thus making the task of comparing the text with the plates more difficult. On this entire matter see W. G. Spencer, "The 'Epitome' of Vesalius on vellum in the British Museum Library"; *Essays on the History of Medicine presented to Karl Sudhoff*, etc., edited by Charles Singer and Henry E. Sigerist, Zürich, Seldwyla (1924), pp. 237-44.

† That is, the skeletal figure, while it shows all the bones, is drawn to a smaller scale since it was taken from the *Fabrica*, where the plates are smaller.

‡ The plates are not numbered; if they were, these would be two and one respectively, not four and five.

§ For the reason why Vesalius here skips the second muscle figure, see W. G. Spencer, *op. cit.*, and especially Larkey, *op. cit.*

nutrition with food and drink is maintained, then the heart and the parts subserving its functions, together with the nervous system, are shown in figures on the plates following that of the nude woman. Therein are also to be seen the female organs of generation, and likewise the male organs occur in a picture to be cut out and pasted to the fifth muscle figure.

As for the portrayal of those parts which are contained in the skull, what is not carried by the plate prepared for demonstrating the nerves is presented in sufficient fullness in the plates showing the muscles. These should be taken in the following order: the head of the first figure, then of the second, then of the fourth, together with the images which the hands of that figure hold; next, that image which appears in the left hand of the fifth figure and the other image lying on the ground beyond the picture of the parts of the eye. Farewell, and use these, my efforts, as frankly as they are offered.

THE EPITOME OF HIS BOOKS ON THE FABRIC OF THE HUMAN BODY BY ANDREAS VESALIUS OF BRUSSELS

TO THE MOST SERENE PRINCE PHILIP, SON AND HEIR
OF THE DIVINE EMPEROR CHARLES THE FIFTH,
MIGHTIEST AND MOST INVINCIBLE
ANDREAS VESALIUS SENDS GREETINGS:

WITHIN the slender compass of these pages, greatest prince Philip, adorned with the splendor of your immortal name and under its good auspices, there is sent forth unto the common use of learning the description of the human body, which I have so divided in the manner of an enumeration, and singly related, that the principal branch of natural philosophy, treating the finished product of a creation most perfected and nigh the most worthy of all, may in the manner of an image be set before the eyes of those studious of the works of Nature. This has been done with as much conciseness as possible, and with less labor it describes those matters which I have embraced more amply in my seven books upon the subject. To those books this *Epitome* is, as it were, a footpath, or, as it will also be rightly considered, an appendix, gathering into summary form the chapters which are set forth with detail in those books; it lays out everything in such a fashion I may prophesy that you, with the amazing liberality of culture in which you eagerly welcome whatsoever slightest offering of the writer's craft, will not utterly cast it from your sight. Moreover, as you are now entering upon a period in your life distinguished by such various virtues, you are held fast by a wondrous and most generous love of all art and learning. And when your spacious spirit shall one day rule the whole world, you may perhaps at times consider it pleasant to be acquainted with my work

and to regard it as a situation wretched and unworthy of the greatest Em-
perors, Kings, and Consuls, that in the pursuit of studies so varied, the harmony of the human body which we shall publish to the world should lie
constantly concealed; that man be completely unknown to himself; and that
the structure of instruments so divinely created by the Great Artificer of
all things should remain unexamined: since it is by the function of these
instruments that those things we look upon as most, and almost solely, important are brought to pass.

Truly, although for this reason my undertaking will perhaps be not wholly
displeasing to your admirable judgment, if I should nevertheless refuse to
give forth this companion to physicians because, while I strive to be useful
to them yet at the same time I am anxious to snatch opportunity from the
hands of certain rascally printers who may later seize in possession upon
the labors of another to reduce them ineptly into small space and publish
them under their own names (creatures born for the destruction of letters!),
I might in either case prove a grievous hindrance. For no one is ignorant
how much is lost in all sciences by the use of compendiums. Though indeed
they seem to provide a certain way and systematic approach to the perfect
and complete knowledge of things and seem to contain in short and in sum
that which is set down elsewhere with more space and prolixity and are for
this reason considered in the light of an index or the very abode of memory, in which matters written down at length are fitly reduced to their proper
place, nevertheless, compendiums do signal injury and wreak a great havoc
upon literature; for, given to the use of compendiums alone, we read scarcely
anything else through to the end these days. This is true even for those who
have delivered themselves completely to learning, to this degree aspiring
only to the shadow and superstructure of science, digging little or not at
all beneath the surface.

However, although this evil wanders widely amid almost all studies, it is
a charge to be laid most gravely at the door of the mob of physicians that
they perform their duty so carelessly in distinguishing the parts of the human
body that not even enumeration is made use of in learning them. For when,
beyond the function and use of each part, its location, form, size, color, the
nature of its substance, the principle of its connection with the other parts,

and many things of this sort in the medical examination of the parts may never be sufficiently perceived, how many can be found who know even the number of the bones, cartilages, ligaments, muscles, and veins, arteries, and nerves running in a numerous succession throughout the entire body and of the viscera which are found in the cavities of the body? I pass over in silence those pestilent doctors who encompass the destruction of the common life of mankind, who never even stood by at a dissection: whereas in the knowledge of the body no one could produce anything of value who did not perform dissections with his own hands as the kings of Egypt were wont to do and in like manner busied himself frequently and sedulously with dissections and with simple medicines. Whence also those most prudent members of the household of Asclepius will never be sufficiently praised, who, as children in the home learn reading and writing, so they exercised the dissection of cadavers and, learned in this wise, under the happy auspices of the Muses, they bent to their studies. Furthermore, whatever our sloth in the thorough mastery of Anatomy as the basis and foundation of the medical art, I have assumed that no demonstration is required of how necessary the knowledge of human parts is for us who have enlisted under the banner of medicine, since the conscience of each and all will bear full testimony to the fact that in the cure of illness the knowledge of those parts lays rightful claim to first, second, and third place; and this knowledge is to be sought primarily from the affected portion, without, of course, neglecting the due application of subsidiary remedies. Indeed, those who are now dedicated to the ancient study of medicine, almost restored to its pristine splendor in many schools, are beginning to learn to their satisfaction how little and how feebly men have labored in the field of Anatomy to this day from the times of Galen, who, although easily chief of the masters, nevertheless did not dissect the human body; and the fact is now evident that he described (not to say imposed upon us) the fabric of the ape's body, although the latter differs from the former in many respects.

But as to my own audacity, by virtue of which this slight offering, unworthy of your majesty and uniquely commended by such a patronage, hazards the dubious fortune of critical judgment, I shall defend myself with no excuse except that this is the grain and salt whereby I am permitted to obtain favorable omens for my systematic studies; and meanwhile I should wish this book to be an indication of my complete obedience and sense of duty toward my country's ruler until such time as it shall be possible to offer incense also.

At Padua, on the Ides of August, in the Year of the Virgin Birth, MDXLII. [August 13, 1542]

THE EPITOME OF
ANDREAS
VESALIUS

CONCERNING THE BONES AND CARTILAGES,

OR THOSE PARTS WHICH SUPPORT THE BODY

CHAPTER I

ALL of the parts of the human body are either *similar,* or simple to the senses,* such as the bones, cartilages, ligaments, fibers, membranes, flesh, and fat, or *dissimilar,* instrumental agencies, such as the veins, arteries, nerves, muscles, individual fingers, and the remaining organs of the entire body. These latter parts are made all the more instrumental to the degree that they (e.g., the hand and head) are composed of many similar parts and also of many functional mechanisms [1].

The bones are the hardest and driest parts of the entire body. The cartilages are softer than the bones, but of the parts of the body they are next in hardness to the bones. The whole body is supported by bones and carti-

---

* I am indebted to the kindness of Professor Henry E. Sigerist, former director of the Institute of the History of Medicine, Johns Hopkins University, for the following answer to my question about this passage: "I think that *sensu ue* refers to the senses of the anatomist, that is to say, these parts are simple as judged by the senses; the anatomist cannot perceive any simpler parts composing them. For this interpretation we have a good parallel in Galen, ed. Kühn, Vol. 4, p. 741: εἴη ἂν οὖν ἀρίστη κατασκευὴ τοῦ σώματος, ἐν ᾗ τὰ ὁμοιομερῆ πάντα (καλεῖται δ' οὕτως δηλονότι τὰ πρὸς αἴσθησιν ἁπλᾶ) τὴν οἰκείαν ἔχει κρᾶσιν. Vesalius' 'sensu ue simplices' stands for πρὸς αἴσθησιν ἁπλᾶ, which expression the Latin translator of the Galenic text renders by: 'sensu simplices.' I should therefore be inclined to translate the beginning of the sentence: 'All parts of the human body are either similar or simple to the senses as bone, cartilage. . . .'"

Professor Sigerist quotes both the Latin text and the translation of this passage into German by Albanus Torinus in his article "Albanus Torinus and the 'Epitome' of Vesalius," *Bulletin of the History of Medicine* XIV (1943), 663-64, and comments on the virtues of each passage.

Professor Saunders writes me as follows: "The classification of the parts of the body into 'similars and dissimilars' was standard terminology almost to the time of Bichat. The terms are of course derived from Galen. What is meant is parts of similar temperaments and elements. This passage is typical of one of the difficulties of the modern translator when dealing with the humoral doctrine; the very terms have disappeared from our language with the development of newer anatomical and physiological concepts even in everyday language. Contemporary sixteenth century English is as above: 'similars and dissimilars.' Cf. animal, spiritual, natural—all terms with special meaning differing from that of customary Greco-Latin usage. The same difficulty as above is presented with 'functional.' 'Instrumentum' is not quite 'functional.' The term is derived from Aristotle, *De Gen. Animal.* I, ii, 716a: ' . . . the bodily parts are the instruments or organs to serve the faculties. . . .' According to Galen, *Method, Medendi* I, vi, instruments are those parts of the body capable of carrying out a complete action; hence the arteries, veins, and nerves are collectively instruments for the distribution of the vital, natural, and animal spirits; the eye, and all pertaining to it, the instrument of sight. This was the customary usage of the *Fabrica.*"

lages in combination, and all its parts are attached to, and stabilized by, them. The skull, which contains the brain and the sense organs, is composed of several bones; one bone frequently makes up the forehead, especially in women [2]; in the occiput of the head there is likewise one; two bones are at the vertex, and one at each ear or temple [3], in which a cavity is formed suitable for the reception of the organ of hearing. This cavity encloses two small bones, one of which resembles an anvil or molar tooth, while the other is like a small hammer [4]. The bone of the temple has connected to it the cartilage supporting the structure of the ear. In addition it has three processes: first, it bears the mastoid process posteriorly; second, the styloid process, like a bodkin or cock's spur; third, a process which turns anteriorly, is closely joined in the external structure of the orbit to the bone of the upper jaw, and at the level of this junction constitutes the part of the skull which we call the os jugale [5]. Inferiorly the temporal bone joins the base of the occipital bone to form that region of the skull which we may compare to a broken rock, not only from the standpoint of hardness but also in appearance [6]. In the base of the skull is a noteworthy bone which professors of dissection compare to a wedge [7]; it is polymorphous and gives forth projections very much like the wings of a bat [8]. Near it, above the nose, there is another bone which is pervious in form like a sieve or more like a sponge [9]; it forms the septum of the nose, and in company with the seven bones previously listed it makes up the cavity which contains the brain.

In the upper jaw we count twelve bones in addition to the teeth: one on the lateral and two on the medial aspect of each eye socket [10], and one pair in the inferior part of the orbits; these last bones are regarded as by far the largest of the group [11] and contain small cavities for the reception of the upper teeth. A pair of bones is found at that end of the palate at which the apertures of the nasal cavities become continuous with the pharynx [12]. Finally, the prominent part of the nose is composed of two bones which connect with the cartilages of the nose by which the wings of the nostrils are supported; like the other bones of the upper jaw, they have no special name [13].

Thus far most of the bones mentioned are held in place by sutures, of which the one passing transversely in the sinciput [14] is called the coronal; the one creeping transversely in the occiput receives its name from its resemblance to the Greek letter Λ [15]; and the one passing along the length of the skull from the top of the occiput to the middle of the coronal suture is called the sagittal. Those bony junctions which are equidistant from the sagittal suture and which pass superior to the ears do not look like sutures but are more like two overlapping scales, from which appearance they are called squamous conglutinations [16]. The remaining connections between the bones of the skull do not show the appearance of a suture as well as do the three which have been named; in fact, in some places they appear more like a simple line and should receive the name of "harmony" rather than that of "suture" [17].

The lower jaw consists of a single bone, with the exception of very young children, in whom it forms from two bones fusing at the point of the chin; indeed, most of the bones of children are composed of several bones which later unite into single bones in those who have reached their full growth [18]. The lower jaw articulates on either side with a bone located near the ear, and in addition with its special cartilage intervening here, where the heads of these bones and their corresponding sinuses fit together [19], the articular surface is covered in the manner of a rind and a joint is thereby provided that turns readily, rendering it free from the injuries of continuous friction of the bones against each other. There are at most sixteen teeth in each jaw: four incisors, two canines, and ten molars; not only do they differ in appearance when examined in place in the mouth, but they are also fixed in their sockets with differing numbers of roots.

In the pharynx, the bone at the root of the tongue has more the shape of the Greek letter υ than of Λ [20]; it is bound together with many small bones. The lower of these are joined at their extremities to the rough artery of the head [21] (which we call the larynx rather than the gullet or throat) and, more specifically, to a cartilage which resembles a shield. This cartilage is called the first cartilage of the larynx and can be palpated in its entirety [22]. The second cartilage makes up the greater part of the posterior portion of the larynx and resembles the ring which the Thracians fit on their right thumbs when shooting arrows [23]; it lacks a name and from this fact

3

actually receives one [24]. The third cartilage, which is made up of two parts, resembles the orifice of vessels used for pouring water in washing the hands [25]; it forms an opening in the middle of the larynx for structures like the reeds of a flute [*tibia*] or pipe [*fistula*] [26]. This opening is like the aperture of pipes which are held to the mouth, and because of this we call it the "little reed" [27]. On these cartilages an operculum is laid like a lid, composed of cartilage [28], fat, and ligamentlike structures. The remaining cartilages of the rough artery, making up both its trunk and the branches running to the lungs, present the semicircular shape of the letter C or the Greek sigma [29].

The backbone, which provides the best passage for the dorsal medulla [30], is like a keel of the body and is divided into the regions of the neck or cervix, the thorax, the loins, the sacrum, and the coccyx or cuculus [31]. It is composed of thirty-four bones, which we call vertebrae. The neck has seven bones, furnished with several processes (not all bones having the same number); by means of the first of these bones [32] (which, unique among the vertebrae, has no spine and has quite protuberant transverse processes) we move the head directly forward and backward. By the use of the second vertebra (to which a prominent process resembling a canine tooth is attached) we turn the head [33]. By the function of the remaining vertebrae the head is carried to the side but only in a slight degree.

The thorax has twelve vertebrae, with which the ribs articulate. Usually the lowest of these vertebrae [34] is supported by the adjacent vertebrae through its ascending and descending transverse processes (with which the vertebrae are articulated in turn in addition to the connections between their bodies) just as the first cervical vertebra supports the bones contiguous to it above and below. The remaining vertebrae of the backbone above the twelfth thoracic are supported from above and in turn support those below, while those below this level are supported below and support those above them. Below the twelfth vertebra are five vertebrae of the loins, followed by the os sacrum, formed, at most, from its own six bones firmly fused together. The coccyx is a bone the extremity of which terminates in cartilage; it is frequently composed of four meager ossicles which provide no foramina for nerves and have no path for the dorsal medulla.

Furnishing a suitable location for the heart and the organs subsidiary to the heart, the breastbone occupies the anterior region of the thorax. It is composed very rarely of seven bones [35], usually fewer, receiving the seven articulations of the ribs on either side. Of the twelve ribs on each side ending in cartilage, the seven upper ones attach to the breastbone by their own cartilages and therefore have been given the name of true or genuine ribs. The ribs which do not come in contact with the breastbone, but fall short of it and of the anterior region of the abdomen in a degree corresponding to the lower position which they occupy, are called false ribs [36]. The lower portion of the breastbone terminates in cartilage and resembles the blunt point of a sword (because of which the entire breastbone is compared to a sword) [37]. At the upper extremity of the bone, where it is broadest and strongest [38] and where the throat lies, a clavicle is attached on each side, holding the shoulder joint away from the thorax.

The scapula has the form of a triangle and occupies the posterior region of the thorax on either side; it ends in a neck in which a socket is molded [39], suitable for the reception of the head of the humerus. From its own back the scapula sends out a process projecting above the shoulder joint and called the summus humerus [40]. It is articulated through a special cartilage of the clavicle (as is also the case with the connection between the clavicle and the breastbone); by means of the clavicle the shoulder joint is held away from the thorax. The inner process of the scapula is compared to an anchor, or the letter C, or the Greek sigma [41].

The bone of the arm, or humerus, articulates with the scapula; inferiorly it is furnished with several sinuses and tuberosities [42]. Two bones are joined here, the radius and the ulna (the other name of which is cubitus, from the name of the entire member). The cubitus is flexed and extended on the humerus in a fashion similar in both man and quadrupeds. In its upper portion, in the posterior aspect of the arm joint, it has a process which many call the gibber [43]. Similarly, its lower portion has another process which takes its name from the shape of a stylus.

The wrist articulates almost exclusively with the radius and is separated from the ulna by its own cartilage [44]; it is made up of eight bones which are entirely different from each other in shape and size. The four bones of

5

the postbrachial metacarpals, together with the first bone of the thumb, join the wrist at its lower aspect. The thumb, as well as the other four fingers, is composed of three bones placed serially, as it were, in a line [45]. The total number of bones of the fingers is fifteen; to this we add the two small bones comparable to sesame seed [46] which are found at the second inter-node of the thumb. Bones which are similar, but much smaller and quite cartilaginous, are found in the inner portion of the first four internodes of the fingers and in the third internode of the thumb; one connected near the wrist to the external side of the metacarpal bone which supports the little finger is found by those who dissect the body. There is rarely one in the remaining internodes of the fingers, except that such may be observed in the fingers of very old men [47].

A large bone is attached on each side of the os sacrum; where this bone is broad and faces the flanks, it is called the ilium, but where the head of the femur enters a deeper socket, it is called the hipbone. That aspect of the bone which, with the bone of the opposite side, forms the pubis (which has a conspicuous perforation) is called the pubic bone. Henceforth, however, under the name of coxendix we include the entire bone [48].

The rounded head of the superior aspect of the femur is continuous with the broad neck; it grows inward in an oblique direction and articulates with the coxendix. At its inferior end, the femur enters the sinuses [hollows] of the tibia by means of its own two heads [condyles], with a certain sinus lying between them where a tuberosity of the afore-mentioned tibia is received, as well as by means of the special cartilages in this joint, which is very similar to the knee of quadrupeds and of birds [49]. A large process is seen near the external part of the neck of the femur, called the rump or the great pulley [rotator] [50]. Inwardly, the bone has also another process, much smaller than the one on the external aspect; because of this fact we call it the minor or internal rotator.

In the leg, just as in the forearm, two bones are seen; the inner of these is much thicker than the outer one and goes by the name of the entire member [51]. The outer bone, which is not articulated to the femur, is called the fibula. A round bone called the mola or patella, similar to a shield, is located in front of the joint of the tibia with the femur. The lowest portions of the tibia and fibula, which have prominences on their outer aspects protruding from the fleshy parts, are called the malleoli.

The talus lies in the same region in man and in beasts and is put to the same use in both creatures. Under it lies the os calcis [52], extending posteriorly far beyond the straightness of the tibia. The anterior part of the talus ends in a round head; it enters the sinus of the navicular bone, which is joined to three bones of the tarsus [53]. The fourth, an external bone of the tarsus, resembles a cube or a die and adjoins the heel. Five metatarsal bones [ossa pedii] [54] are joined with the four bones of the tarsus; by means of these five the toes are supported.

The great toe is formed from two internodes [55], while three are assigned to each of the remaining toes. Moreover, there are the same number of these bones in the foot (which is much shorter in man than in quadrupeds) and in the hand. Small bones occur, which we compare to sesame seed [56]; the two which lie beneath the first internode of the great toe are far larger than in the hand. Of these, the inner may be the one which followers of occult philosophy affirm to be subject to no sort of corruption; foolishly they contend that it must be long preserved in the earth until, in the manner of a seed, it produces a man at the time of resurrection [57]. To the bones of the digits, in the foot as well as in the hand, nails are attached; we refer to them here not inopportunely on account of their substance, just as among the parts bracing something we mention the cartilages of the eyelids, supporting the lids so that they may not fall together flaccidly.

MUCH has been written about the splendid title pages of Vesalius' *Fabrica* and *Epitome*. Some see them as representing symbolically the divisions of Vesalian anatomical teaching into three phases: the skeleton, in its central position of dominance, represents the foundation of most anatomy teaching, osteology; the cadaver, the dissecting-room; the nude living figure, surface and regional anatomy. Whatever the intent of the author may have been in designing this plate, we may see some traces of the organization in the text of the *Epitome*. The first chapter concerns the skeletal parts, the succeeding five chapters describe structures disclosed by dissection, and the book closes with a section on topographical and surface anatomy. The modern encyclopedias of anatomy follow almost exactly, chapter for chapter, the order in which Vesalius describes the systems of the body.

Another influence which may be observed in the organization of this book is that of Mondino de' Luzzi, whose *Anathomia* of 1316 starts with parts associated with digestion, the *natural members;* following this come the contents of the thorax, or *spiritual members,* and then the nervous system, the *animal members.* This order is exactly that of the *Epitome*'s Chapters III, IV, and V, and the general interpretations of these chapters will show the relationship to the three "spirits," which may be compared with the system of "members" of Mondino.

Immediately on beginning the reading of the *Epitome,* the question arises: for whom was this text intended? According to Vesalius, in his dedicatory introduction, it is a compendium of anatomy for physicians and may be treated as an index to the *Fabrica*. Singer, in *The Evolution of Anatomy,* believes that it was "intended for those who were not students of medicine" (p. 123). However, the first thing which arouses the curiosity of the reader is Vesalius' restraint in naming the parts described. Except for those structures the names of which are in common, even household, use, almost no names are given directly. Instead, the derivation of the anatomical name is often given by the device of descriptive comparison. In illustration, the "second cartilage" of the larynx "resembles the ring which the Thracians fit on their right thumb when shooting arrows" in spite of the fact that the term "cricoid" was already available (Gr., κρίκος, "a ring").

In this connection, a communication from Professor J. B. deC. M. Saunders of San Francisco informs me that in his experience with the *Fabrica* he has found the *Onomasticon* of Julius Pollux of great value in dealing with nomenclature. Singer (*op. cit.,* p. 107) says that this work, while written in the time of Galen, first became influential after its publication in 1502. Its section on anatomical terms became the storehouse from which the Humanists replaced the current Arabic terms. For example, "cricoid" was thus introduced.

The conclusion seems tenable that in the *Epitome* Vesalius has employed this picturesque device in the introduction of new terms much in the way that modern teachers do. We feel often that teaching is made more vital and the student's interest and retention of **fact** increased if we explain, as far as possible, the derivation of the term; we mourn the lack of training in the classical languages (both in teacher and in student) which prevents this from reaching its maximum utility. According to such an interpretation, the *Epitome* was written not for barber-surgeons and bonesetters, for whom sheer rote memorization of names and methods would serve, but instead for the medical student, for whom the greatest effort in offering a basic understanding of fact pays manifold dividends in the form of a well-trained physician.

Another teaching method introduced in the first chapter is enumeration of parts. Vesalius feels strongly that this is of value in anatomy teaching, as shown by the third paragraph of his dedication. It reaches its highest and most complex form in the second chapter on muscles; an attempt has been made to preserve its full force in the annotation. The method has been dropped, almost completely, in anatomy (an outstanding exception is the enumeration of twelve cranial nerves) but is in use in pathology teaching, where the student learns the four cardinal signs of inflammation, the five diseases which show leukopenia, the five types of cirrhosis of the liver, and other similar enumerations.

In connection with Vesalius' methods of teaching, it would be gross negligence to omit his manikin plates in the *Epitome*. We can imagine the great pride he took in this "first instance in which the type of demonstration by moveable layers is adopted" (Singer, *op. cit.*, p. 126). While the vascular system rather than the skeleton is the basis for this pair of male and female manikins, much care has been taken in designing the various portions of the plates so that they may be cut out and superimposed. The instructions on how to assemble them are written in great detail. Singer's comment that "It is not a useful method, and has since fallen into desuetude save for popular purposes" may be modified on the basis of the recent appearance of three volumes of this type, the first a detailed study of the body and the other two a series of anatomical transparencies of the eye and the ear. The use of transparent mediums in these demonstrations may yet bring about the reintroduction into anatomical teaching of a method invented by Vesalius.

1. THE first few lines contain an idea which is now commonplace in elementary anatomy, viz.: organs are composed of tissues. Probably it was the first great generalization in the analysis and synthesis of the main anatomical facts.

2. Frontal bone. Vesalius appears to expect metopism (persistence of the metopic suture) but finds many skulls, especially female, which do not show it. Metopism is actually the exception, and significant sex differences are not now claimed for it.

3. Parietal and temporal bones.

4. Vesalius recognized the existence of the third auditory ossicle, the stapes, in his letter to Fallopius some twenty years later.

5. The zygomatic processes of the temporal and maxillary bones, yoked together by the zygomatic bone.

6. The petrous portion of the temporal bone, with special reference to the appearance of its inferior aspect.

7. The sphenoid bone, wedge-shaped or irregular in form (σφήν, "a wedge").

8. Compare the ancient name of this bone: sphecoid (from σφήξ, "a wasp").

9. The ethmoid bone, lamina cribrosa and lamina perpendicularis. The comparison to a sponge refers to the ethmoid air cells. See Chap. V, note 18.

10. "Upper jaw" here is the topographic equivalent of face, exclusive of mandible. The bones indicated are, laterally, the malar or zygomatic bone, and medially, the lacrimals and laminae papyraceae of the ethmoids.

11. Maxilla, with the alveoli.

12. Palatine bone.

13. Nasal bones.

14. Sinciput: *semi* + *caput,* the opposite of occiput; forehead or calvaria.

15. Lambdoid suture.

16. The squamous part of the temporal bone: *squamosae conglutinationes.* The term refers to a union of thin scalelike bones. See Morris' *Human Anatomy* (10th ed., 1942), p. 268.

17. Harmony: smooth union along a nearly straight line. This concept has continued to be the same to the present time. It reflects the Greek concept of fitness in joining or fastening, as in carpentry or masonry (and in anatomy), by mere apposition. Morris, *loc. cit.:* "In harmonic suture, the even, regular edges of the apposing bones. . . . "
18. Separate centers of ossification in the mandible and other bones; Vesalius' experience was not limited to the dissection of the adult body.

19. Mandibular fossa of the temporal bone and condyloid process of the mandible.

Sinuses here mean hollows, articular fossae. The word has long had many meanings in anatomy.

20. The hyoid bone; more curved than sharp at the convergence of its cornua. Vesalius would correct the old name of "lambdoid bone."

21. Trachea or windpipe; the idea is a derivative of the concept of arteries as air passages. "Rough" (Latin, *aspera*) is descriptive of the cartilaginous rings.

22. Thyroid cartilage (θυρεός, "a shield").

23. Cricoid cartilage (κρίκος, "a ring").

24. Old name, *cartilago innominata* (Fr., *cartilage anonyme*).

25. Arytenoid cartilages; *arytaena*, "ladle-shaped."

26. Corniculate cartilages and vocal folds (or cords). The diminutive of *cornu*, "little horn"; compare this with other terms applied, such as *tibia*, "flute," and *fistula*, "pipe." Both of these last appear to have been lost; they are not found in Motherby (*A New Medical Dictionary*, 2d ed., London, 1785), though they may be found as synonyms in Dunglison (*A Dictionary of Medical Science*, rev. ed., 1874).

27. Glottis or lingula: the mouthpiece of a pipe.

28. The epiglottis.

29. I.e., the uncial capital sigma.

30. *Medulla*, marrow, representing the concept that the white, fatty material filling bone cavities is comparable to that found in the cavity of the vertebral column.

31. From its fancied resemblance to the bill of a cuckoo (*cuculus*, κόκκυξ).

32. The atlas.

33. The epistropheus (axis), with the odontoid process (dens); odontoid means tooth-like.

34. Vesalius is here referring to the transitional vertebrae of the thorax. His qualification of "usually" indicates his full realization that this may be either the eleventh or twelfth thoracic vertebra. The remainder of the paragraph is doubtless a description of the differing inclinations of the various articular processes, but here, as all too frequently in the *Epitome*, the clarity of his concepts has been lost in overcondensation.

35. The sternum is "composed very rarely of seven bones"; a concession to Galen, who so described its composition.

36. I.e., the lower the rib, the shorter it is, and hence the less it extends toward the mid-line.

37. Xiphoid process. *Gladiolus* ("little sword") was the old name for sternum. Ensiform process carries the same meaning.

38. Manubrium, the "handle" of the sword.

39. The glenoid cavity.

11

40. *Summus humerus*: the acromion process. According to Professor Saunders, Galen described a third bone in the shoulder, the summus humerus, which Vesalius concluded was the acromion. There was a long dispute on this subject, and some concluded that the summus humerus was the cartilage of the acromioclavicular joint.

41. Coracoid process; other names indicative of its shape which have been in use are uncinate, corniculate, anchoralis, rostriformis, ancyroïdes. Cf. Vesalius, *Fabrica* I, xxi, on Galen's use of the term.

42. Including (as sinuses, see note 19) the coronoid, radial, and olecranon fossae, and (as tuberosities) the epicondyles, trochlea, and capitulum.

43. The olecranon process.

44. The articular disk.

45. On comparative anatomical and ossification bases, Vesalius holds the view, more recently advanced (and criticized), that the thumb has no metacarpal but is like the fingers in having three phalanges. Hence, the "four bones of the postbrachial" equal our second through fifth metacarpals.

46. Sesamoid bones. Nodes are joints; hence internodes correspond to phalanges.

47. Can Vesalius have referred here to the finding in arthritis (and especially ascribed to gout) of Heberden's nodes? The reason for the unusually large number of "sesamoid bones" found in connection with the other digits is not evident; there may be some confusion with epiphyseal ossification centers.

48. The limits of the three bones described here do not exactly correspond to those at present specified for the os coxae, but the principle of fusion of three bones is clearly defined. The "perforation" is the obturator foramen.

49. The description of this hinge joint is always one of the most difficult to accomplish with clarity because of its complexity; Vesalius is describing the method by which the two condyles and intercondylar fossa of the femur fit on the condyles and intercondylar eminence of the tibia, with the interposition of the cartilaginous menisci.

50. Greater trochanter (old name, *glutus*, "rump"); followed by lesser trochanter.

51. "Tibia" is not only a specific term for a single bone but also a generality for the leg region. This is explained also in the topographic or surface anatomy section at the end. The principle holds for several parts of the body, and the differentiation of bone or region is usually made from the presence or absence of the word *os*.

52. Calcaneum, which extends posteriorly beyond the perpendicular line formed by the posterior aspect of the tibia.

53. In the anatomy of the period, the tarsus is not so extensive as in modern terminology; it is limited to the navicular, the three cuneiforms, and the cuboid and excludes the calcaneum and talus.

54. *Ossa pedii* does not refer to all of the bones of the foot since the term is strictly limited to the metatarsal bones, in the same way that the "bones of the postbrachial" are always to be rendered as metacarpal bones in translation.

12

55. Note that he does not attempt to homologize the thumb and the great toe in particular, with respect to number of bones forming these digits (see note 45).

56. See note 46. The sesame seed was often symbolic in medieval metaphysics not only of minuteness but also of fertility and hence immortality. On this last meaning depends his next statement.

57. Surely Vesalius contributes here his own sardonic joke; he comments on the old superstition of the incorruptible bone, upon the foundation of which the whole body will be recreated on Resurrection Day. His training in philosophy must have been such that he would have appreciated the reference Butler made later to the os sacrum (holy bone, Vesalius' "meagre ossicle" of the coccyx) in his satirical poem:

> The learned Rabbins of the Jews
> Write there's a bone, which they call luez,
> I' the rump of man, of such a virtue,
> No force in nature can do hurt to. . . .
> —SAMUEL BUTLER, *Hudibras*, Part III, Canto II

Vesalius's transference of the property of indestructibility to an insignificant bone lying in a tendon under the big toe would have been adequate comment to answer (by anticipation) the questions of contemporary metaphysicists regarding his findings on incorruptible bones. The corresponding passage from the *Fabrica* will be found in translation in Clendening's *Source Book of Medical History*, p. 150. See Richard Burton's translation of *The Thousand and One Nights* (notes on the 449th night) and Dr. Nash's notes on *Hudibras* for interesting additional reading on this subject.

CONCERNING THE LIGAMENTS OF THE BONES

AND CARTILAGES, AND THE MUSCLES WHICH ARE THE
INSTRUMENTS OF VOLUNTARY MOVEMENTS

CHAPTER II

THE ligaments, no less than the sinews of the muscles and the organs by means of which the animal spirit is led from the brain, are commonly called nerves [1]. They are made of similar particles, originating from bone and cartilage [2], almost entirely devoid of sensation, hard (but nevertheless softer than the cartilage), and white; they serve various purposes in the fabric of man in binding together, containing, covering, and forming the muscles. For the muscle is regarded as the instrument of voluntary motion, formed of fibers interwoven with flesh and with many membranes having the nature of a ligament [3]. In order that the muscle may contract and lead the part that is to be moved [4], it requires the assistance of the nerves which carry the animal force from the brain no less than it requires the sense organs. Similarly, in order that the rest of the parts which require nutrients may be nourished, it is irrigated by veins and arteries. Further, the tendon of the muscle is a certain type of sinew and is, as it were, composed of fibers except for the intervening flesh. The tendon is distinct from the muscle only at the point where it reaches a position far enough from its origin (which it takes from a bone, cartilage, or some membrane) toward the insertion (which the tendon makes on the part that is to be moved) that its fibers attain continuous traction through the whole muscle; this is obtained by virtue of its interconnection with the proximal fleshy portion of the muscle. In proportion to their length, muscles end in tendons now round, now broad and membranous, now shorter, now longer; the short muscles spread out in a continuous expansion and terminate in no sinew worthy of mention.

A membrane augmented with fleshy fibers lies under the skin of the

14

forehead. The skin is the natural outer covering of the body and sends out a thin little skin growing upon its own surface, like an efflorescence of the true skin itself [5]. Inwardly, throughout the entire body, a certain membrane lies under the skin; because it is increased with fleshy fibers (as here in the forehead), it has been thought to be called carneous elsewhere [6]. The largest part of a man's fat is placed between this membrane and the skin [7]. Also, the upper eyelid is moved by means of the membrane just mentioned, for in that place where this [carnea] reaches the inner region of the eye socket, it raises the eyelid [8]; where it is augmented at the external aspect of the eye by fleshy fibers drawn into the image of our letter C, it is the originator of the downward motion of the eyelid [9].

Seven muscles move the eye [10]: the first leads to the side inward, the second outward, the third upward, the fourth downward; the fifth and sixth are somewhat curved around the eye and render moderate assistance to the function of the first and second muscles. These six correspond to each other in form, being elongated and almost round; they spring forth from the tough membrane which surrounds the nerve of vision [11]. They pass by membranous tendons to the anterior portion of the scleral tunic of the eye in a ring near the border of the iris. The seventh muscle is covered by these and surrounds the visual nerve along with the six muscles at the same time [12]. The carneous muscle is implanted in the posterior portion of the scleral tunic of the eye; it is chief among those six muscles, making almost the same motions as they do.

A muscle draws one ala of the nose upward and outward, arising from the inner aspect of the cheekbone and inserting at one side into the ala, on the other into the upper lip where the latter lies below the ala of the nose [13]. A membranous muscle draws the alae together inwardly, lurking in the broad part of the nostrils beneath the tunic which girdles them from below [14].

Four muscles on either side move the cheeks and lips [15]. The first is composed of fleshy membrane reinforced for the most part with carneous fibers in the anterior portion of the neck and face as far as the cheeks; it resembles a muscle. The second arises from the cheeks and is implanted in the upper lip. The third extends from the lower jaw to the lower lip. The

15

fourth, somewhat different, lies in that part of the cheeks which we puff out. To these muscles there approaches a portion of that muscle which, as we learned, moves the outer ala of the nose; this, together with those mentioned, produces those marvelous and varied movements of the cheeks and lips.

There are also four muscles on either side which move the lower jaw [16]. The first is the temporal, arising from the bone of the vertex and also of the forehead, as well as from the bone shaped like a wedge; it is broad and flat at its origin from the bones of the temple and inserts in an acute process of the lower jaw. The second is called mansorius [17], from chewing [a mandendo]; it proceeds from that part of the skull called the os jugale and is inserted in the external aspect of the jaw. The third comes from the processes of the skull which have the shape of wings; it is implanted in the internal aspect of the jaw; it raises the jaw, together with the muscles named, and moves the jaw laterally and forward and backward. The fourth, with its companion, depresses the jaw. It takes its origin from the process of the skull which resembles a stylus and inserts at the apex of the chin; it is furnished with two bellies for itself.

The hyoid bone [18] is drawn straight downward by two muscles, close to each other and arising from the top of the chest bone. Two others, coming from the lower jaw, draw this bone upward. At the sides it is drawn upward by one muscle on either side, originating from the styloid process of the skull. Having origin from the upper border of the scapula, one muscle at each side moves it downward. All eight of the above muscles are inserted in the anterior portion of the hyoid bone.

A fleshy mass, coming from the middle of the bone just mentioned, is inserted in the root of the tongue [19]; this mass can be regarded as two muscles and moves the tongue straight inward and downward. From the sides of the hyoid bone one muscle is also inserted into the root of the tongue inwardly but nevertheless moving the tongue more to the side. The fifth and sixth muscles of the tongue come from the styloid processes of the skull on either side; they are implanted in the root of the tongue and move it upward or, as the one or the other is contracted, to either side. The seventh and eighth muscles originate from the sides of the lower jaw near the root of

16

the molar teeth on either side. They are inserted along the length of the tongue on the lower side and move downward and laterally that part of the tongue which is conspicuous in the gaping mouth before dissection. The ninth muscle arises from the inner aspect of the lower jaw near the tip of the chin; it is thick and has a few furrows or wrinkles. It is inserted in the lower part of the tongue and moves the tongue outward; its body as seen before dissection is interlaced with fibers of such a sort that by the great workings of Nature the tongue is very readily carried in every direction of movement [20].

Four muscles contracting the little crevice of the larynx join the first cartilage of the larynx to the second. Four muscles opening this crevice bind the third cartilage to the second. Two closing the little crevice connect the third cartilage to the first. Two others set in the base of the third cartilage contract the crevice tightly. These twelve muscles are said to belong to the larynx [21]. Two additional ones proceed together from the hyoid bone and insert into the first cartilage; they elevate it in front and also retract the crevice of the larynx [22]. Two muscles arising from the breastbone extend to the same cartilage [23]. Then two arising in turn from the posterior region of the esophagus (completely fleshy, as are almost all of the laryngeal muscles) are also inserted into the sides of that cartilage [24], together with the two already mentioned as contracting the larynx. Two others extend from the hyoid bone and insert into the root of the epiglottis; they pull the latter up and forward [25].

In the group of muscles which move the head are also those which move the first cervical vertebra separately [26]. There are seven pairs of them in all, because the same number, of course, is reckoned on each side. The first pair passes from the spines of the upper five thoracic vertebrae; ascending gradually in an oblique direction outward, they are implanted on the occipital bone. The second pair, apparently formed not of two but of a number of muscles, is relatively different; a special portion of it arises from the transverse processes of the four upper thoracic and five lower cervical vertebrae and, passing inward somewhat obliquely, inserts on the occipital bone. The third pair arises from the spine of the second cervical vertebra and, creeping outward somewhat obliquely, also inserts on the occipital bone. The fourth pair, likewise inserted on the occipital bone, passes from the first vertebra at the place which, in other vertebrae, ends in a spine. The fifth pair is carried somewhat transversely from the middle of the occipital bone to the lateral processes of the first vertebra. The sixth pair extends from the spine of the second vertebra to the same processes; like the five pairs just mentioned, it is located in the posterior region of the neck; like the third, fourth, and fifth pairs, it is composed of muscles which are completely fleshy, round, and slender. The seventh pair is more noteworthy; from the top of the breastbone where the clavicles articulate, two muscles (one on each side) have their origin and, borne obliquely upward, they extend to an insertion on the mastoid process of the head. When the first four pairs are tensed at the same time, the head is moved back; when the muscles of the first three pairs are tensed from the opposite side they assist in turning the head, and in that movement the fifth and sixth pair turn the first cervical vertebra and the head circularly. The function of the seventh pair of muscles, operating together, is to direct the head straight forward, but when they work alternately, they turn the head around. The muscles of the neck subserve the motion of the head to the extent that the latter is turned with the neck secondarily and is led laterally toward the shoulders [27].

Among the eight pairs of muscles which move the back, these muscles are to be classed [28]. The first pair, beginning from the sides of the fifth thoracic vertebra, extends to the first cervical vertebra below the esophagus and flexes the upper part of the back. The second extends on either side from the first rib of the thorax and inserts on the inner portion of the trans- verse processes of the cervical vertebrae; it turns the neck to the side but rather more in front. The third, taking its origin from the transverse proc- esses of the upper six thoracic vertebrae, is implanted in the external region of the transverse processes of the cervical vertebrae; it leads the neck back- ward, inclining the neck to the side. The fourth pair extends from the spine of the seventh thoracic vertebra to the second cervical vertebra, inserting into all intervening vertebrae, as does the first pair, and originating from them also; it extends the upper part of the back. The fifth pair has a muscle on either side from the iliac bone to the transverse processes of the lumbar vertebrae and inserts on the lowest rib of the thorax; it flexes the lower part of the back. The sixth, arising in the back from the lowest aspect of the os sacrum, extends to the neck; it inserts on the transverse processes of the lumbar vertebrae and even more distinctly on those of the thorax. When both muscles of this pair contract, the back is extended; when only one of the pair is in action (as among the other pairs also), this provides an oblique movement or toward the sides. The seventh, hidden beneath the sixth, originates from the posterior aspect of the os sacrum; attached to all the intermediate spines, it ascends as far as the spine of the eleventh thoracic vertebra and, by successively drawing the spines together, it extends the back in this region. The eighth pair, extending from the eleventh thoracic vertebra to the seventh cervical vertebra, is completely joined to the intervening spines in the same fashion as is the seventh.

One muscle moves the scapula to the chest [29]; it arises from the second, third, fourth, and fifth ribs of the thorax before their cartilaginous termination and is inserted in triangular fashion on the inner process of the scapula. A second muscle of those which move the scapula arises from the occiput and, following along the length of the neck to the spine of the eighth thoracic vertebra, originates from the apexes of the vertebral spines as well; it inserts on the spine of the scapula, the acromion, and a portion of the clavicle. All of that part of it lying in the neck pulls the scapula upward; that part below the neck in the posterior portion of the thorax and which resembles a monk's hood, draws the scapula downward. The third springs from the transverse processes of the upper cervical vertebrae; this muscle inserts into the upper angle of the base of the scapula and lifts it upward. The fourth arises from the spines of the fifth, sixth, and seventh cervical vertebrae and especially from the spines of the first three thoracic vertebrae; this muscle inserts at the base of the scapula and draws it somewhat backward.

The first author of the movements of the arm [30] arises from the middle region of the clavicle nearest the breastbone and from the breastbone; narrowed into somewhat of an angle, it draws the arm to the chest. The second muscle, originating from the other part of the clavicle, the point of the shoulder, and from the spine of the scapula, is inserted transversely by its apex into the humerus; beautifully covering the shoulder joint, it lifts the arm upward in various directions. Its shape is not unlike that of the

19

Greek letter Δ. The third muscle proceeds from the lower border of the scapula; it draws the arm straight backward. The fourth muscle takes its origin from the spine of the sixth thoracic vertebra to the lower aspect of the os sacrum and from the apexes of the intermediate spines. It is drawn together into the vertex of a triangle and is inserted into the humerus where the three muscles just enumerated insert, far below the articulation of the head of the bone with the scapula. This muscle draws the arm downward in various directions, since its base is quite broad and not led from a point in such a fashion that the muscle would exercise a wholly simple movement. The fifth muscle occupies the entire cavity of the scapula facing the ribs. The sixth appropriates to itself the entire gibbous part of the scapula lying below the spine. The seventh fills the conspicuous sinus between the spine of the scapula and its upper border. These three are inserted by a broad implantation into the ligaments surrounding the shoulder joint; they accom-plish the rotation of the arm [31], and the seventh seems to be of some assistance in raising the arm.

The first muscle of those which move the thorax [32] originates from the clavicle and is inserted into the first rib of the thorax; it moves this rib upward, at the same time assisting the dilatation of the thorax. The second arises from the base of the scapula and is inserted with digitations into the upper eight ribs long before they terminate in cartilage; it moves the ribs outward and dilates the thorax. The third muscle takes its origin as a broad membrane from the apexes of the three lower cervical spines as well as from the first thoracic vertebra and inserts with three digitations into the three interspaces of the four upper ribs beneath the base of the scapula; it moves these ribs obliquely upward and enlarges the thorax. The fourth originates on the iliac bone and passes upward to the neck, it is inserted into the twelve ribs where they first leave the vertebrae, and it contracts the thorax. The fifth originates from the apexes of the spines of the two lowest thoracic and some of the lumbar vertebrae. It is membranous, passes transversely, and is inserted into the ninth, tenth, and eleventh ribs at the place where they turn back into the deep parts; it dilates the thorax. The sixth lies back in the breadth of the thorax; it extends to the cartilages of the true ribs and to the side of the breastbone and contracts the thorax.

Internal and external muscles lie in the intervals of the twelve ribs [33]. Those external ones which are in the intervals between the bony ribs send their fibers from the upper rib obliquely to the lower rib straight opposite; the internal muscles send their fibers from the lower rib obliquely upward in the anterior direction to the upper rib. In the six intervals of the cartilages which are allotted to the true ribs, the fibers of the external muscles creep from the lower cartilage to the opposite upper cartilage in an oblique direction, but the internal fibers extend in reverse from the upper cartilage to the lower.

Hence, muscles in groups of four are counted in the intervals of the six true ribs. In the interspaces of the false ribs, however, there are groups of only two. All the intercostal muscles on one side total thirty-four; all of them have the function of contracting the thorax. Forty muscles are enumerated thus far on one side of the thorax; there are the same number on the other side, and to these eighty muscles one is added, to wit, the septum transversum [diaphragm] itself [34], inserted into the lowest part of the breastbone and the cartilages of the false ribs as well as into the upper lumbar vertebrae. In the middle it is sinewy [35] but fleshy circumferentially toward the insertion; it divides those organs which serve for making blood and for generation from the region of the heart and of the parts which minister to the heart [36]. It has the function of dilating the thorax.

To these are added eight muscles of the abdomen [37], four on each side. The first or outermost sends its fibers obliquely downward and forward, forming with its mate a covering for the abdomen. The second sends its fibers obliquely upward in the opposite direction and with its mate forms a covering for the abdomen. The third sends its fibers straight upward from the pubic bone to the chest. The fourth has its fibers distributed transversely and with its mate forms a covering for the abdomen, as do the oblique muscles; it renders assistance, no less than the other abdominal muscles, to the constriction of the thorax [38].

Two muscles flex the elbow [39], of which the anterior derives one head from the higher region of the neck of the scapula and another head from the internal process of the scapula; formed with these heads, it is inserted into the radius. The posterior muscle originates from the humerus and is inserted into the anterior region of the elbow joint or, rather, into the ulna. Three muscles extend the elbow [40]; one originates from the lower border of the scapula, and the second from the posterior aspect of the neck of the humerus. These merge together in their descent and a third joins with them, arising from near the middle of the length of the humerus and inserting together with them into the posterior process of the ulna.

In the inner aspect of the elbow lies a slender muscle which arises from the inner protuberance of the humerus and turns into a flat tendon lying beneath the internal skin of the greater part of the hand. By its function it is believed that this skin is rendered less movable and more fitted for grasping [41].

The radius is led into pronation by two muscles [42]. One arises from the inner region of the elbow joint and is implanted obliquely on the radius; the other is borne from the ulna transversely to the radius near the wrist. The radius is led into supination [43] by two other muscles, one of them long and extending from the humerus to the lower part of the radius, to which the wrist is articulated. The other extends obliquely from the outer aspect of the elbow joint to the middle of the length of the radius and inserts there.

The wrist is moved by four special muscles [44]; the first two grow forth from the inner protuberance of the humerus. One is inserted in the postbrachial bone which supports the index finger [second metacarpal], the other on the smallest bone of the wrist [pisiform]. The third arises from the humerus and is inserted with a bifid tendon into the postbrachial bones which sustain the index and middle fingers. The fourth, passing from the external tuberosity of the humerus and extending along the ulna, forms an insertion on the postbrachial bone which supports the little finger. The first two simultaneously flex the wrist; when the third and fourth are simultaneously contracted, they extend it. When the first is tensed with the third, the wrist is moved toward the inner side; when the second and fourth act together, it is inclined to the outer side.

The first of the muscles which move the fingers of the hand [45] arises from the inner and anterior region of the elbow joint; proximal to the root of the wrist it splits into four tendons, inserted into the second internodes of the four fingers and flexing the internodes. The second arises from the same place as the first but is more slanting and lies under the first muscle. It is also divided into four tendons, lying under those of the first; they pierce those tendons proximal to the root of the second internode of the fingers. Finally they form an insertion in the third bones of the four fingers and flex them. The third arises from the radius near the elbow joint, is inserted into the third joint of the thumb, and flexes it. Thirteen other muscles follow the third muscle in series; they lie in the hand, and of them, two are inserted into the first bone of each of the five fingers and flex them. Three insert into the second internode [first phalanx] of the thumb also and move it. The seventeenth muscle of those which move the fingers arises from the external protuberance of the armbone; it is inserted in the index, middle, and ring fingers especially and extends those fingers. The eighteenth muscle proceeds from the same region as the muscle just mentioned; it is the prime originator of the extension of the little finger and, blended to a varying extent with that tendon of the seventeenth which is inserted into the three bones of the ring finger, it subserves therein the abduction of that finger toward the exterior. The nineteenth, along with the twenty-first, has a common origin from the ulna; it arises near the region of the wrist. Almost divided into two tendons, it sends one to the outer side of the index, the other to the side of the middle finger, and is considered the author of the abduction of those fingers to the external side. The twentieth arises from the wrist; it extends along the external side of the postbrachial bone which supports the little finger, inserts on the first bone of that finger, and moves it outward to the side. The twenty-first is inserted on the outer side of the thumb as far as the third joint; it extends the thumb toward the index finger. The twenty-second proceeds from the ulna a little above the muscle just mentioned, and soon splits into two parts, one part ends in a tendon; it inserts on the bone of the wrist which supports the thumb and, passing to the place where the hand follows the motion of the radius in pronation, it lends assistance to that motion. The other part is likewise split into two parts which form one tendon each. Of these, the one inserts into the external side of the outer region of the first bone of the thumb; the other grows on that bone and is inserted on the second and third bones of the thumb. By

23

the function of these tendons, the thumb is flexed inward. The twenty-third occupies the region near the inner side of the first bone of the thumb and distinctly separates the thumb from the index finger. The twenty-fourth springs from the bone of the postbrachial which supports the index finger, is inserted chiefly into the first bone of the thumb, and brings the thumb close to the index. There remain four slender muscles extending in the palm from the four tendons of the second muscle of those which move the fingers. They are inserted on the inner side of the first bone of the four fingers, serving the abduction of those fingers thumbward.

On the internal aspect of the elbow lies the muscle which forms the broad tendon of the hand: the first and second muscles which cause the movements of the wrist; the first, second, and third of those which move the fingers; and two muscles which pronate the radius. In the external aspect lie the seventeenth, eighteenth, nineteenth, twenty-first, and twenty-second of the muscles which move the fingers; the third and fourth of those which have charge of the movements of the wrist; and two which supinate the radius. These total nine; there are ten if you distinguish from the twenty-second of those muscles which move the fingers that portion which offers a tendon to the bone of the wrist which supports the thumb. In the hand itself ten muscles are observed which flex the first joints of the fingers; three flex the second internode of the thumb. Then there are the twentieth, twenty-third, and twenty-fourth of those which move the fingers, and four muscles by which the four fingers are moved toward the thumb.

Each of the male testes, with their seminal vessels, is covered by a tunic which proceeds from the peritoneum [46] and is nourished by some straight fleshy fibers [47] inserted into the lowest region of the vessel carrying the semen [48]. One muscle of the testis is made up of these fibers; by its function the testis is drawn upward closely. Thus also the membranes which secure the uterus are equipped on either side with fleshy fibers, and in this way the uterus has one muscle on either side by the assistance of which it is easily drawn upward toward the ilia [49]. One muscle, preventing the untimely excretion of the urine, arises circularly on the neck of the bladder [50]. Likewise, there is also a muscle which encircles the end of the rectum;

it prevents premature expulsion [51]. Two other muscles pull the rectum quickly upward after expulsion [52]. A slender muscle is inserted at the root of the penis from the pubic bone on either side, assisting its erection very slowly [53]. Likewise, two muscles arise close to each other from the anterior region of the muscle which embraces the rectum circularly; they are inserted at the urinary passage where it turns back and upward under the bones of the pubis. They dilate the passage during the ejaculation of semen so that it may not be shut off at the bend [54].

The first of the muscles which move the thigh [55] arises from the outer-most aspect of the iliac bone and the posterior region of the coccyx; it passes to the posterior region of the greater process of the femur and also is attached by a broad insertion into its root. The second muscle is hidden under the first, in large part, but extends rather more forward from the anterior region of the iliac bone and is inserted into the greater process of the femur. The third is much smaller than the second muscle and is completely hidden by it. It arises from the iliac bone near the posterior region of the acetabulum of the coxendix [hipbone]; it is also inserted on the greater process of the femur. Like the two previously mentioned, it extends the femur, moving the latter outward to the side. The fourth muscle extends from the three lower bones of the os sacrum, also inserts on the greater process, and extends the femur and turns it outward to some extent. The fifth is the largest of all the muscles of the body and, with many parts, it takes its origin from the bone of the coxendix [ischium] and of the pubis and is inserted into the posterior region of the femur as far as its lower heads [condyles]. This muscle is the author of extension of the femur, holding it upright and moving it inward with a portion of it especially thrust forward from the lower region of the pubic bone. The sixth muscle takes its origin from the two lowest thoracic vertebrae and from some of the higher lumbar vertebrae; inserted into the lesser process of the femur, together with the seventh muscle, it flexes the thigh. The seventh muscle proceeds from the entire internal aspect of the iliac bone; it also is inserted on the lesser process, higher than the sixth. The eighth passes from the pubic bone and is im-planted with a long insertion below the lesser process of the femur; it flexes the thigh and also moves the thigh strongly inward. The ninth muscle occupies the anterior region of the foramen of the pubic bone; inserted into the greater process of the femur, it turns the femur inward. The tenth occupies the posterior or internal aspect of the foramen just mentioned and is very securely bent around the posterior part of the coxendix bone [ischium]. Like the other muscles here, it is increased by muscles arising from it. It is inserted on the greater process of the femur and turns the thigh outwardly.

The first muscle of those which move the leg [56] proceeds from the anterior region of the spine of the iliac bone and passes somewhat obliquely along the internal region of the thigh; it is inserted into the anterior region of the tibia and is at once the most slender and the longest muscle of the entire body. The second muscle proceeds from the union of the pubic bones: it inserts into the same region as the first. The third muscle begins from the appendix of the coxendix bone [ischium]; it is also implanted in the same region of the tibia. The fourth muscle passes forward from the same region of the coxendix bone and in its descent receives a portion of its substance from the bone of the femur; it is inserted into the articulation of the tibia with the fibula, but especially into the fibula. The fifth muscle originates also in the same region and is inserted on the anterior aspect of the tibia with the first three muscles but in a less slanting direction. The sixth grows out from the spine of the ilium; it is covered by a sort of membrane along with the muscles investing the femur and is inserted in the knee joint rather near the outer side. The seventh muscle originates from the root of the greater process of the femur and occupies the external side of the thigh; it forms a tendon with the eighth and ninth, to which the patella is attached. The eighth arises from the neck of the femur and from the base of the latter's greater process; this muscle closely encircles almost all of the femur. The ninth, taking origin conspicuously in the anterior region, arises from the protuberance of the hipbone above its joint with the femur; lying on the seventh and eighth muscles, the ninth muscle is carried to the anterior region of the knee. Implanted very firmly on the anterior region of the tibia, this muscle turns into a tendon, forming one with the two muscles just mentioned. Thus the first, sixth, seventh, eighth, and ninth muscles are considered the agents of the extension of the tibia, while the second, third, fourth, and fifth clearly flex the tibia.*

The muscle which is hidden in the popliteal region [57] and which extends obliquely from the external ligament of the knee joint to the tibia, does not flex the leg; if it does anything, it vaguely imitates the motion of the first muscle which pronates the radius.

Of the muscles which move the foot [58], the first originates from the inner head [condyle] of the femur near the knee joint, as the second begins from the outer head; both form the posterior part of the calf of the leg, and joining with the tendon of the fourth muscle which moves the foot, they are inserted on the heel. The third is a small muscle also proceeding from the external head of the femur and here in the popliteal region terminates in a very slender tendon which is inserted into the inner side of the os calcis. The fourth, the largest of those which move the foot, begins from the articulation of the fibula with the tibia; it ends in a very strong tendon which is united with the tendon of the first two muscles likewise inserted, together with it, into the heel. The fifth muscle is placed very deeply in the posterior region of the tibia and the fibula. It originates from those same bones where they first separate, and near the rear of the internal aspect of the malleolus, it sends forth a tendon to a bone of the tarsus; the tendon is inserted in this bone, which is contiguous to the bone resembling a die [59]. The sixth, proceeding from the tibia where the fibula is articulated with it superiorly, is situated in the anterior region of the leg; its tendon inserts on the root of the metatarsal [os pedii] which supports the great toe. The seventh arises from the fibula, occupies the external side of the leg, and inserts a tendon, reflected under the inferior part of the foot, on the bone which supports the great toe. Inserting a tendon on the root of the bone which supports the little toe, the eighth is hidden under the seventh and also arises from the fibula. The ninth is part of that one which, as I am about to describe, extends the toes of the foot; it is inserted at almost the

---

* . . . . *atque ita primus, sextus, septimus, octavus et nonus tibiae extensionis opifices habentur, secundo interim, tertio, quarto et quinto tibiam liquide extendentibus* is the reading in the Latin text.

To avoid the repetition of idea in *extensionis* and *extendentibus* which makes nonsense of this passage as it stands, I am forced to conclude that Vesalius meant to write *flectentibus* instead of *extendentibus*. I therefore emend the passage to read *flectentibus* and translate accordingly.

middle of the length of the metatarsal supporting the little toe. The foot is extended with the first five muscles or is firmly set upon the ground, although the third muscle performs this function feebly and, if it contributes at all to the movement of the foot, it turns the foot obliquely inward. The foot is flexed by the sixth, seventh, eighth, and ninth muscles, and by their function it makes lateral movements, in so far as each muscle moves it.

The first of the muscles which move the toes [60] is located entirely in the sole of the foot and in its lowest part possesses an exceedingly thick membrane acting as an intimate covering not unlike the broad tendon in the hand. This muscle arises from the bone of the heel and sends single tendons to the second internodes of the four toes; these tendons flex the toes. The second and third muscles creep through the posterior region of the leg; the second arises from the tibia more than the fibula and, having arisen from it, sends into the sole of the foot a tendon which then divides into four tendons. One of these is inserted into the third bone of each of the four toes; the tendons, as happens also in the hand, pierce the tendons of the first muscle and flex those bones. The third arises from the joint of the fibula to the tibia and, extending more from the fibula, it sends a tendon to the sole of the foot, whence a small portion of it mingles with tendons which flex the third internode of the index and middle toes. The remainder of the muscle is inserted as a whole into the second bone of the great toe and flexes it. Ten muscles, mutually intermingled in a remarkable way, succeed these; attached to the metacarpals, they flex the first bones of the toes, with two muscles extending to each of the toes. The fourteenth muscle, of which the ninth muscle of those which move the foot was reckoned a part, arises from the anterior region of the tibia and is divided into four tendons inserted into the four toes and regarded as the cause of their extension. The fifteenth also proceeds from the anterior region of the tibia; this muscle inserts on the great toe and is the master of this toe's extension. The sixteenth muscle lies in the upper region of the foot and is a fleshy mass divided into four tendons; of these, one is inserted on the external side of the upper aspect of the great toe, the second in that of the index, the third in the middle toe, and the fourth on the annular digit. These tendons move these toes toward the outer side. The seventeenth muscle occupies the external side of the foot and is inserted on the first bone of the little toe; it moves this toe away from the other toes. The eighteenth muscle extends from the internal side of the foot; it abducts the big toe straight from the others. Then in the sole of the foot is a fleshy substance [61] divided into four slender portions which cling to the tendons by the function of which the third bones of the four toes are flexed. These portions are inserted on the inner side of the four toes at the first joint; they are considered the authors of the adduction of the toes toward the great toe.

If you will count this last as four portions instead of four muscles, you will observe in the posterior region of the leg the first, second, third, and fourth of those muscles which move the foot, the second and third of those which move the toes, and under these the fifth of those which move the foot. In the anterior region lie the sixth, seventh, eighth, and ninth muscles which cause the movements of the foot and the fourteenth and fifteenth of those which move the toes. In the foot you will have the first of those muscles which move the toes and the ten muscles which flex the first bones of the toes and the sixteenth, seventeenth, and eighteenth also of those which move the toes, unless it be proposed to divide the sixteenth into more than one muscle.

In the description of the muscles, I have not made mention at all points of the ligaments, since for the most part they are mutually related with the joints. In all the joints is a ligament [62] running circularly from one bone to another or to a cartilage or from a cartilage to a bone, or the cartilage insertion extends from it separately. Special ligaments are an accession to a few joints. In the joint of the skull is a certain smooth round ligament running from the dens of the second cervical vertebra to the occipital bone [63]. Along the posterior region of the dens, another one is carried transversely in the first vertebra [64]. The bodies of the vertebrae are joined by somewhat cartilaginous ligaments [65]; the ascending and descending processes of the same bodies are connected with strong ligaments, but these only go roundabout in circular fashion [66]. Then a membranous ligament is situated in the intervals of the spines, as also in the forearm and the leg, where the bones are separated from one another [67]. In addition, in the foramen of the pubic bone occurs a ligament, or rather a membrane, of this nature [68]. In the joint of the humerus, three special ligaments are observed [69]. The first is round, arises from the internal process of the scapula, and runs to the external aspect of the head of the humerus. Two others arise from the higher region of the neck of the scapula; they extend to the same head, and one also is here led from the internal process of the scapula to the acromion [*summus humerus*]. In the joining of the bones of the wrist among themselves and with the metacarpal bones, as also in the foot, cartilaginous ligaments intervene. From the os sacrum two roundish ligaments extend to the ischium [70]. From the superior part of the head of the femur, a round ligament is inserted into the acetabulum of the hipbone [71]. A cartilaginous ligament is in the middle of the knee joint, and in the posterior region of that joint and on both sides, a special ligament is obvious to dissectors [72]. In the number of the ligaments covering the tendons transversely and containing the tendons, lest they slip from their seat [73], there is one in the inner region of the wrist which may be considered one and continuous, following the entire inner aspect of each digit [74]; six occur next to the root of the wrist in the outer aspect of the radius and ulna [75]. A ligament is also observed in the anterior region of the leg near the talus [76], and three between the heel and the internal malleolus [77]. There is one between the heel and the external malleolus [78]. Also, ligaments of this nature are observed in the internal or inferior aspect of the toes.

GENERAL INTERPRETATION

IN attempting the identification of the muscles described in this chapter, a technique of annotation has been adopted which is well illustrated by note 16. The identifying name of the muscle group given in the text is stated briefly, and the numbers following correspond to the order in which the muscles themselves are described. The method serves the three following purposes:

1. By reducing the number of footnote reference marks, the continuity of the text is less disturbed.
2. Since, in subsequent chapters, the text makes several references to muscles by statements such as "the third muscle of those which move the jaw" and since the legends for the muscle plates are in similar form, it is intended that more rapid identification of the structure to which reference is made may result. It should be stated here that a complete collation of notes and plate legends has not been possible but that in a number of trials the device has proved useful.
3. Emphasis is placed where the text places it, on muscle groups which act on, and across, joints. The text's discussion of individual muscles is minimized; instead of directing attention to the minute details of their bony relationships, they are treated as functional masses. An increasing number of anatomists at present is recognizing the soundness of this view not only in kinesiology but as a basic philosophy of human biology. Yet this is only a rediscovery of a principle derivable from Vesalius' text and stated more than two centuries earlier with conciseness and clarity by Mondino: " . . . . we must first gain an idea of the whole, and then of the parts. For all our knowledge doth begin from what is known. For though the known is oft vague and though our knowledge of the whole is of a surety vaguer than that of the parts, we yet begin with a general consideration of the whole" (Charles Singer, "Fasciculo di Medicina," *Monumenta Medica,* series Vol. II, Part I, Florence: R. Lier and Co., 1925, p. 59).

While the outline of Vesalius' text corresponds to the "systematic" anatomy, the chapters themselves are written as functional anatomy (or, to borrow a term noticed recently, "dynamic morphology"). Vesalius' conception of muscles as contractile masses associated with a joint and acting across it in co-ordination is more in accord with our ideas of synergy than is the treatment of them as single structures. The reasoning which derives a muscle's action by considering it as an isolated contractile element tending to shorten the distance between its points of attachment is incorrect physiologically (for it is rare, except in pathologic states of major paralysis, for a muscle to act alone); it is incorrect embryologically and neurologically; finally, it has served to introduce errors which have been carried forward through many editions of the standard encyclopedias of anatomy. The modern student has difficulty in finding in any of these great reference texts as clear a concept of integration as was available to the Renaissance student who owned a Vesalian *Epitome;* only with effort do we lead the student from the morass of isolated osteologic and myologic textual statements to the terra firma of synergy.

We are now being offered texts which are regional and functional rather than systematic anatomies. Some teachers are becoming more outspoken in their criticism of the teaching of anatomy as a discipline in morphology alone. To select one from many, a recent discussion of the approach to the teaching of anatomy states that "Stress is laid on the movements at joints and on their limitations. . . . The muscles are considered in functional groups rather than as separate units. . . . In this department we have tended to neglect . . . the memorizing of muscular attachments in relation to a bone instead of to a joint. . . . " (Sheehan, "The Physiology of Anatomy," *J. A. Am. M. Coll.*, XV [1940] 363).

The whole field of integration of muscle group activity is being subjected to the laboratory investigation it so badly needs, and we may anticipate in the not so distant future the time when all anatomists take up where Vesalius left off with the teaching of this aspect of functional anatomy.

NOTES

1. **VESALIUS** follows the old view which confused ligaments and nerves, or regarded the terms as synonymous. The Greek word from which comes our "nerve" originally meant *tendon* or *sinew;* hence the confusion. Observe (*a*) the relic of this usage which remains to us in the term "aponeurosis"—the flattened and membranous type of fibrous muscular attachment as opposed to "tendon" (example: the *aponeurosis* of the external abdominal oblique muscle, the *galea aponeurotica* of the epicranium); (*b*) the students' nickname for the slender, shining long tendon of the plantaris muscle: "Freshman's nerve."

2. "Originating from": *principium ducens*—not in the histogenetic sense of originating, but "leading forth from," in the modern anatomical sense of a muscle's origin.

3. Tendinous membranes to which are attached the muscle fibers, as in a multipennate muscle such as the deltoid.

4. Lead: compare the modern colloquial name for tendons, "leaders."

5. Dermis and epidermis.

6. The deep fascia; the extended argument is presented in the *Fabrica,* and Vesalius does not consider it to be carneous.

7. The superficial fascia, with its panniculus adiposus.

8. Levator palpebrae superioris muscle.

9. Orbicularis oculi muscle. The meaning of the paragraph is thus: where the connective tissue of the tendon attached to the upper border of the superior tarsus (and the fascia-sheath overlying this tendon) is followed back into the orbit, the fleshy (muscular) portion encountered is the levator; however, outside the palpebral fascia may be seen the incomplete circle of the sphincterlike muscle opposed to the levator —the orbicularis oculi.

10. Muscles which move the eye: (1) rectus medialis, (2) rectus lateralis, (3) rectus superior, (4) rectus inferior, (5) and (6) obliqui superior et inferior.

11. The fibrous ring annulus tendineus communis and the optic nerve. It is, of course, incorrect to include the inferior oblique as among the muscles arising from the annulus, for the former's origin is much more anterior, just lateral to the lacrimal sulcus. It is thus more equatorial in direction as compared to the meridional orientation of the first five named.

12. The seventh muscle of the eye is the retractor oculi (or *choanoides,* "funnel-shaped"), not present in human beings. In the sheep's eye it may be dissected out as a sheet of muscle underlying the other six, incompletely divided longitudinally, attaching into the sclera behind the recti, and passing back to surround the optic nerve. See Sisson and Grossman, *The Anatomy of Domestic Animals* (1938), p. 883, for discussion of this muscle. Cf. *Fabrica* XII, xi; also Cushing's *Bio-Bibliography,* pp. 186

and 190 for the exchange of opinion between Fallopius' *Observationes Anatomicae* and Vesalius' *Examen* (1561).

13. Quadratus labii superioris: angular head on the one (medial) side, and infraorbital and zygomatic heads on the other (lateral) side.

14. Nasalis, especially its alar portion.

15. Muscles which move the cheeks and lips: (1) platysma, including the risorius, which is not always well separated; (2) zygomaticus; (3) mentalis, quadratus labii inferioris, and triangularis, treated as a single mass; (4) buccinator—observe the correctness of its inclusion with the other muscles now known to arise from the second branchial arch and innervated by the facial nerve. The origin of the name is from *buccinare:* "to sound the trumpet"; compare Vesalius' observation on "inflate" (the cheeks). The muscle is set aside as "somewhat different," as if it is recognized that it is less a mimetic muscle than one associated with the next group, the muscles of mastication.

16. Muscles which move the jaw: (1) temporalis, (2) masseter, (3) pterygoidei, (4) digastricus.

17. Dunglison (*A Dictionary of Medical Science,* rev. ed., 1874) gives *buccinator* as the synonym. However, the muscle referred to is obvious from attachments given in the text, the buccinator has already been described, and Motherby (*A New Medical Dictionary,* London, 1785) indicates the masseter, as also Cooper, *et al.* The name "mansorius" is not found in Hyrtl's *Onomatologia Anatomica,* usually a rich source of anatomical synonyms.

18. Muscles moving the hyoid bone: (1) sternohyoids, (2) geniohyoids, (3) stylohyoids, (4) omohyoids.

19. Extrinsic muscles of the tongue, in pairs: (1) aponeurotic fibers of genioglossus and hyothyroid membrane; (2) hyoglosus; (5 and 6, the third pair) styloglossus; (7 and 8, the fourth pair) mylohyoids (which do not actually insert into the tongue but form a raphe inserting on the hyoid bone and make a diaphragm on which the tongue rests). The "ninth muscle" is the genioglossus.

20. The intrinsic muscles (generally oriented in three directions: vertical, longitudinal, and transverse).

21. Muscles belonging to the larynx: first four are the cricothyreoidei (pars obliqua et pars recta) paired, second four are the cricoarytaenoidei laterales et posteriores, next pair is the thyreoarytaenoidei, and the last pair the arytaenoidei. This makes the total of twelve (six pairs).

22. Thyrohyoidei.

23. Sternothyroidei.

24. Constrictor pharyngis, probably inferior.

25. Hyoepiglottic ligament.

26. Muscles which move the head and first cervical vertebra: (1) splenius capitis et

34

cervicis, (2) probably semispinalis capitis, (3) rectus capitis posterior major, (4) rectus capitis posterior minor, (5) obliquus capitis superior, (6) obliquus capitis inferior, (7) sternocleidomastoidei.

Observe that Vesalius probably turned the cadaver after demonstrating the hyoid and laryngeal musculature, since all of the pairs above except the seventh are most easily approached posteriorly.

27. I.e., indirectly rotate the head by rotation of the neck and do not directly act on the head.

28. Muscles which move the back: (1) longus colli, (2) scalenus anterior (and possibly including scalenus medius; these muscles vary in attachment and arrangement of fibers), (3) longissimus cervicis (portion of sacrospinalis), (4) semispinalis cervicis, (5) quadratus lumborum, (6) longissimus position of sacrospinalis, (7) multifidus, especially the more prominently developed lumbar portion, (8) semispinalis dorsi. The meaning of the last sentence is that these last two named are not uninterrupted bands of muscle but composed of many slips, with attachment to all vertebrae intervening between their termini.

29. Muscles which move the scapula: (1) pectoralis minor, (2) trapezius, (3) levator scapulae, (4) rhomboidei major et minor. The monk's hood is an apt comparison for the trapezius; some readers may be more familiar with the shape of the (derived) hood worn with academic dress and may carry the likeness forward from that. The text reads as if the trapezius functions either to elevate or to depress the scapula; its mechanism is not always clearly defined today. Actually, it probably *rotates* the bone, the upper part elevating the outer portion of the scapular spine, the lower (thoracic) part simultaneously depressing the inner portion of the spine. The center of rotation is in the spine and receives the predominantly aponeurotic, nonmuscular portions of the trapezius, acting to stabilize the fulcrum. By thus rotating the scapula (moving the inferior angle laterally), the trapezius aids the deltoid in its task of abduction of the humerus.

30. Muscles which move the arm: (1) pectoralis major, (2) deltoideus, (3) teres major, (4) latissimus dorsi (the site of insertion described means "at the place where the first three muscles form a continuous line or mass of insertion extending far down the humerus from near its head"), (5) subscapularis, (6) infraspinatus, (7) supraspinatus.

31. The fifth, sixth, and seventh of the group actually reinforce the ligaments of the shoulder joint and are concerned with internal and external rotation.

32. Muscles which move the thorax: (1) subclavius, (2) serratus anterior (modern texts reverse the order of origin and insertion here), (3) serratus posterior superior, (4) probably iliocostales lumborum et dorsi, (5) serratus posterior inferior, (6) transversus thoracis.

33. The enumeration of the intercostal muscles is at first glance somewhat formidable. By the term "true ribs" (costae verae) we mean the seven which connect to the sternum by separate costal cartilages. By "false ribs" (costae spuriae) we indicate the

eighth, ninth, and tenth, all sharing a cartilaginous connection, and the eleventh and twelfth "floating ribs," devoid of cartilaginous segments. There are, then, six interspaces for the true ribs and five associated with the false ribs. (The distinction between true and false ribs can be traced back at least as far as Gerhard's translation of Avicenna's *Canon;* see Singer's *Evolution of Anatomy,* p. 81.)

Each of the six interspaces is occupied by an external and an internal intercostal muscle. Vesalius subdivides each layer into two muscles: first, the fibers between the ribs proper; and second, the fibers between the costal cartilages. He thereby obtains four muscles per interspace. This division has validity for the internal intercostals (Wiggers' *Physiology in Health and Disease,* in the chapter on "Respiratory Movements and Mechanics of Lung Inflation," differentiates internal intercostals into interchondral and interosseous parts on the basis of functional differences during respiration), but the interchondral portions of the external sheet are aponeurotic and nonmuscular "external intercostal ligaments" in modern conception (Morris, *op. cit.,* p. 488). Nevertheless, it being clear that Vesalius regards them as muscles, we find four muscles per interspace in six interspaces, a total of twenty-four muscles.

In the five interspaces associated with the false ribs, there are no appreciable interchondral spaces, with consequent lack of muscles in this category. Therefore, there exist only the two (external and internal) between each rib, a total of ten in all five interspaces.

The figure thirty-four is the sum of twenty-four plus ten muscles. To list forty, include the six muscles listed in note 32; doubling this forty (to include both sides), we obtain the eighty.

34. The term "septum transversum" is now an embryologic one; the diaphragm is related to it but the two are not identical.

35. The central tendon.

36. The relationship of the alimentary canal to hematopoiesis is set forth in Chap. III; this, plus the liver-spleen system of blood formation and the urogenital system, completes the abdominal contents. The lungs minister to the heart in several ways; according to Plato (one of Vesalius' authorities), they even serve mechanically as a shock absorber (*Timaeus*). We speak frequently of the cardiorespiratory system.

37. Muscles of the abdomen: (1) obliquus externus abdominis, (2) obliquus internus abdominis, (3) rectus abdominis, and (4) transversus abdominis. Observe that in this text no light is thrown on the superior attachment of the rectus abdominis. Vesalius' plates on muscle in the *Fabrica* have been criticized as showing this muscle ascending as high as the manubrium.

38. Compare here the training of singers, speakers, and wind-instrumentalists in diaphragmatic and abdominal breathing, rather than intercostal. Vesalius seems to attribute to these muscles only the accessory respiratory function, along with a passive containing of the abdominal viscera. Other functions, such as in efforts of expulsion (childbirth, defecation) and in lifting of weights, have been neglected.

39. Muscles which flex the elbow: (1) the anterior, biceps brachii, (2) the posterior, brachialis, probably including coracobrachialis with the short head.

40. Muscles which extend the elbow: the triceps brachialis—(1) long head, (2) lateral head, (3) medial head. The "posterior process" of the ulna is the olecranon.

41. The palmaris longus; see note 5 of this chapter on "true skin." It is worth while to note here the first use of a device employed several times in subsequent text; that is, the contrast of "it is believed" to "the professors of dissection believe." The phrases are so used as to appear that in neither case is Vesalius as yet prepared to make a positive statement; however, in the first case he suggests in an affirmative sense, while the second is indicative of doubt and partial denial.

42. Muscles which pronate the radius: (1) pronator teres, (2) pronator quadratus. The forearm is being described in the anatomical position (radius and ulna parallel, thumb out, and palm anterior).

43. Muscles which supinate the radius: (1) brachioradialis (old name, "supinator longus"), (2) supinator (supinator radii brevis).

44. Muscles which move the brachial (wrist): (1) flexor carpi radialis, (2) flexor carpi ulnaris, (3) extensor carpi radialis longus et brevis, (4) extensor carpi ulnaris. Several points of confusion and ambiguity enter in attempting to define this group.

45. Muscles which move the fingers: (1) flexor digitorum sublimis; (2) flexor digitorum profundus; (3) flexor pollicis longus (for "third joint of the thumb" see Chap. I, note 45); (4-16, incl.) the text is not adequate for exact identification, but the group probably includes for the thumb the extensor pollicis brevis, abductor pollicis brevis, flexor pollicis brevis (lateral head), opponens pollicis, and adductor pollicis (transverse head); for the index finger, one dorsal and one volar interosseus; and for the little finger, a volar interosseus and probably the flexor digiti quinti brevis and opponens digiti quinti considered together; (17) extensor digitorum communis; (18) extensor digiti quinti proprius; (19) extensor indicis proprius; (20) abductor digiti quinti; (21) extensor pollicis longus et brevis; (23) flexor pollicis brevis (medial head, also sometimes described as interosseus volaris primus); (24) adductor pollicis (oblique head) [?]; (25-28) lumbricales.

Some of the difficulty in understanding this section arises from inconstant use of the anatomical position in determining direction.

46. The tunica vaginalis.

47. Cremaster muscle.

48. Ductus (vas) deferens.

49. This is probably not the broad ligament and uterine tube. While Vesalius did not recognize the significance of the tubes until they were described by Fallopius, he did consider them as uterine horns, as indicated in his letter to Fallopius. More likely he means here the smooth (involuntary) muscle which may be found in the uterosacral ligaments.

50. Sphincter urethrae.

51. Sphincter ani; the internus and externus are probably not differentiated.

52. Levator ani.

53. The original text uses extreme emphasis in the idea of "very slowly"; the sense is that of "lazily." Vesalius seems uncertain of the effectiveness of the muscle. This is probably the ischiocavernosus muscle (which does have some pubic origin) although the ambiguity might admit identification of a ligament of the penis, such as fundiform or suspensory.

54. Bulbocavernosus muscle. Present ideas of function attribute an ejaculator mechanism to this muscle.

55. Muscles which move the thigh: (1) glutaeus maximus (which passes over the greater trochanter with the interposition of a bursa and inserts instead just below on the gluteal tuberosity), (2) glutaeus medius, (3) glutaeus minimus, (4) piriformis, (5) the adductor group (including brevis, longus, magnus, and probably quadratus femoris—the upward continuation of the adductor magnus), (6) psaos major, (7) iliacus, (8) pectineus and adductor longus, perhaps including brevis, (9) obturator externus (which turns the femur *outward*), (10)' obturator internus (which is "increased" by the superior and inferior gemelli).

56. Muscles which move the leg: (1) sartorius, (2) gracilis, (3) semitendinosus, (4) biceps femoris, (5) semimembranosus, (6) tensor fasciae latae (the membrane is, of course, the fascia lata proper), (7) vastus lateralis, (8) vastus intermedius et medialis (except for the lower portion of the medialis, which has a slightly different function, the consideration of these two as a unit is as defensible as the modern separation of them), (9) rectus femoris. The statement that the last-named "turns into" a tendon has the force of "degenerates"; following the Aristotelian idea of more and less noble parts, muscle is superior to tendon, just as bone is to cartilage.

57. Popliteus.

58. Muscles which move the foot: (1 and 2) gastrocnemius (medial and lateral heads), (3) plantaris, (4) soleus, (5) tibialis posterior, (6) tibialis anterior (into the base of metatarsal I), (7) peronaeus longus, (8) peronaeus brevis, (9) peronaeus tertius (quite accurately defined; see later the fourteenth of those which move the toes—extensor digitorum longus, of which this is a part; note 60 below).

59. The insertion of the muscle is into the navicular bone. Probably the "bone resembling a die" is the cuboid, in spite of the fact that the talus is also contiguous and that its old name is astragalus (ἀστράγαλος, "a die"). This identification is based on the fact that the tarsus is indicated and that to Vesalius the talus or astragalus is not a part of the tarsus proper (see Chap. I, note 53). In either case, the "die" is not used in the sense of printing or mechanics but should be compared to another old name for talus, πεσσός, a small stone or other substance for playing at draughts. Note also the old Roman game of "knucklebones."

60. Muscles which move the toes: (1) flexor digitorum brevis (with the plantar aponeurosis); (2) flexor digitorum longus; (3) flexor hallucis longus; (4-13) for the first toe the flexor hallucis brevis and adductor hallucis; second toe, the two interossei dorsales; third toe, one interosseus dorsalis and one interosseus plantaris; fourth toe, the same; fifth toe, plantar interosseus and flexor digiti quinti brevis; (14) extensor digitorum

longus; (15) extensor hallucis longus; (16) extensor digitorum brevis; (17) abductor digiti quinti; (18) abductor hallucis.

61. Quadratus plantae and lumbricales.

62. Capsular ligament and collateral ligaments.

63. The apical odontoid ligament.

64. The transverse ligament of the axis.

65. Intervertebral fibrocartilages.

66. That is, they are not specialized accessions; falling in the class of the first-named they are capsular ligaments, between articular processes.

67. The interspinous ligaments, compared to the interosseous membranes of forearm and leg.

68. The obturator membrane.

69. The coracohumeral is the first; the next two are glenohumeral; and possibly the last of the group is that portion of the glenohumeral which arises from the base of the coracoid process and attaches near the lesser tubercle.

70. Sacrospinous and sacrotuberous ligaments.

71. Ligamentum teres femoris.

72. Menisci and collateral ligaments.

73. The various retinacula and mucous tendon sheaths are not differentiated here, as appears by inspection of the text.

74. Transverse carpal ligament and digital extension of palmar fascia.

75. The six tendons sheathed on the dorsum of the wrist are, from medial to lateral: extensores carpi ulnaris, digiti quinti proprius, digitorum communis and indicis proprius, pollicis longus, carpi radialis longus et brevis, pollicis brevis and abductor pollicis longus.

76. Transverse crural ligament (and mucous sheath of tibialis anterior muscle).

77. Mucous sheaths for tibialis posterior, flexor digitorum longus, and flexor hallucis longus.

78. More likely the mucous sheath of the peronaeus longus than the retinaculum peronaeorum superius.

CONCERNING THE ORGANS WHICH MINISTER

TO NUTRITION BY FOOD AND DRINK

CHAPTER III

SINCE man has been unable to form the substance of an immortal being by means of the genital semen and the menstrual blood (the origins of our generation and of those parts of which we are composed [1]), the great Creator of things has carefully devised that man should live as long as possible and that his species, never failing, should continue to exist forever. In order that man might attain to the stature for which he was intended and that those elements upon which his innate heat is continually fed might be restored as quickly as possible, he possesses organs which serve to nourish him in many ways.

The food is broken up by the teeth in order that the task may later be completed more easily. Food, as well as drink, passes from the mouth to the stomach as into a storehouse along a path called the esophagus or gullet [2]. This is extended by two special tunics appropriately formed to descend from the fauces behind the rough artery [3] and then along the vertebrae of the thorax through the transverse septum to the upper, or left-hand, orifice of the stomach.

The stomach lies between the liver and the spleen under the septum. It is particularly roomy and rather long transversely, larger on the left-hand region of the body than on the right; it is equipped with two tunics suitable for distending and contracting [4] and enclosed by a third covering derived from the peritoneum. The stomach is intertwined with many veins, arteries, and nerves. It concocts what is sent down to it from the mouth and changes this by an innate force into a thick milky juice [5]. This passes through the lower orifice of the stomach from the higher region of its right side and is sent into the intestines.

The intestines are rounded, extending from stomach to anus in a continuous course made tortuous by innumerable coils and turns; like the stomach, they are fashioned from two tunics. To these is added from the peritoneum a third tunic adapted for relaxing and contracting no less than the first two tunics proper to the intestines but not everywhere equally extensive [6]. The origin of the intestines proceeds from the stomach; along the posterior side of the stomach, reflected toward the back, lies the organ we call the duodenum. Following this is the part of the intestines known as the jejunum and that which is called the ileum or volvulus. The coils of the latter fill the ilia and the region lying under, and contiguous on all sides to, the umbilicus; it is of almost constant diameter. The narrowness of this organ provides the reason for designating as small intestines the parts just mentioned. The part of the intestines in which the terminus of the ileum lies is broad and very thick; in its entire course it constitutes the colon. Joined to it is a small appendage, narrow and curled like an earthworm; this has one orifice and is therefore called blind by the masters of dissection [7]. The thick part of the intestines itself ascends from the region of the right kidney to the concavity of the liver. Thence it proceeds along the base of the stomach to the region of the spleen, then turns downward along the region of the left kidney, and bends back to the left region of the pubis in a sort of coil [8]. This last passes above the beginning of the os sacrum straight down to the anus, thereby obtaining the name of the straight and principal intestine [9].

Thus, whatever has been prepared in the stomach is sent down through these intestines to be forced through their various coils. Veins in innumerable series pass from the concavity of the liver, together with the arteries drawn off from the great artery, between the two membranes which fasten the intestines to the back. These veins are quite thick and dense, abounding in much fat and glands; they are called the mesentery and extend to the intestines [10]. The veins suck out from the intestines (especially the small ones) whatever is suitable for the making of the blood [11], together with the aqueous and thin refuse of the stomach's concoction, and carry it to the workshop of the liver, where the blood is made. But that refuse which is thicker and less adaptable to suction is gradually collected in the thick intestine; it is kept there only until, it becoming troublesome to man, the muscle surrounding the rectum in circular fashion relaxes, and the refuse is borne forth at once and completely at the will of man.

The liver is not divided into fibers or lobes [12]; it occupies a position higher than that of the organs ministering to it [13] and for the most part lies in intimate relation to the stomach; the liver is placed close beneath the transverse septum and fills the right, rather more than the left, region of the body. It is gibbous above and hollow below, conforming exactly to the shape of the parts lying near it [14]. It is formed by the intertwining of many veins and is surrounded by the substance proper to the liver, similar to recently coagulated blood [15]. It is clothed with a thin membrane [16] proceeding from the ligaments with which it is secured to the peritoneum. It admits two small nerves [17] and one artery. It is the tinder of the natural or nutritive faculty or, as Plato said, of the part of the soul which desires the pleasures of love, food, and drink [18].

One series of veins diffused through the liver lies in its gibbous part, extending to the vena cava [19]. Another series forming the stem of the portal vein lies in the hollow of the liver. This vein sends two branches first to the bladder which receives the yellow bile [20], then to the lower region of the stomach near its lower orifice [21].

Thence a branch runs to the right part of the base of the stomach [22], from which small branches spread out to the stomach and the upper membrane of the omentum [23]. The omentum is a membranous body fashioned like a sack and especially adapted for conducting vessels in safety. However, since it is full of veins, arteries, and the fat attached to them, it also assists in preserving the warmth of the intestines. It is borne in a circular fashion, beginning from the middle of the back under the posterior region of the stomach, through the hollow of the liver, to the base of the stomach (from the third tunic of which it here arises). Then it is carried down to the hollow of the spleen and thence to the middle of the back where it started [24]. Like a sack stretched downward, the omentum covers the anterior region of the intestines, or there where the colon is stretched under the stomach, it arises, joining the back in place of a mesentery. The stem of the portal vein, after having been supported by the omentum, sends out the branches just mentioned.

The stem is divided into two trunks; the right one [25], which is larger, is carried in various ways through the mesentery and is offered to the intestines (first the duodenal intestine); the right trunk also presents a branch to the beginning of the jejunum. The right trunk is supported by a glandulous body stretched out in this region of the intestines [26]. The left trunk, having been woven into the lower region of the omentum, sends a small branch to the posterior region of the stomach, where the latter faces the right part of the back, then also to the inferior membrane of the omentum. Next the branch goes to the glands, fleshy in color, which are in charge of the safe distribution of the vessels here. A branch ascends from it along the posterior side of the stomach; this branch sends out other branches to the region of the stomach which faces toward the middle of the back and embraces the upper orifice of the stomach in the manner of a crown [27]. From this, in addition to the branches sent upward and downward, one creeps forward along the posterior side of the stomach to its lower orifice.

The left trunk of the stem of the portal vein, extending ever to the left [28], sends an outstanding vein woven into the omentum and the colon; it is divided into various branches and sends an offshoot as far as the lower membrane of the omentum [29]. It is inserted into the hollow of the spleen by means of its own offshoots before they enter the spleen. To the left side of the stomach, it sends little branches [30], among which a notable one creeps along the base of the stomach in the left region and sends shoots to the stomach and to the upper membrane of the omentum [31].

Offshoots of the portal vein are distributed through the substance of the liver; within them is contained whatever is brought to the liver from the intestines, to say nothing of the stomach. The liver, concocting the best part of that chyme, changes it into blood, obtaining also a twofold refuse of its concoctions, such as we see in all wines and other similar concoctions. One is thicker than the other and, because it is considered, as it were, the dross and offscouring of the blood, is commonly called the black bile. It is carried through the portal vein to the spleen, which lies below and behind the left side of the stomach. The spleen looks like a rather thick tongue [32]; it adjusts itself to the shape of the organs lying close to it, just as the liver does. It is likewise interwoven with many veins and arteries, by which the proper flesh of the spleen is rendered similar to muddy blood. The spleen is

43

covered with a thin tunic sent forth from the omentum [33]. We believe [34] the spleen draws to itself the thicker refuse of the liver and converts it into nourishment for itself, and whatever it cannot assimilate, it throws up into the stomach.

The thinner refuse of the liver, which is regarded as a sort of flowers of the wine, is the yellow bile. It is drawn into passageways between those offshoots of the portal vein and the vena cava which are distributed through the substance of the liver. These passageways, gathered together, end in a single channel which proceeds from the hollow of the liver and extends to the gall bladder [35]. This, like a rather long pear in the concavity of the liver, arises in the middle of the liver's breadth and is provided with a body adapted for distending and relaxing. The professors of anatomy are convinced [36] that, in the case of this bladder, the bile is preserved until, by the action of its special duct, it is thrust forth into the duodenum. The bile must be carried out along with the dry refuse of the stomach. With its biting quality it irritates the intestines for propelling this refuse and frees them from the phlegm which clings to the refuse [37].

The blood, cleansed of the excrement just referred to, rushes from the narrowest branches of the portal vein into the smallest offshoots of the vena cava [38]. The blood uses as a vehicle [39] the thin watery refuse which it had taken up to the liver from the intestines. This refuse, accompanying the blood thus far and ascending together with it into the vena cava, renders a signal service to it in these narrow passages. For since, thus far, this refuse aids the blood in the function of a prompt distribution, it is also suitable for this refuse to carry off whatever overabundant supply of itself [the refuse] the blood does not require and to purge the blood of that which would be a burden.

This office of purgation is most fitly performed by the kidneys, one each on either side of the vena cava and very close to the liver. They quickly draw the greater part of the serous humor of the liver toward themselves and strain it from the blood [40]. In order that they may accomplish this more handily, a notable vein and likewise an artery are extended to the kidney; the kidney receives the serous blood into a membranous sinus which is broad and hollow and divided into many offshoots concealed by the substance of the kidney and covered over with a double tunic [41]. By its function the urine is expelled and led off into another sinus which is prolonged as the urinary passage constructed like a vein [42]; this urine is going to be carried to the bladder.

The bladder, situated at the posterior region of the pubic bone, gradually receives the urine [43]. Shaped like a rotund flask, it is formed of its own simple and sinewy tunic, interwoven with a threefold type of fibers, ready to be distended or contracted [44]. Another membrane is drawn over it from the peritoneum or the membrane of the abdomen, which is the covering and protection of the organs thus far mentioned. Single passageways from each of the kidneys are carefully inserted in the posterior portion of the bladder not far from its neck. This collects the urine only so long until it troubles man either by its abundance or its quality; then it is completely voided by the opening of the muscle which surrounds the neck of the bladder in circular fashion [45].

The blood, purified by this operation, is distributed through the branches of the vena cava or its rivulets over the entire body in order that the separate parts may drain from the blood that which is proper to them; changing and applying it to themselves, they then convert it to their own nourishment. Finally, also, they drive off the refuse of this concoction from themselves by their own functions.

The series of the vena cava is for the most part as follows: while it is located in the posterior region of the liver, it sends forth branches from its own anterior aspect distributed in a numerous series to the gibbous part of the liver. Then ascending and perforating the transverse septum and the pericardium, it sends two offshoots to the septum [46]. At the level of the right auricle of the heart, the vena cava opens toward the right ventricle with an opening wider than the circular width of the vena cava elsewhere. From the posterior region of its implantation (unless you prefer to say rising [47]), a vein proceeds surrounding the base of the heart in the manner of a crown and sending little branches downward along the upper surface of the heart [48]. The vena cava, rising upward from the heart, there where it pierces the pericardium, sends off from the right side, the azygous

vein, which nourishes the eight, more commonly lower, intervals of the ribs *
on both sides.

In the throat the vena cava is divided into two parts [49], sending veins
from its anterior region to the pectoral bone and to the membranes dividing
the thorax, and creeping through the upper part of the abdomen [50]. From
the root of the one branch of the division into two parts in the throat arises
a notable vein running above the first rib to the armpit [51] but first sending
into the cavity of the thorax a branch which disappears in the three upper
intervals of the ribs of its side [52], and another branch through the transverse processes of the cervical vertebrae all the way to the skull [53], and
another spread out in the posterior part of the thorax near the root of the
neck [54]. The present vein, having meanwhile, passed out of the thorax,
here sends forth the shoulder vein [humerariam uenam] [55] and a branch
to the muscles spread over the anterior region of the thorax [56]; then,
hastening on into the armpit, it sends another to the posterior region of
the thorax and the hollow of the scapula [57], and then another to the side
of the thorax [58].

The remaining branch of the trunk split into two parts in the throat
is again divided into two unequal branches. Of these, the inner and more
slender one forms the internal jugular vein. It enters the skull, with two
offshoots passing to the dural membrane of the brain. The outer branch
sends an offshoot from its outer side; from this the humeral vein [humeralis
uena] is derived [59]. It goes upward, forming the superficial jugular,
running in various ways up to the fauces, and distributed to the tongue,
the larynx, the palate, the face, the temples, and the vertex and entering
the skull with three veins.

The humeral vein, before it is carried under the clavicle and the acromion
into the arm, extends a branch to the posterior region of the neck [60]
and another to the gibbous part of the scapula. Another branch goes to the
upper region of the acromion [61], and a second creeps under the skin,
following along the outer side of the anterior muscle of those which flex
the elbow [62]; bringing forth slender shoots to the skin, it divides in front
of the elbow joint. Sometimes one branch lies deeper and soon disappears,

* . . . . octo frequentius inferiora costarum intervalla.

passing to the elbow joint. Another runs obliquely under the skin to the middle of the bend of the elbow [63] to meet with the branch of the axillary vein and to form one vein in common with it [64]. A third passes under the skin along the radius to the posterior aspect of the forearm, finally to the root of the wrist near the end of the ulna [65]; it mingles there with the offshoot of the axillary vein and rises to the outer side of the little finger and the ring finger [66].

The axillary vein lies hidden in the armpit and sends a branch to the skin covering the anterior region of the arm toward the inner aspect. It presents an offshoot to the heads of the muscles which extend the elbow and another at almost the middle of their length [67]. Then the axillary vein sends another offshoot, with the fourth nerve that proceeds to the arm, along the posterior aspect of the arm up to the exterior region of the forearm [68]. It is soon cut into two veins, one of which sinks completely into the depths in its entire length, continually accompanied by an artery [69]. This vein passes through the middle of the bend of the elbow joint; before it reaches the middle of the length of the forearm, it is cut into two offshoots, one of which stretches along the radius [70], the other along the ulna toward the wrist [71]. Here it is again split into offshoots [72], distributed to the inner region of the fingers in such a way that it offers two twigs to each of them; one shoot, extending to the external region of the hand, is distributed between the first internode of the thumb and the metacarpal bone supporting the index finger.

Extending under the skin all the way, the other branch from the axillary vein [73] is divided into two branches near the elbow joint. One of these branches runs obliquely toward the bend of the elbow joint and merges with the branch of the humeral vein which is composed of those two middle veins, forming a common vein with it [74]. Running obliquely downward along the radius, this is divided into two offshoots like the letter Y in the external region of the forearm. One of these runs for the most part to the external region of the middle finger; the other runs to the thumb and index finger and sends an offshoot into the internal region of the hand to mingle with the small branches encircling the sacred hill of Venus [75]. The other branch from the axillary vein formed by the division near the elbow joint sends various offshoots to the internal region of the forearm [76]. In association with these branches, a vein often occurs arising from the other branch constituting a common vein which the axillary sends forth. These offshoots come close together in various ways at times; again, they separate in turn and are interwoven in the skin in the inner aspect of the forearm. Finally they creep forward to the skin of the internal part of the hand. The more outstanding offshoot of this branch extends to the ulna and sends offshoots in similar fashion into the external region of the forearm. It merges with the branch of the shoulder vein [humerariae] near the root of the wrist as that branch runs to the little finger and the ring finger.

A part of the vena cava runs downward below the liver. It sends a branch from the left side to the fatty tunic of the left kidney and the region contiguous to it [77]. Then a large vein is borne to each of the kidneys. From the superior aspect of the vein seeking the right kidney (which vessel frequently originates higher than the vein belonging to the left kidney), an offshoot approaches the fatty tunic of the right kidney [78]. From the inferior aspect of that vein which passes to the left kidney, a seminal vein arises; the right seminal vein originates much lower down from the trunk of the vena cava [79]. Further, where the vena cava lies upon the lumbar vertebrae, it gives offshoots to the latter in clusters which finally disappear into the nearby muscles and sides of the abdomen [80]. The most outstanding of these are those which arise from the vena cava where it divides into two equal trunks [81] above the union of the os sacrum and the lumbar vertebrae. Both the right and left trunks send some offshoots to the foramina of the os sacrum [82].

Each trunk is divided into two branches, of which the inner [83] sends an offshoot which ends in the muscles occupying the posterior regions of the iliac and sacral bones [84]. Another offshoot goes to the bladder and penis [85]; in women it extends to the uterus in the form of many smaller shoots [86]. That which is left of this branch anastomoses with the external branch and is led through the foramen of the pubic bone to the thigh [87], where it sends offshoots to the skin and muscles occupying the inner femoral region. Proximal to the knee joint, it ends, joining its terminus with the branch of another vein which extends to the leg, as I shall soon describe.

The external branch [88] of the left trunk of the vena cava, when it is about to pass through the groin to the thigh, sends to the peritoneum an offshoot which terminates in the lower region of the abdomen up to the umbilicus [89]. Extending downward upon the thigh, the external branch sends a shoot to the skin of the pubis and to the hillocks of the female pudenda [90]. It sends a notable vein under the skin through the internal aspect of the thigh, knee, and leg as far as the end of the toes [91]; in its progress it distributes other branches here and there to the skin. Another vein is also sent under the skin to the anterior region of the hip joint [92]. Itself more deeply submerged among the muscles, the trunk [93] sends an offshoot to the muscles located in the external region of the thigh and to the skin [94]; it sends another offshoot to the muscles which appropriate to themselves the inner and anterior region of the thigh [95]. With this offshoot is joined the end of that vein which descended through the foramen of the pubic bone. Thence the large vein [93] winds back to the posterior part of the thigh and sends offshoots to the muscles of that region; from these offshoots little branches extend to the skin, upward and downward as far as the calf.

This large vein is divided into two trunks between the lower heads of the femur. The lesser outer one extends to the fibula [96]; from it, in addition to small branches extending to the anterior aspect of the knee [97], a branch is separated which proceeds posteriorly under the skin covering the external region of the leg and which is variously divided toward the upper part of the toes [98]. That portion of it which remains hidden higher up among the muscles extending toward the external region of the fibula runs past the middle of the length of the leg. The inner of the two trunks is quite large [99]; along the inner region of the tibia, it sends a branch spread out posteriorly under the skin as far as the toes. Another branch is sent forth, somewhat hidden through the calf and stretching as far as the heel. Especially worthy of note concerning this trunk is the fact that it extends to the muscles which occupy the posterior aspect of the leg. It sends a branch from its anterior aspect down through the membranous ligament which binds the fibula to the tibia. The branch hidden under the anterior muscles which surround the tibia extends to the upper part of the foot [100].

The vein itself, running down along the posterior part and thence sending shoots to the skin and the contiguous muscles, finally enters the lower portion of the foot between heel and tibia and is there distributed to the muscles and toes in such a way that two offshoots are sent to each toe.

GENERAL INTERPRETATION

IN THIS and the following chapters, the physiology departs sufficiently from modern
concepts and is so dispersed through the text that it seems appropriate to bring it
together in brief abstracts. To these are joined such remarks of general nature as may
refer to the subject and yet find no specific place in the serial notes.

The Vesalian discussion of blood and bile is an effort to bring to the prevailing
humoral theory of physiology and pathology some degree of anatomical specificity.
The theory, which probably originated with primitive man, was used in Vedic medicine, proclaimed to the West by Hippocrates, "proved" by Galen, and held in good
repute until the time of Virchow. It is not surprising to find that, in the main, Vesalius
accepts it; his position is to carry forward the efforts of Erasistratus to take it out
of the realm of metaphysical speculation.

Vesalius believes that the mesenteric vessels carry material absorbed from the intestines to the liver (via the portal vein). Blood is formed in the liver and enters the
circulation through the hepatic vein. In the liver is obtained a refuse which consists
of two parts, comparable to the flowers (or supernatant scum) and lees (or dregs) of
wine. The thicker is the black bile, which is sent back through the portal vein to the
spleen; no effort is made to explain this two-way flow in the portal vein (intestine to
liver and liver to spleen). It is not difficult to understand the "black bile" (atra bilis,
melancholia) of the splenic vein when one remembers that the blood coming from
the spleen actually contains a high concentration of hemoglobin breakdown pigments.
Anything in the black bile not usable by the spleen is sent (via the left gastroepiploic
vein?) to the stomach.

The thinner decoction of the liver is the yellow bile, which is sent to the gall bladder.
While Vesalius has some doubt as to the role of the gall bladder as a storage organ,
he recognizes that bile is the "physiological laxative," acting as an irritant (through
its "biting quality") to increase intestinal motility.

The noncellular component of blood leaving the liver contains some waste material,
which is carried to the inferior vena cava and then to the kidneys for excretion. In a
later chapter Vesalius states that the two kidneys have slightly different functions
with respect to this excretion; he thereby accounts for the difference in right and left
internal spermatic veins and explains the method by which erotic activity and formation of seminal fluid are stimulated by its acrid quality.

The blood is now freed from all useless or harmful substances and is distributed to
all parts of the body by the veins. The various tissues extract from blood useful substances and return to it their own refuse from metabolism.

Phlegm, the fourth humor, is mentioned only in passing; the account of its origin
is contained in a later chapter.

The only authority named in the Epitome,* Plato, is cited in this chapter in connection with the discussion of the liver. While the exact source is not given, I believe
it to be the Timaeus. This dialogue, while starting with cosmogony, mathematics, and

* With the exception of a passing mention of Galen in the section on regional anatomy.

51

astronomy, devotes its last third to anatomy, physiology, and pathology. Without doubt Vesalius is as familiar with the content as he is with the work of Hippocrates, Aristotle, and Galen. Plato believes the soul is tripartite, with special regions of the body as the seat of each part. The head, being spherical and most perfect in shape, is the seat of reason and intellect, the most perfect part of the soul. It is above the other seats of soul-portions, and hence reason is placed in a dominant position. The breast is the seat of the nobler passions; it is not to be identified with the head, and hence the neck has been interposed. The diaphragm divides the nobler soul from the coarser base soul, with its bodily appetites and sensuality, seated in the abdomen. The liver has a degree of control over this last in that: (*a*) it contains "bitter," which it uses to restrain the cravings; (*b*) it contains "sweet," to be discharged when desires conform to reason; (*c*) it is like a mirror, smooth and bright (note the pathologist's phrase, "smooth, moist, and glistening"), and may thus reflect the thoughts.

In the *Symposium* of Plato, the myth of the Charioteer and the two horses is thought to be an allegorical statement of this theory of the soul.

The reader interested in the history of medical concepts will, if not already familiar with the *Timaeus,* find much delight in reading it.

NOTES

1. BY Aristotelian teaching (as in *De Generatione Animalium*), the semen of the male is a pure secretion containing the soul principle, while the catamenia is a female semen lacking this principle. Introduction of the soul principle to the secretion of the female results in conception and formation of the embryo.

2. The "path" itself is the lumen, and the two tunics the mucosa and the muscularis-adventitia.

3. Trachea; "rough" because of its cartilage rings, "artery" because it is an air passage.

4. The same two layers as in note 2, plus the serosa, a reflection of the peritoneum.

5. The acid chyme.

6. This is a brief statement of the fact that not all of the intestine is in a broad mesentery but in a number of places becomes almost retroperitoneal.

7. The cecum, "blind," as in a "blind alley" or cul-de-sac. The appendix vermiformis is the part here designated in particular as blind.

8. The sigmoid colon.

9. Intestinum rectum.

10. The mesenteric vessels, within the two sheets of serosa making up the mesentery. The glands are mesenteric lymph nodes.

11. "Suck out": compare the observation of H. S. Wells, *Am. J. Physiol.*, XCIX (1931), 209, that the osmotic pressure here is enough to balance a negative intra-intestinal pressure of 8 to 26 cm of normal saline solution. While we would not say "suck," the concept of some of the absorptive mechanism is suggested.

12. In correction of a standing anatomical error of the time, probably deriving from dissection of lower mammals.

13. "Ministering to it" via the portal venous system.

14. The many impressions on the surface of the liver.

15. The Galenic concept of the nature of liver parenchyma.

16. The tunica serosa—Glisson's capsule.

17. From the left vagus and the sympathetic (celiac plexus) via the hepatic plexus.

18. The *Timaeus;* see general interpretation to this chapter; also *Republic* 439a-440.

19. The intralobular veins join to form the hepatic vein.

20. Gall bladder; cystic vein.

21. Pyloric vein.

22. Right gastroepiploic vein.

23. "The upper membrane" is the anterior portion of the gastrocolic fold.

24. Successively, the gastrohepatic, gastrolienal, and lienorenal "ligaments" or portions of the omentum.

25. The superior mesenteric vein.

26. Pancreaticoduodenal vein; the pancreas.

27. The coronary vein.

28. The lienal (splenic) vein.

29. The inferior mesenteric and left colic veins.

30. The short gastric veins.

31. The left gastroepiploic; the vein is "notable" because of its part in the relationship of spleen to stomach (see text and general interpretation).

32. That is, it has a broad side and an opposing sharp border.

33. The capsule is formed by a reflection of the dorsal mesogastrium.

34. See Chap. II, note 41.

35. The bile ducts and hepatic duct.

36. See Chap. II, note 41. To bring the sentence on the gall bladder up to date, one would have only to say that "the professors of anatomy are convinced but the professors of physiology doubt, etc." The words which have been exchanged over just such controversies as this are those which prompted Truthful James to remark:

> I hold it not quite wise in any scientific gent
> To say another is an ass, at least to all intent.
> —Bret Harte, "The Society upon the Stanislaus"

37. Note the recognition of the laxative function of the bile salts.

38. The confluence of the hepatic arterial and portal venous blood into the central veins and thence via the hepatic vein to the vena cava.

39. Vehicle, in the (present) pharmaceutical sense of a fluid "carrier" for the active constituents.

40. The liver effluent blood contains wastes for excretion by the kidney; for example, the liver is a prime source of urea, one of the discards of protein metabolism.

41. The outer "tunic" was the peripelvic tissue; the inner, the kidney pelvis and calyces.

42. Ureter.

43. Observe the contrast in Vesalius' expressions of rate of activity: blood "rushes" "quickly" in speaking of liver and kidney circulation in the two preceding paragraphs, but urine is secreted "gradually." Vesalius performed a number of physiologic observations as well as anatomies. (Lambert, "The Physiology of Vesalius," *Bull. New York Acad. Med.,* XII, No. 6 [June, 1936].)

44. Nerve: a connective tissue sheet like an aponeurosis; see Chap. II, note 1.

45. Chap. II, note 50. The detrusor muscle and the sphincters.

46. The inferior phrenic veins.

47. Using the Aristotelian idea of a vena caval origin at the heart, rather than the Galenic concept of a hepatic origin.

48. Great cardiac vein and especially the coronary sinus.

49. The innominate veins.

50. Internal mammary and superior phrenic veins.

51. Axillary vein.

52. Highest intercostal vein.

53. Vertebral vein.

54. Superficial cervical vein. From this point in the description of the veins of the upper extremity, it has not proved possible to identify every vessel with certainty. This is due partly to the considerable variability of even larger veins in this region and partly to obscurities in description and form of outline. In consequence, only the vessels which seem most certainly identified are noted.

55. Cephalic vein.

56. Anterior pectoral vein.

57. Subscapular vein.

58. Lateral thoracic vein.

59. Subclavian, axillary, and brachial (in succession).

60. Transverse cervical vein.

61. Acromial and deltoid veins.

62. Basilic vein.

63. Median cubital vein.

64. Median antibrachial vein.

65. Accessory cephalic vein.

66. The most medial of the dorsal metacarpal veins, from the dorsal venous network.

67. Humeral circumflex and muscular rami.

68. Deep brachial vein, with the radial nerve (Chap. V, note 71).

69. Ulnar vein.

70. Dorsal interosseous vein.

71. Volar interosseous vein.

72. Superficial volar arch.

73. Radial vein.

74. Anastomosis with the superficial circulation, especially the median antibrachial vein.

75. The deep volar, with an offshoot to the thenar eminence.

76. The venous anastomosis around the elbow joint, and the cutaneous and muscular rami.

77. Left suprarenal vein; the subsequent account differs from the modern in two main points: (*a*) Modern texts show the right suprarenal as a branch of the inferior vena cava; Vesalius just reverses this. (*b*) Modern texts place the left renal higher than the right; again this is reversed in the *Epitome*.

78. Right suprarenal vein.

79. The internal spermatic veins.

80. Lumbar veins.

81. The common iliac veins.

82. Lateral sacral veins.

83. Hypogastric vein.

84. Gluteal veins.

85. Internal pudendal and vesical veins.

86. Uterine veins and venous plexuses of pelvic viscera.

87. Obturator vein; Vesalius must have followed a branch to an anastomosis with some of the superficial veins of the thigh, perhaps an accessory saphenous.

88. External iliac vein.

89. Deep epigastric vein.

90. Superficial external pudendal vein.

91. Great saphenous vein.

92. Superficial circumflex iliac vein.

93. Femoral vein.

94. Lateral circumflex femoral vein.

95. Deep femoral vein, especially the medial femoral circumflex branch as the anastomotic channel.

96. Peroneal vein.

97. Genicular veins.

98. Small saphenous vein.

99. Posterior tibial vein.

100. Anterior tibial vein.

CONCERNING THE HEART AND THE ORGANS

WHICH MINISTER TO ITS FUNCTION

CHAPTER IV

O F THE organs which are created for rekindling the natural heat within us and for the restoration and nourishment of our spirits, the heart is considered by far the most important part of the agitative faculty. It is like a pine nut, compressed in front and behind, located with its base under the middle of the breastbone and its apex inclining sharply forward to the left side. The substance of the heart is fleshy, but like the substance of muscles, and is interwoven with a tougher, threefold type of fibers [1] provided with its own veins and arteries.

The heart has two sinuses or ventricles [2]. One is located on the right side; this is broader and appears to be covered with a thinner and looser substance of the heart [3]. The orifice of the vena cava extends to this ventricle and is furnished with three membranes drawn inward [4]. Likewise, a vessel which is like an artery in form but performs the function of a vein [5] and hence is called the arterial vein proceeds from this ventricle; this vessel sends toward the orifice of the ventricle also three small membranes facing outward [6]. The other ventricle, surrounded by a special thick substance of the heart, lies on the left side. It, too, has two orifices, of which the lower, with two membranes closing inward [7], belongs to a certain vessel, an artery. While it is formed like a vein, this vessel holds the air and performs the function of an artery [8]; hence it is called the venous artery; this artery sends two membranes that close inward to its own orifice. The higher orifice is dedicated to the beginning of the great artery, to which Nature has also given three membranes facing outward [9]. These ventricles are separated by a very thick septum adapted for distending and contracting and (like the ventricles of the heart) built up within of many pits of ample size [10].

The entire heart is covered with a certain membranous involucrum, to which it is joined at no point [11]. This involucrum is much more ample than the heart and is moistened within by an aqueous humor. The lower region of the involucrum is attached on the outside to a transverse septum of no small breadth; on its two sides the involucrum is contained by the membranes interposed in the cavity of the thorax, supporting this involucrum in order that the heart may be supported in position [12].

The lung fills the rest of the cavity of the thorax not occupied by the heart, the membranes just mentioned, and the descending esophagus. The lung adapts itself on all sides, as the liver does, to the shape of the parts lying close by; on both right and left sides it resembles the hoof of a cow or some other cloven-hoofed animal. Each lung is divided into two fibers or lobes [13] built up from many interweavings of vessels. The rough artery [14] is led down from the top of the throat (where also the tonsils and two other types of glands are located) to the thorax; it is partly cartilaginous so that the voice may be produced. In order that the lung may be expanded and relaxed and thus may assist breathing, it is partly membranous, filled here and there with branches. The arterial vein, proceeding from the right ventricle of the heart which prepares the blood familiar to the lung, offers the blood to the lung; it is distributed in an innumerable series to the latter. Similarly, the venous artery intertwines the lung with an abundant series. These vessels are surrounded by the spongy, soft, foamy, and quite pliable substance proper to the lung. A quite small thin tunic lies next to this substance, not hindering the dilatation and compression of the lung in any way; this tunic is always contiguous to the tunic which lines the ribs [15].

The lung causes a motion of the thorax dependent upon our wills; it dilates to produce a vacuum, and by virtue of this the air from outside ourselves passes along the uvula. When we breathe deeply, the air is attracted through the mouth as though into a bellows. A small part of the air seeks the brain through the foramina of the skull [16], while the remainder [17] enters the rough artery [trachea] by way of the upper throat and completely fills the cavity of the lung made by the latter's dilatation. The substance of the lung changes this air by force peculiar to itself, adapting the air to the use of the heart. This allows the best part of the air to be taken up by the branches of the venous artery from the offshoots of the rough artery extending throughout so that, by the intervention of the former artery, the air may be carried to the left sinus of the heart, where it is going to perfect the material of the vital spirit.*

The heart attracts this air and draws a large supply of blood from the right ventricle into the left ventricle. From the steamy vapor of that blood and from that air, by the inborn virtue of its own substance, the heart creates the spirit which the blood with a rushing flow distributes, thus accompanied and nourished, to the entire body through the great artery; the heart tempers the native heat of each part in the same way that the respiration restores the tinder of the innate heat to the heart. Thus the respiration and the pulse have the same use; by their rhythms the great artery of the heart is dilated and constricted. The heart therefore uses the air for making the vital spirit, and the fiery heat of the heart is tempered by the air. Whatever is sooty and unsuitable for production of the spirit is returned to the lung through the venous artery and, together with the air which had remained in the lung, is driven forth by the compression of the thorax; this is agreed by professors of dissection. To be sure, as the tireless heart by its own dilatation draws the blood into its right ventricle from the vena cava and part of the blood passes to the left ventricle, part of it in fact is appropriately prepared by the heart itself as suitable nourishment for the lung and is offered to the lung through the arterial vein by the contraction of the heart. The dilated heart takes air from the lung into the left ventricle, but when constricted it propels the vital spirit into the great artery with the rushing flow of the blood. In order that the rapid contraction of the heart may not bring harm to the vena cava and the venous artery, Nature has created the auricles as storerooms placed close to the heart [18].

We believe that four membranes guard the orifices of the cardiac vessels so that the heart's labor may not be in vain [19]. The membranes guarding the orifices of the vena cava and of the venous artery prevent the blood from flowing back into the vena cava during the contraction of the heart and prevent the vital spirit from flowing back into the venous artery. Those membranes which guard the orifices of the arterial vein and of the great

* . . . . *spiritus vitalis idonea futurus materia.*

artery prevent the blood carried to the lung and the vital spirit already sent forth from being regurgitated into the heart during its dilatation.

The great artery grows forth from the heart, which it resembles. It sends forth two shoots which girdle the base of the heart and send branches downward through its substance [20]. The stem of the artery divides into two trunks a little above the heart [21]; the larger turns leftward to the spine, and branches [22] extend from it to the eight lower ribs on either side. As this trunk is borne downward below the septum, it sends offshoots to the latter [23]. From one root it sends shoots to the omentum, stomach, liver, gall bladder, colon, and finally to the spleen, it being accompanied by the branches of the portal vein [24]. Then another trunk here sends a root to the mesentery [25] and one to each kidney somewhat lower [26]; seminal arteries are sent forth from the anterior region of the trunk [27]. Then another branch lower down is sent to the mesentery [28]. The trunk, sending offshoots in its course to the lumbar vertebrae and the muscles lying on them [29], arrives at the beginning of the os sacrum; the artery is set on the left side of the vena cava and thus creeps on more safely. It is divided into two parts in the same manner as the vena cava and makes an equal distribution with that vein to the very end of the foot [30]. However, no branch of this trunk of the great artery passes to the skin [31]. That part of this trunk which proceeds separately to the offshoot passing through the foramen of the pubic bone and joins the artery to it, descends from the umbilicus along the side of the bladder; this is regarded as belonging to the fetus [32].

The other trunk of the stem of the great artery goes upward [33]; it soon sends from its left side a branch extending obliquely to the highest rib on this side [34]. From this branch there first goes an offshoot to the upper ribs [35], and next another offshoot to the transverse processes of the cervical vertebrae [36], which finally disappears in the dural membrane of the brain; still another offshoot passes along the left side of the breastbone, is always placed deeply, and extends to the umbilicus [37]. Where the main branch passes over the cavity of the thorax, it sends, an offshoot to the muscles which occupy the posterior region of the neck [38]. For the rest, just as the axillary vein is distributed to the very ends of the fingers (if you will except those branches of the vein which reach the skin), so may you understand the arterial branches, which lie only deeply covered here [39].

A sizable portion of the trunk being described ascends to the root of the neck and is divided into two unequal branches [40]. The left and more slender one constitutes the carotid artery of the left side. The right one sends an offshoot from its right side to the first rib [41], where the offshoot completely disappears in the same way in which that former branch of the trunk was said to reach obliquely to the first rib of the left side. The remainder of the right branch forms the carotid artery of this side; like the one on the left, it seeks the upper part of the throat along the side of the rough artery. Deeply into the face it sends a branch which becomes absorbed in the skin of the temples up to the vertex [42]. The artery itself sends offshoots to the larynx, tongue, and the threefold types of glands lying here [43]; it then enters the skull* and, divided into two offshoots, sends the lesser to disappear in the first or right sinus of the dural membrane [44]. The larger offshoot, without an accompanying vein, disappears into the skull through a foramen of its own, and here offshoots soon separate from it and go to the side of the dura [45]. Another offshoot hastens through a peculiar perforation to the cavity of the nostrils toward the end of the nose [46]. But the offshoot itself, not spread out over the base of the skull and not distributed into any intertwining network, passes forward and sends a branch to the eye with the second pair of nerves of the brain [47]; then it ascends, perforating the dural membrane. Here, part of it disappears into the thin membrane [48]; part creeps into the right ventricle of the cerebrum and forms a plexus laid down in this ventricle and compared to the outermost covering of the fetus [49]. The offshoot brings the vital spirit to the brain so that, as I shall now say, the animal spirit may be prepared by the function of the brain.

* Cf. *Fabrica* III, xiv, Tertia Arteriae Series (marginal rubric).

GENERAL INTERPRETATION

THIS chapter deals with the structure and function of the cardiorespiratory system and with the distribution of the arteries.

The heart is described as a two-chambered organ; the atria are not distinguished from the great veins which enter them. The right and left ventricles are the primary chambers of the heart, into which the great veins open. The atrioventricular valves (tricuspid on the right, bicuspid on the left) are placed between the vena cava and the pulmonary veins on the one hand, and the right and left ventricles (respectively) on the other. The auricles (auricular appendages) are chambers close to the heart, serving the function of taking up the shock of systole and thereby protecting the great veins. The right and left ventricles have separate outlets, which are the pulmonary artery (arterial vein) and aorta, respectively. The intrinsic structure of the heart is described as having a muscular wall, thicker on the left than the right, and a septum which shows pits (which, in the *Fabrica,* are denied to be septal perforations or foramina of any degree of importance). The heart is surrounded by a pericardial sac in which fluid is found. The lung is a spongy, bilobate structure which assumes the shape of the space it occupies. It is covered with a pleural membrane, and its substance is made up of the complex intertwining of many branches of the pulmonary artery, pulmonary veins, and bronchi.

The slight hesitance with which Vesalius approaches the question of the preparation and circulation of blood reflects the beginning of the dissatisfaction with Aristotelian and Galenic physiology which was appearing in the scientific world. At the time of this publication, Vesalius' ill-fated contemporary and former fellow student, Michael Servetus, was setting down his ideas on the circulation through the lungs. The crucial points which Vesalius handles diffidently were, perhaps, already taking form in Servetus' mind during the year which the two spent in Guenther's laboratory in Paris (1532), and the manuscript of *Christianismi Restitutio,* in which the passage concerning pulmonary circulation appeared, was written before 1546. At about the same time, Canano of Ferrara informed Vesalius of the discovery of valves in the veins; their significance was missed by Vesalius and Fallopius; the latter probably observed them and communicated the information to his student, Hieronymus Fabricius. (Cf. Fabricius, *De Venarum ostiolis;* translated by K. J. Franklin, D.M. Springfield, Ill.: Charles C. Thomas, Publisher, 1933.) In 1598 the English student, William Harvey, entered Padua and came under the influence of Fabricius; through such a chain of groping uncertainty, teacher may have passed to student the seed of the idea which flowered in 1616 as a report on the circulation of blood—"the greatest discovery in the annals of medicine" (Fulton).

The cardiorespiratory physiology of Vesalius is dependent on the idea of the three-fold "spirit" (Gr., *pneuma*) in man, associated with the three parts of the soul (see Chap. III, general interpretation). The *pneuma physicon,* or natural spirit, is that associated with the lowest or vegetative side of man: it is a vapor formed in the liver and carried with the humors along the veins. The *pneuma zoticon,* or vital spirit, is produced in the heart, the seat of the passions. The source and character of the *pneuma psychicon,* animal spirit, will be examined in connection with Chapter V.

According to Vesalius, the lung expands by activity of the thorax comparable to a bellows, and air rushes in. While some inspired air passes to the cerebrum by way of perforations in the skull, much of it goes through the trachea to the lung. The lung acts on this air and a part of it passes by way of the pulmonary vein to the left ventricle, where the vital spirit is prepared through the interaction of the air and the natural-spirit–bearing blood from the liver; the nonusable part of the air drawn by diastole to the left ventricle returns to the lung during systole by the same route it came and is expelled by thoracic compression in expiration. The blood, now bearing vital spirit, also leaves the left ventricle during systole and passes through the aorta; that which reaches the brain is transformed to animal spirit.

It is in getting blood to the left ventricle that the discussion encounters the greatest difficulty; it is so great, in fact, that Vesalius omits any attempt at explanation in the *Epitome.* The only account given here of the movement of blood which has entered the right heart states that a part of it is sent, in systole, through the pulmonary artery for the nourishment of the lung substance. An explanation is found in the *Fabrica,* where we are informed that air is drawn from the lungs through the pulmonary vein by the left ventricle, whence it "together with the blood which soaks plentifully through the septum from the right ventricle into the left may be assigned to the great artery (the aorta) and so to the whole body." Later, in denying the existence of per-forations in the interventricular septum, he says, "We are driven to wonder at the handiwork of the Almighty, by means of which the blood sweats from the right into the left ventricle through passages which escape human vision."

Several excellent references relating to the development of ideas on the relationship between heart and lungs may be found in Sir M. Foster, *Lectures on the History of Physiology* (1901), from whose first lecture the extracts from the *Fabrica* are taken; in J. F. Fulton's *Selected Readings in the History of Physiology* (1930), especially Chapter II; and in Arturo Castiglioni's *History of Medicine* (1941), where the *pneuma* is described (p. 221). See also Samuel W. Lambert, "A Reading from Vesalius and the Physiology of Vesalius," *Bull. New York Academy Med.* (1936), vol. 12, pp. 345–415.

NOTES

1. UNDERSTANDING of what Vesalius meant by the "threefold type" mentioned in Chapters II and III and twice in the present chapter must await annotation of the corresponding sections of the *Fabrica*.

2. The atria are not considered as parts of the heart; the right atrium was, to Vesalius, a part of the vena cava with "an opening wider than the circular width of the vena cava elsewhere" (see Chap. III, p. 45 and note 47); consistent with this, the left atrium is an expansion of the pulmonary vein. The auricles correspond to the auricular appendages of modern terminology.

3. The wall of the right ventricle is the thinner.

4. Tricuspid valve: "drawn" inward means "directed."

5. That is, carries venous blood (to the lungs); pulmonary artery. See the Leake translation of Harvey's *De Motu Cordis*, footnote 7 to the introductory section.

6. Pulmonary valve.

7. Mitral (bicuspid) valve.

8. That is, carries arterial blood; pulmonary vein. Actually the left atrium; see note 2 above.

9. Aorta and aortic valve.

10. The spaces between the trabeculae carneae.

11. Parietal pericardium.

12. The transverse septum is the diaphragm; the lateral membranes probably indicate mediastinal pleura.

13. The three lobes of the right lung are not recognized.

14. Trachea: see Chap. I, note 21.

15. In order, the visceral and parietal pleurae.

16. For the fate of the "small part of the air" see Chap. V, p. 69.

17. For this and following, see general interpretation to this chapter.

18. The auricles (indicating the auricular appendages) are thought to form a kind of recoil mechanism or shock absorber.

19. That is, to prevent regurgitation and retrograde blood flow.

20. Right and left coronary arteries.

21. The innominate artery and (larger) arch of the aorta. See note 33 below.

22. Intercostal arteries (usually nine pairs).

23. Superior and inferior phrenic arteries.

24. The celiac artery, with left gastric, hepatic, and lienal (splenic) arteries and their branches.

25. Superior mesenteric artery.

26. Renal arteries.

27. Internal spermatic (or ovarian) arteries.

28. Inferior mesenteric artery.

29. Lumbar arteries.

30. Compare this sentence with statements in modern texts (such as Morris, p. 729) that "veins accompany the arteries, and have practically the same relations as those vessels." This, together with the brevity of the present chapter compared with the foregoing chapter on veins, affords excellent illustration of the reversal of emphasis on blood vessels which resulted from the discovery of the circulation of blood.

31. Except for the subcutaneous venous system, the arteries of the extremities correspond to the veins; the superficial veins have no arteriae comitantes.

32. The hypogastric artery, which has the obturator as a branch, is much larger in the fetus, and at birth only its pelvic portion is left; the remainder, "which descends from the umbilicus," is the obliterated hypogastric artery, or lateral umbilical ligament (a fibrous cord).

33. The following text appears confused at first; examination of a Vesalian plate of the arterial system (such as may be found preceding p. 65 in *Icones Anatomicae, Tabulae Libri Tertii*) will establish the point of view from which the description pro-

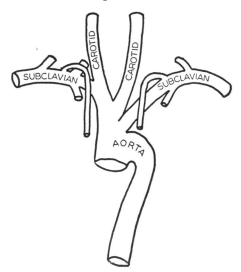

ceeds. Essentially it is as follows: the arch of the aorta and its descending portions have been described as the larger of the two trunks of the stem of the great artery which comes from the heart. The stem is considered to include the ascending aorta and that portion of the arch which gives rise to the great vessels of the head and upper extremities; the aorta, as already described, starts at the point where the left sub-clavian is sent forth. Consequently the lesser of the two trunks, which is now to be described, includes not only the innominate artery but also the left common carotid and subclavian arteries and that portion of the aortic arch from which they arise. The adjacent diagram, adapted from the plate referred to, may aid here. If this concept of the aorta and its branches requires any defense, Morris (*loc. cit.,* p. 607), may be cited: "The innominate and left carotid arise close together—indeed, so close that, when seen from the interior of the aorta, the left subclavian arises a short distance beyond the left carotid."

34. Left subclavian artery.

35. Superior intercostal artery.

36. Vertebral artery.

37. Internal mammary artery.

38. Deep cervical artery.

39. See note 31 above.

40. The two common carotids; there is no named equivalent to the "sizable portion of the trunk" which includes the innominate artery and a portion of the aortic arch.

41. Right subclavian artery.

42. Not only the superficial temporal but the major part of the external carotid artery.

43. Superior thyroid and its laryngeal rami, lingual, and internal maxillary arteries. While positive identification of the "threefold types of glands" cannot be made from the *Epitome,* inspection of *Fabrica* VI, v, suggests that the first type is the thyroid gland, the second is the palatine tonsils, and the third a group of glands which includes the cervical lymph glands and all of the major salivary glands. There is also a refer-ence to what may be the thymus.

44. From this point the description is confusing and inadequate. The present vessel may be the anterior meningeal artery.

45. Middle meningeal artery.

46. Ethmoidal arteries(?).

47. Ophthalmic artery.

48. The cerebral arteries (anterior and middle). The arterial circle at the base of the brain is not described.

49. Choroidal artery and choroid plexus (compared to the chorion).

CONCERNING THE BRAIN AND THE ORGANS

FORMED FOR FURTHERING ITS FUNCTIONS

CHAPTER V

THE brain, the seat of the animal and the principal faculty, lies in the skull and admirably fits the form of the cavity in the upper region of the head which it occupies throughout its length. Anteroposteriorly it is divided into right and left parts but is continuous at its base in the mid-line. Here is the beginning of the dorsal medulla [*oblongata et spinalis*], entirely different from the medulla [marrow] of the bones. Rather less than a tenth of the brain [1] and completely beneath it in its posterior aspect, the cerebellum is joined to the dorsal medulla. The cerebellum extends backward no farther than does the brain itself.

A tough membrane [2] surrounds all these parts of the brain, closely lining the skull and sending fibers through its sutures which end in the skull's own involucrum [3]. This membrane is separated only far enough from the thin membrane of the brain that it may not hinder the motions of the latter's vessels [4]. It sends a process between the right and left parts of the brain [5] and likewise another between the superior region of the cerebellum and that aspect of the cerebrum which rests upon the cerebellum [6]. Performing the service of veins and arteries at the same time and distributing a varied series of vessels to the thin membrane of the brain, four special sinuses lie in this membrane [7]. The substance of the brain, which is continuous, white, and intertwined by no veins, is covered over very intimately by this thin membrane [8]. Weaving here and there through the convolutions of the cerebrum, which are very much like the windings of the intestines [9], it contains the cerebral vessels.

The cerebrum is furnished with three outstanding and spacious cavities or ventricles; of these, one is located in the length of the right part of the cerebrum. It bends back from the posterior portion through the substance of the cerebrum and is carried to the middle of the base of the brain [10]. The second is located in the left part of the cerebrum in a similar fashion. Where they face each other inwardly, they are separated in the upper region by a certain thin substance of the cerebrum [11]; this is called the septum and is continued superiorly to that part of the cerebrum which, because it is somewhat harder and more whitish than the other parts of the brain lying on the surface, is called the corpus callosum [12]. The lower region of the septum is joined to, and continuous with, that part of the cerebrum which is formed like an arch or a tortoise shell (or vault) [13]. It proceeds with a broad base [14] on both sides from the posterior region of the two first ventricles of the cerebrum; gradually passing forward, it fuses at an acute angle and in its inferior aspect overhangs the cavity to be discussed, like the hollow of an arch.

The lower regions of the ventricles mentioned are not partitioned from each other by the septum but come together in a common sinus [15] lying under the body formed like an arch; this space extends directly downward as a prominent channel through the substance of the cerebrum into a funnel or basin formed by a thin membrane of that shape [16]. The phlegm of the brain descends through this channel; it is distilled by a quadrate gland lying on the bone shaped like a wedge [17] and thence flows down to the palate and the broad part of the nostrils through notable perforations, which, however, are not like the holes of a sponge [18]. This present cavity, common to both right and left ventricles, is the third ventricle of the brain. It ends posteriorly in a canal [19] which reaches through the bodies of the brain which are not unlike the nates and the testes [20] to the fourth ventricle. The latter is common to the cerebellum and the beginning of the dorsal medulla; it is furnished in its anterior and posterior region with a process of the cerebellum which, because of its windings, we compare to a worm born in wood [21].

The gaze of the dissector encounters no peculiar body in this fourth ventricle such as may be found in the three former ventricles [22]. For in the right ventricle (as also in the left), a rather noteworthy branch of the soporal artery [23] extends through its inferior and posterior region, destined to form a plexus or network which we compare to the outermost covering of the fetus [24]. It is constituted of that branch of the artery and a portion of its vein which fashions a gland shaped like a pine nut [25] and supported by the testes of the overlying cerebrum. It is led through the third ventricle of the cerebrum from the end of the fourth sinus of the dural membrane [26], which extends along the length of the cerebellum. From that sinus, as from a press [27], it receives the content of the vein and the artery. Then it divides into two portions, of which one extends to the right, the other to the left, ventricle, and with the branches of the arteries passing to the same place it forms the plexus just mentioned in each ventricle.

From the vital spirit adapted in this plexus to the functions of the brain and from the air which we draw to the ventricles of the brain when we breathe in, the inborn force of the brain's substance creates the animal spirit, of which the brain makes use partly for the functions of the chief portion of the mind. Part of it the brain transmits by means of the nerves growing forth from itself [28] to the organs which stand in need of the animal spirit. (These are chiefly the instruments of the sense and of voluntary movement [29].) A not inconsiderable part of the animal spirit spreads from the third ventricle under the testes of the brain into the ventricle common to the cerebellum and the dorsal medulla. This is subsequently distributed to all the nerves drawing their origin from the dorsal medulla [30].

From the middle of the base of the brain a long, rounded process arises on either side and is led along the base of the brain anteriorly; it lies on the corresponding sinus of the eighth bone of the skull and is the organ of smell. Since it does not pass from the cavity of the skull, it has not been given the name of a nerve by professors of dissection [31].

The first of the seven pairs of nerves which are ascribed to the brain has its origin from the base of the brain a little behind the process corresponding to the substance of nerves, of which mention has just been made. It constitutes the optic nerves, which end in the tunic of the eye similar to a net in appearance [32]. The eye has a crystalline humor in its center, the anterior region of which is covered by a tunic corresponding to the very thinnest membrane of an onion [33]. The posterior region of this humor is held in by a vitreous humor, around the posterior aspect of which runs an involucrum corresponding to the substance of the brain and in which the substance of the visual nerve is dissipated [32]. The thin membrane of the brain covers up the visual nerve and extends to a tunic very similar to the skin of a grape [34]. Although it completely surrounds the eye, it is seen to be perforated in its anterior region with an opening which we call the pupil. The dural membrane of the brain surrounds the visual nerve and ends in the hard tunic of the eye [35], which covers up the eye completely; in the anterior region of the eye it is transparent in the manner of horn [36]. This is circumscribed by the iris, the larger circle of the eye, to which clings the white of the eye or the tunic growing in the anterior region of the eye. Between this cornea and the anterior region of the crystalline humor is the aqueous humor, which is separated from the vitreous by a certain thin tunic bearing cilia which is joined in circular fashion to the crystalline humor; this tunic arises from the uvea [37].

The second pair of nerves serves for moving the muscles of the eye [38]. The third pair grows out on either side with two roots separate from each other [39]; it sends the lesser root by certain little openings to the skin of the forehead [40], to the upper jaw and upper lip, to the breadth of the nostrils [41], and to the muscles which raise the lower jaw [42]. The larger root is sent to the tongue; by the function of this root the tongue is made the instrument of taste [43]. Also, from this root a branch twisted inward in the manner of a tendril is sent to the muscles just mentioned, and another branch to the upper teeth [44], another to the lower jaw and to the teeth fixed in it, and finally to the lower lip [45].

The fourth pair of nerves ends in the covering of the palate [46]. The fifth pair proceeds with a double root also [47], as does the third pair, and distributes the lesser root to the muscles which raise the lower jaw [48] but sends the thicker root to the organ of hearing [49]; from this root it also sends two offshoots extending through different openings to the muscles just mentioned.

The sixth pair [50] is increased by a portion of the seventh pair beyond the little branches sent out from itself to certain muscles in the neck and to the larynx [51]. Near the top of the breastbone it sends certain offshoots to the muscles issuing thence [52]. To the roots of the ribs it sends down a branch [53] which is well distributed to the organs which have charge of making the blood. Thus far, each nerve of the sixth pair is equally distributed. The right nerve separately turns back a portion of itself to the artery which extends to the right arm, from which the nerve is carried up along the right side of the rough artery and proceeds to the larynx; for this reason it is called the recurrent nerve [54]. The remaining part descends from this right nerve and sends little branches to the right part of the lung and to the covering of the heart [55]; this part finally joins the esophagus after passing through the septum and giving many offshoots to the left side of the superior orifice of the stomach [56]. The left nerve turns back those portions of itself which constitute the recurrent nerve of the left side to the trunk of the great artery extending to the back [57]. From the nerve of this side a slender offshoot belonging to the heart is distributed [58]; that which remains of it is interwoven in the right side of the superior orifice of the stomach and sends a little branch as far as the liver along the upper part of the stomach. The seventh pair, in addition to the fact that it increases the sixth pair considerably, ends especially in the muscles of the larynx and the tongue [59].

The nerves which draw their origin from the dorsal medulla contained in the vertebrae include thirty pairs [60]. Of these, seven are dedicated to the cervical vertebrae, twelve to the thoracic vertebrae, five to the lumbar vertebrae, six to the os sacrum; no nerve, however, springs from the coccyx. The pairs which begin to descend from the cervical vertebrae are distributed to the muscles which rise very close to these pairs; one nerve, belonging to the transverse septum, is formed on either side from the fourth, fifth, and sixth offshoots of the pairs [61]. Then from the fifth, sixth, seventh, and next from the eighth and ninth, or from the first and second pairs of the thorax, a varied plexus of nerves arises [62] from which six nerves sprout forth into the arm, in addition to various offshoots dispersed to the hollow and to the gibbous part of the scapula.

The first nerve which seeks the arm [63] sends from its own offshoots to the muscle which raises the arm a very slender shoot to the skin covering the external region of the arm. The second nerve enters the arm through the axilla [64]; it sends little branches to the first muscle of those which flex the elbow. It imparts a notable portion of itself [65] to the third nerve

71

which approaches the arm, and itself [66], hastening to the elbow, sends a branch to the first muscle which leads the radius in supination; it runs under the skin and, divided into various offshoots, it intermingles with the skin of the superior and internal region of the forearm as far as the hand [67]. The third nerve also descends through the axilla [68]; it sends little branches to the skin of the anterior region of the arm. Increased by a portion of the second nerve and communicating an offshoot to the posterior muscle of those which flex the elbow, it hastens to the forearm through the anterior aspect of the inner tubercle of the humerus [69]. Together with the fifth nerve, it sends shoots to the muscles which draw their origin hence; extending along the radius and led into the palm of the hand, it sends two offshoots to the internal aspect of the thumb, the same number also to the index finger, and one offshoot only to the external side of the inner [palmar] region of the middle finger; not infrequently, however, it offers two little branches to the middle finger and one to the ring finger [70]. The fourth nerve of the arm is much thicker than the rest [71]; sending branches to the muscles which extend the elbow, it enters through the armpit. First sending two offshoots to the skin [72], it hastens along the posterior aspect of the arm to the external tubercle of the humerus. The nerve placed at this external region of the elbow joint distributes a branch to the skin of the external region of the forearm as far as the wrist [73], and soon dividing into two trunks [74], it gives offshoots to the muscles growing forth from the external tubercle of the humerus. To the ulna it extends one trunk [75]; from this trunk little branches are distributed to the muscles arising from the external region of the ulna; the trunk itself ends near the root of the wrist. The upper trunk [76] reaches to the radius; except for the slender shoots which it offers to the overlying muscles, it seeks the wrist and imparts two little branches to the external region of the thumb, two likewise to the external region of the index finger, and one to the internal side of the middle finger. The fifth nerve [77] lies hidden in the armpit, nearest to the artery of the arm. It sends out no offshoots from itself to the arm. It extends into the forearm along the posterior region of the internal tubercle of the humerus [78] and, together with the third nerve, communicates branches also to the muscles growing forth here. It runs along the ulna to the wrist, sending out in the middle of its course a branch which dwindles by giving off two shoots to the exterior [dorsal] region of the little finger, two likewise to the same region of the ring finger, and one shoot to the external side of the exterior region of the middle finger [79]. Whatever portion of the fifth nerve reaches the internal region of the wrist offers small branches to the interior [palmar] region of the little finger as well as of the ring and middle fingers [80]. The sixth nerve is especially slender [81]; it is led along the internal aspect of the arm under the skin, and in its progress it extends some little branches to the skin. It reaches to the forearm, in the skin of which it is disseminated with numerous shoots along the ulna as far as the wrist.

From the nerves which spring forth from the thoracic vertebrae, with the exception of branches which are stretched backward to the spines of the vertebrae and hence to the muscles which draw their origin from them [82], single intervals of the ribs appropriate to themselves single branches stretch-ing in circular fashion to the middle of the chest and abdomen and dispers-ing shoots to the muscles laid down in the thorax, to the muscles of the abdomen, and finally to the skin. Small portions are distributed to these intervals from the intercostal nerves, which augment the offshoots of the sixth pair of nerves of the brain extending to the roots of the ribs [83].

The distribution of the nerves proceeding from the lumbar vertebrae cor-responds in large part to the nerves of the thorax, for the former send branches backward and these ascend along the ilia in a circular fashion to the middle of the abdomen, furnishing little branches to the contiguous muscles and to the skin. From the first pair of these [84], very small offshoots extend to the testes with the seminal arteries. The nerves which proceed to the thigh [85] take their origin from the four lowest pairs, although the greatest nerve [86] of all arises from the first four pairs, of the nerves of the os sacrum. The first pair of sacral nerves, like those of the thoracic and the lumbar region, descends from the vertebrae. The five lowest pairs of the os sacrum do not spring from the sides but issue forth with one root ante-riorly and another root posteriorly [87]; the posterior roots are dispersed to the muscles which attach to the bones of the sacrum and ilium and to the skin [88]. The anterior branch of the first pair, together with the anterior roots of the three succeeding pairs, constitutes the [sciatic] nerve just mentioned. The roots of the lowest pairs disappear into the bladder, anus, and penis, or in women into the neck of the uterus [vagina] and the hillocks of the pudenda [89].

Of the four nerves which proceed to the thigh, the first is led along the sixth muscle which moves the femur and sends a branch into the external aspect of the skin of the thigh [90]; it disappears in the muscles which occupy the external side of the femur. The second enters the thigh along with the larger vein and artery of the thigh [91]; it soon sends a branch through the internal aspect of the thigh, the knee, and the leg as far as the foot and the ends of the toes. It descends under the skin, together with a vein which has been mentioned as creeping forward here, and sends little branches here and there [92]. That which is left of the second nerve ends in the muscles covering the anterior region of the femur. The third nerve creeps through the foramen of the pubic bone and offers branches to the muscles which occupy it [93]. Distributed here and there, it sends an offshoot to the internal aspect of the skin of the thigh. The rest of that nerve is divided and sent to the muscles located in the internal region of the thigh. The fourth nerve [94] is easily the thickest of all the nerves of the body which are composed of more than one nerve; it is led into the posterior part of the thigh where the bone of the coxendix splits away from the sacrum. To the posterior aspect of the skin of the thigh, it sends a branch which presently ends a little below the middle of the femur [95]. Another branch propagated from the fourth nerve is offered to the lower region [96]. It also sends off-shoots to the muscles arising from the lowest posterior region of the coxen-dix bone [97], as also to the muscles which arise from the inferior heads of the femur. Then in the popliteal region it is divided into two trunks. The more slender outer one is carried to the fibula [98], from which a branch creeps to the external aspect of the skin of the leg as far as the little toe. Another branch is sent to the anterior aspect of the skin of the leg. The rest of that trunk extends to the fibula, where lies the origin of the seventh and eighth muscles of those which move the foot. The larger inner trunk [99] gives off a branch into the internal aspect of the skin of the leg and likewise to the skin of the calf as far as the heel. The trunk itself is hidden in the muscles which form the calf and sends a branch along the membranous ligament where the fibula is joined to the tibia [100]. The branch is here hidden in the muscles which occupy the anterior region of the leg; finally it reaches the upper part of the foot and is hidden there in the toes. The greater portion of that larger trunk [101] runs down along the posterior part of the leg and sends some offshoots here and there to the muscles. It approaches the lower part of the foot between the heel and the inner malleolus; it offers quite small offshoots to the muscles lying therein and communicates two offshoots to the inferior aspect of each of the toes.

In this manner, indeed, the great Creator of things has fashioned our body not only that it may live but that it may, subject to corruption, live properly. But what means he has fashioned for the continuation of our species and how he has joined them with the organs of nutrition far from the seat of the senses and of the reason [102], I shall now relate below, summarily and in so far as this enumeration of the parts of the human fabric admits.

GENERAL INTERPRETATION

T HE brain, the source of activity and the seat of consciousness, is seated in the spherical, "most perfectly formed" portion of the body, the head. In addition to its protection within the skull, it is surrounded by membranes, the outer tough and the inner thin and more fragile. These membranes are not named by Vesalius but correspond to our "dura mater" and "piarachnoid." These terms may be referred to a philosophic concept employed by the Arabic anatomists: the membranes which cover a given structure are those in which the structure was originally formed. Our modern terminology utilizes this in naming the layers of the uterine wall "endometrium" and "myometrium"; both the term "mater" and the combining form "metrium" are cognates of our word "mother" and have equivalent value in the Arabic concept; the idea was carried across with the translation of the Arabic term. Mondino does not use the idea, although the names are employed; he does point out the function of the pia mater in nourishing the brain substance. It is noteworthy that Vesalius not only omits these terms but also avoids using the term "involucrum," which carries somewhat the opposite meaning of a membrane which has been derived from the structure it encloses.

Among the products of the brain's activity is phlegm, one of the four humors. It passes down the infundibular ("funnel-shaped") recess of the third ventricle and is "instilled" by the pituitary gland, passing thence to the palate and nostrils through inadequately described foramina.

The circulation of the brain is somewhat confused; the arterial circle is not recognized, and the dural sinuses perform both arterial and venous functions for the brain substance. The carotid artery sends a branch to make up the choroid plexus. This structure is remarked especially in the two lateral ventricles and the third ventricle but not the fourth ventricle (all of which spaces in the brain are described in a manner conformable with modern anatomy; this is not the case in the work of Mondino). The choroid plexus is the site in which the vital spirit, carried in the arterial blood from the heart, is turned into animal spirit (*pneuma psychicon*), which is adapted to nervous function. This is accomplished by interaction with that part of the inspired air which has entered the cranium (see Chap. IV, general interpretation) and has reached the ventricles. The animal spirit thus created is distributed along the cranial nerves.

The seven cranial nerves correspond closely to those of Galen and Mondino. The only one in which data are lacking for a fairly positive identification is the fourth. It is interesting to observe here a discrepancy in the text of Mondino. In his section "Of the Nerves Arising in the Brain," he describes the fourth nerve as our "vagus" (the key to the identification is the presence of the *nervi reversivi* or recurrent laryngeal); the sixth pair "go to the palate to give it feeling." Yet earlier, in treating "Of the Trachea Arteria," the vagus is enumerated as the sixth nerve. Vesalius says, of the fourth nerve, only that it "ends in the covering of the palate." Singer, in annotating his translation of Mondino, does not follow the confused listing of the section on cranial nerves.

76

In the comparative table below, the fourth and sixth nerves of Vesalius are not presented as positive and with complete identification; the description in the *Epitome* is inadequate for this purpose. The portion ascribed to Galen is taken from Charles Singer's *The Evolution of Anatomy* (1925), page 56; that of Mondino is from the same author's translation and annotation (note 97) of the "Anathomia," found in *Monumenta Medica,* Volume II, Part I (1925); this text was also quoted in the preceding paragraph. The development of anatomical thinking on the subject of the cranial nerves from Galen through Mondino and Vesalius to modern times will be made apparent at a glance from this table.

COMPARATIVE TABLE OF CRANIAL NERVES

MODERN USAGE	GALEN	MONDINO	VESALIUS
I. Olfactory	Not regarded as separate nerves	Not regarded as separate nerves	Not regarded as separate nerves
II. Optic	"The soft nerves of the eyes"	First pair	First pair
III. Oculomotor	"The nerves moving both eyes"	Second pair	Second pair
IV. Trochlear	Not described	Not mentioned	Included with "second pair"
V. Trigeminal	"Third pair of nerves"	Third pair	Third pair, which has two roots
	"Fourth pair of nerves"	Fourth pair	Fourth pair
VI. Abducens	United with second (II)	Not mentioned	Included with second pair
VII. Facial	"Fifth pair of nerves"	Fifth pair	Fifth pair
VIII. Auditory			
IX. Glossopharyngeal	"Sixth pair of nerves"	Sixth pair	Sixth pair; also includes sympathetic trunk (note 83) with this cranial nerve
X. Vagus			
XI. Spinal accessory			
XII. Hypoglossal	"Seventh pair of nerves"	Seventh pair	Seventh pair

1. THE average weight of the cerebellum is 140 gm; average weight of the encephalon is slightly less than 1,400 gm, although varying from 1,100 to 1,700 gm.

2. The dura mater.

3. In the cranial vault the endocranium (outer layer of the dura, which is here separable into two layers) is continuous through the sutures with the pericranium (periosteum, the "skull's own involucrum").

4. The subdural space is only a potential one.

5. The falx cerebri.

6. The tentorium cerebelli.

7. Just which dural sinuses are meant is not clear; probably we are dealing with the right and left transverse sinuses, the superior sagittal, and the straight sinus (and possibly in this numerical order). Some readers may need to be reminded that the term "sinus" in anatomy is used in many different senses and does not necessarily refer to the accessory nasal air cavities. Here the meaning is an intracranial space filled with venous blood. The reference to veins and arteries is more likely the prevailing concept of blood circula- tion; in only one place is a major artery (the internal carotid) included within the walls of a sinus (the cavernous).

8. The piarachnoid.

9. And serving much the same purpose—that of obtaining an increased area within a limited space.

10. The right lateral ventricle, with its inferior horn.

11. The septum lucidum.

12. The "callous body." By this name a sharp distinction is made between the texture of this white fiber tract and the gray cellular tissue composing the cortex.

13. The fornix; its old name (corresponding to "tortoise shell") was *testudo cerebri;* the parenthetic "vault" is an alternative translation.

14. Like a man standing with a broad base; legs wide apart and diverging from the trunk.

15. The third ventricle.

16. The infundibular recess.

17. The pituitary gland and the sphenoid bone (*pituita,* "phlegm").

18. Through perforations in the sphenoid, not through the lamina cribrosa ethmoidalis; see Chap. I, note 9.

19. The aqueduct of Sylvius.

20. *Nates et testes*, the superior and inferior colliculi (corpora quadrigemina; from a fancied resemblance to the appearance of the buttocks and scrotum of a man bent over, seen from the posterior aspect. It is appropriate here to remember that much of the nomenclature of the brain was established at a time when brains were not subjected to the action of a hardening solution such as formalin. The soft mass assumed shapes which might lend themselves to comparisons not so obvious in the firmer brains with which the present-day dissector is more familiar; hence the cornu Ammonis, calamus scriptorius, hippocampus, obex, clava, and many others. This comment is not to disparage the terms, for the similarities can be observed in formalinized tissue, but to emphasize that there may have been even more stimulus to the imagination of the early dissector. The *nates et testes* comparison is by no means inept.

21. The vermis of the cerebellum; a "worm born in wood" is probably a grub, the larval form of a beetle.

22. The amount of choroid plexus in the fourth ventricle is small.

23. Soporal artery: the artery of sleep (the internal carotid). Carotid is derived from χάρος, "stupor," thought to be produced by pressing on the carotids. Professor J. B. de C. M. Saunders suspects an even older, onomatopoeic derivation. *Carus, or sopor caroticus,* was the final degree of unconsciousness and insensibility (sopor, coma, lethargia, and carus).

24. The anterior choroidal artery, see Chap. IV, note 49. The reference is to the choroid plexus, named from the fetal membrane *chorion*.

25. The pineal gland.

26. The straight sinus. The "vein of Galen," or great cerebral vein, is the forward continuation. The omission of the eponymic is probably without significance; the only man named in the entire *Epitome* proper is Plato. This is definitely not the situation in the *Fabrica*.

27. "Press": not the *torcular Herophili*, the "wine press of Herophilus" (or sinus confluens); while the figure of speech may be the same, the place under description is at the anterior end of the straight sinus, while the torcular is posterior.

28. The history of the concepts of the nerve impulse has shown two main ideas present at various times; nerves have been thought either to be somehow hollow (or pithy), transmitting a vital spirit which obeys the laws of fluids, or (on the other hand) solid, conveying a less tangible and material influence.

29. A clear distinction between sensory and motor functions.

30. The anatomical specificity surely implies some tangible carrier of this animal spirit such as the cerebrospinal fluid. Even if this be true, it does not mean that Vesalius fully accepted either the fluid or the less corporeal concept of nerve impulse propagation. A translation of that portion of the *Fabrica* dealing with this point may be read in Lecture X of Sir M. Foster's *Lectures on the History of Physiology* (Cambridge University Press, 1901), and there Vesalius refuses to commit himself, saying "we will not too anxiously discuss" the question.

31. The olfactory tract; our "first cranial nerve" which is, of course, neither first nor nerve. Vesalius explains that he does not give it the status of a nerve because it does not emerge from the cranium. As previously noted (see note 9, Chap. I), he does not describe emergence of olfactory filaments through the lamina cribrosa ethmoidalis.

32. Optic nerve; retina (from *rete*, "a net").

33. The lens and the anterior portion of its capsule.

34. The choroid tunic. "The skin of a grape" probably indicates its dark pigmentation. Note that the old names, "tunica aciniformis" or "rhagoides" or "uvea," all suggest a grape.

35. Tunica sclera.

36. Cornea (*cornu*, "horn").

37. Zonula and orbiculus ciliaris.

38. The oculomotor (our third cranial) nerve.

39. The trigeminal (our fifth cranial) nerve. This text is difficult to reconcile with the two roots at present distinguished: a large sensory and a smaller motor root ("nervus masticatorius").

40. Ophthalmic nerve.

41. Maxillary nerve, including nasal rami.

42. Masticator nerve.

43. Lingual nerve (not, of course, the nerve of taste as Vesalius thought, but the general somatic sensory innervation of the tongue; the chorda tympani runs with it in its distal portion and carries the taste fibers).

44. Superior alveolar branches of maxillary.

45. Inferior alveolar nerve, with the mental ramus.

46. The brevity of the text does not allow adequate identification of this nerve; it is probably the group of palatine nerves, branches of the trigeminal, and corresponds to the "fourth nerve" of Galen and Mondino.

47. Facial and auditory nerves (our seventh and eighth cranial).

48. A part of the facial nerve going to the mimetic muscles (here the branch to buccinator muscle is emphasized; see Chap. II, note 15, for inclusion of buccinator with the muscles of mastication).

49. The auditory nerve, with part of the facial nerve passing through the stylomastoid foramen and hiatus of the facial canal.

50. Vagus nerve, our tenth cranial, and spinal accessory (or eleventh). See general interpretation.

51. Superior laryngeal nerve.

52. Superior cardiac nerves(?). They are given off at about this level and pass near the trachea and surrounding muscles.

53. Sympathetic trunk.

54. The right recurrent (inferior) laryngeal nerve, passing under the right subclavian artery.

55. Pulmonary branches and right inferior cardiac branches.

56. Gastric branches.

57. Left recurrent laryngeal, passing under the arch of the aorta.

58. The left inferior cardiac branches usually arise only from the recurrent nerve.

59. The hypoglossal (our twelfth cranial) nerve, including (here) the descendens cervicalis portion of the ansa hypoglossi. It is probable that Vesalius considers this a portion of the hypoglossal nerve, thereby omitting the root which we count as first cervical (see following note).

60. We number thirty-one pairs; eight are cervical, of which the first is atypical and arises above the first cervical vertebra, the next being typical and arising below the vertebra. We count five sacral and one coccygeal nerves. In determining the origin of any nerves from the cervical region, we must add one to the Vesalian enumeration to reach the modern count.

61. No system of enumeration exactly accounts for this composition of the phrenic nerve.

62. The brachial plexus; quite definitely postfixed innervation of the arm (see Wilfred Harris' monograph *The Morphology of the Brachial Plexus,* Oxford University Press, London: Humphrey Milford, 1939).

63. The axillary nerve, with branches to the deltoid muscle and lateral brachial cutaneous nerve.

64. The lateral cord of the brachial plexus.

65. The lateral head of the median nerve.

66. The musculocutaneous nerve. The brachioradialis receives its innervation from the radial nerve; perhaps the inconstant branch to the pronator teres is meant.

67. Lateral antibrachial cutaneous nerve.

68. Median nerve.

69. Over the medial epicondyle, near the brachialis.

70. The variation pattern is well described, but the frequency is reversed; the emphasis on the inconstancy should be on the ring finger.

71. Radial nerve.

72. Posterior brachial cutaneous nerve.

73. Dorsal antibrachial cutaneous nerve.

74. Superficial and deep.

75. The deep branch, dorsal interosseous nerve.

76. The superficial branch.

77. The ulnar nerve.

78. Behind the medial epicondyle.

79. Dorsal digital branches.

80. Volar digital branches.

81. Medial antibrachial cutaneous nerve.

82. Dorsal primary divisions.

83. The sympathetic trunk and rami communicantes.

84. Ilioinguinal nerve.

85. The femoral nerve.

86. The sciatic nerve.

87. Through the anterior and posterior sacral foramina, respectively.

88. Such as branches to the multifidus muscle and the middle cluneal nerves.

89. Pudendal nerve, and other branches of pudendal plexus.

90. Lateral femoral cutaneous nerve.

91. Femoral nerve.

92. Saphenous nerve.

93. Obturator nerve.

94. The sciatic nerve, passing through the greater sciatic foramen.

95. Posterior femoral cutaneous nerve.

96. To the buttocks—*humilior;* the inferior cluneal nerves.

97. To the hamstring muscles.

98. The superficial peroneal nerve; inspection of the text will establish several minor errors in the distribution pattern of the terminal branches of the sciatic. The branches of the superficial peroneal here listed are the dorsal cutaneous (medial and lateral) and the muscular branches to peroneus longus and brevis.

99. This will, by necessity, include the tibial nerve and the deep peroneal nerve. The cutaneous branch is the medial sural cutaneous nerve, continued as the sural.

100. The deep peroneal (anterior tibial) nerve, which passes around the head of the fibula to enter the anterior compartment of the leg.

101. The tibial nerve.

102. The reason for this is dependent on the concept of the tripartite soul; see note on Plato's *Timaeus* in Chap. III, general interpretation.

CONCERNING THE ORGANS WHICH MINISTER

TO THE PROPAGATION OF THE SPECIES

CHAPTER VI

IN THE beginning, the Author of the human fabric fashioned two human beings for the conservation of the species in such a way that the male should furnish the primary principle of the infant, the female indeed should fitly conceive it and should nourish the little child arising from this principle as she would nourish some member of her own body [1] until the child should become stronger and could be given forth into the air which surrounds us. Both male and female received instruments suitable for these functions and peculiar to them alone. To these organs was imparted so great a power and attraction of delight in the generative act that the living creatures are incited by this power, and whether or not they are young or foolish or devoid of reason, they fall to the task of propagating the species not otherwise than if they were the wisest of beings.

The male possesses two testes covered by skin which is here called scrotum, surrounded with a fleshy membrane [2], and formed of a white, continuous substance quite peculiar to them. A strong membrane contains this substance, growing very close to it in circular fashion and receiving the insertion and connection of those parts which are near the testis, constituting a covering belonging to each of the testes [3]. Joined to this one is another covering proper [4] to the testis and growing forth from the peritoneum where the latter offers a path for the seminal vessels. Thence grows forth the membrane containing those vessels with the testis; it is at no point fused to the testis nor even to the seminal vessels (except where they escape from the great cavity of the peritoneum). This tunic is attached with its fleshy part only to the lower region of the testis; we consider this the muscle of the testis [5].

83

The seminal vessels consist of one vein and one artery on each side. The vein which seeks the right testis grows forth from the anterior region of the trunk of the vena cava below the place of origin of the veins which extend to the kidneys. But that vein which is offered to the left testis is believed to take its origin from the lower aspect of the vein which approaches the left kidney [6] for the reason that it may not carry the pure blood to the testis in the manner of the right vein but rather the serous blood, which by its salty and acrid quality may bring about an itching for the emission of the semen. Both arteries take their origin from the great artery a little below the right seminal vein; the right-hand one, climbing over on the trunk of the vena cava, joins the right vein, reaching the testis together with this vein. It is complexly intertwined with the vein before it reaches the testis and forms a body showing many dilatations [7]. This body is inserted with its base in the superior region of the testis, offering small branches to the innermost cover-ing of the testis [8]. The body is distributed through the manifold substance of the testis which changes this benign blood and spirit by its own innate faculty into semen not otherwise than the substance of the liver changes the thick juice carried there from the intestines into blood.

The semen, when it is created, is received by a strong vessel like a worm growing in the posterior region of the testis and complexly intertwined like a tendril [9]. This vessel, round like a nerve, rises upward to the great cavity of the peritoneum along that path by which the seminal vein and artery descended [10]. Turning downward to the pubic bone, it reaches the pos-terior region of the bladder, to which a vessel bearing the semen from the left testis also runs. This vessel is attached to the right one [11] and together with it is inserted into the root of the neck of the bladder in the glandulous body covering the neck [12].

For the semen and for the urine there arises a common channel which is led slightly downward and again bends back upward to the joining of the pubic bones outside, lying under the bodies which constitute the penis. There issues forth on either side of the pubic bone a nerve and a round and sinewy body which is seen to be very funguslike within and full of blood [13]. United and fused together, they constitute the penis; by the aid of its sub-stance it provides for its erection and enlargement when it is about to inject the semen into the uterus. Otherwise, when there is no need for its full length, it is flaccid and slender. For the satisfactory use of Venus, it swells in its apex in the manner of an acorn [14]; it is furnished with a skin by which it can be covered and uncovered [15].

The female possesses a uterus, dedicated to receiving the semen and to containing the fetus. The uterus lies between the bladder and the rectum and, like the bladder, is suitably formed with a fundus and neck [vagina] [16] adapted for stretching and relaxing, intertwined with loose membranes and with some fleshy fibers (by the assistance of which the uterus is voluntarily moved somewhat). It is joined at its sides to the peritoneum [17], just as the mesentery contains the intestines. The shape of its fundus is not completely round but flattened in front and behind, obtuse above, and showing two blunt angles (one on each side) which resemble the immature horns on the foreheads of calves [18]. In the fundus of the uterus is a simple sinus [19] corresponding very closely to the shape of the fundus; ending in an orifice and constricting and relaxing itself by a natural force alone and not by the conscious will of the female, it projects like the glans penis into the cavity of the neck of the uterus [vagina]. The fundus of the uterus consists of a simple intrinsic tunic notably thick in nonpregnant women so that it can be stretched to a remarkable extent in the uterus of women who are with child. Another tunic is drawn over this one; it takes its origin from the peritoneum. The neck of the uterus [vagina] is round and smooth; in the nongravid uterus it is not particularly distended, not much smaller than the fundus itself. It receives the insertion of the neck of the bladder [urethra] and is furnished at its orifice with leathery pieces of flesh and hillocks or wings [20].

On each side of the uterus lies one testis to which vessels extend in exactly the same way as in males [21]. Here, however, it happens that only the middle part of the seminal vein and artery is sent to the testis; the other part is interwoven in the fundus of the uterus [22]. The vessel carries a thin and very scanty and watery semen from the female testis; it is inserted into the obtuse angle of the side of the uterus. Veins and likewise arteries in a very rich series interweave the uterus, in addition to those mentioned before; they issue from those distributions of the vessels which are formed below the junction of the os sacrum and the lowest lumbar vertebra [23]. These vessels serve for nourishing the fetus and for the re-creation of the innate heat.

The fetus, contained in the uterus, is covered with three involucra. One of these is commonly called the secundine ["afterbirth"], because it surrounds only the fetus like a wide belt and is notably thick and blackish like the spleen [24]; this is joined to the uterus and receives the vessels extending thereto. By means of it, those vessels which are presently gathered within it are inserted into the umbilicus by two veins and the same number of arteries, and at last with one vein to the liver [25]. Two arteries [26] extend to the offshoots of the great artery as these are about to descend through the apertures of the pubic bones. The second envelope, collecting the fetal urine between itself and the third envelope, is a membrane embracing the entire fetus in the image of a sausage [27]. The urine is carried by a special channel [28] from the upper aspect of the bladder into this cavity so that, the urine of the fetus being contained within this membrane, the fetus is not injured by its acidity. The third envelope is a very thin membrane and is for this reason also called *agnina,* lamblike, by the masters of dissection [29]. It covers the fetus very closely; finally it keeps the perspiration of the fetus [30] between itself and the skin of the fetus, smeared, as it were, with a yellowish scum [31].

When the fetus is given forth into the light of day, it sucks the milk as its own nourishment from the breasts, untaught by anyone. The breasts have their location in the chest and are furnished with nipples; they are built up of a glandulous material which, by an innate force, converts the blood brought to them by the veins into milk.

THE END OF THE ENUMERATION OF ALL THE PARTS WHICH OCCUR
in the fabric of the human body, as far as possible most briefly and in their
completeness set down; the following pages contain the delineation
of these same parts, to be examined in the order we
prescribed at the outset.

GENERAL INTERPRETATION

VESALIUS' ideas on reproductive physiology are Aristotelian in origin. The substances from which the embryo is formed are "genital semen" and "menstrual blood." The former is formed by the testes from the blood coming to them in a manner similar to that in which the liver creates blood from the food brought to it. In addition to the menstrual blood, the female also forms a thin watery semen in the ovaries which is carried to the uterus.

The chapter appears to be the least adequate of the various sections in the *Epitome*. Much anatomy is not described. The significance of the clitoris was at first missed by Vesalius and later denied (after having been pointed out by Fallopius). The vagina goes by the name of "cervix (neck) of the uterus," and the "fundus of the uterus" is equivalent to the entire uterine mass. The uterine tubes are not described. Fugitive sheets published by Vesalius only a few years before the printing of the *Epitome* represent the uterus as bearing horns. The section on fetal membranes is not written from the standpoint of human anatomy.

The *Epitome* does not describe the various male and female reproductive organs in terms of direct homology, although implications are often present. Additional data may be drawn from the manikin-plates, where the reproductive systems have been represented in such a way that homologizing is apparent. From such sources the following table of homologues in the *Epitome* is offered; it is subject, of course, to possible revision and addition by future translators of the *Fabrica*.

MALE	FEMALE
Testis	Ovary—"testis"
Epididymis	Pampiniform plexus of veins
Ductus (vas) deferens	Portion of ovarian artery
Prostate gland	Fundus of uterus
Corpora cavernosa (urethrae et penis)	Body of uterus
Glans penis	Cervix of uterus (modern terminology)
Prepuce	Vagina—"neck of the uterus"—and labia minora

1. THAT is, as if it were an organ of the mother; the independence of maternal and fetal circulation was not known.

2. The dartos tunic.

3. Tunica albuginea.

4. Tunica vaginalis proprius.

5. The cremaster muscle, lying on the internal spermatic fascia (tunica vaginalis communis).

6. See Chap. III, note 79.

7. Pampiniform plexus.

8. The septula, which radiate from the mediastinum testis to the tunica albuginea.

9. The epididymis and ductus deferens (vas deferens).

10. The inguinal canal.

11. The colliculus seminalis.

12. Prostate gland.

13. The corpora cavernosa penis, on the inferior aspect of which is placed the corpus spongiosum (corpus cavernosum urethrae) previously described. The comparison to a nerve refers to the dense fibrous sheath which surrounds the erectile tissue (see Chap. II, note 1).

14. Glans: acorn.

15. Prepuce.

16. The "neck" of the uterus does not correspond to the cervix uteri of modern terminology, although the Latin text uses these words; it is to be identified as the vagina wherever named by Vesalius. To avoid confusion with the cervix, the word has been translated as neck wherever it occurs here.

17. The broad ligaments.

18. The cornua of the uterus.

19. In contrast to the bipartite and bicornuate uteri of lower mammals.

20. The vulva; especially the labia majora and minora. See general interpretation.

21. The uterine tubes were not described by Vesalius but by his student, Fallopius. Vesalius confirmed their existence when pointed out by Fallopius; cf. Cushing, p. 193. The term "testis" in Vesalius is equivalent to our "gonad."

22. The ovarian artery, with a branch to the uterus.

23. The hypogastric arteries, especially the uterine branches.

24. The placenta. The term "secundine" is approximately the Latin equivalent for our "afterbirth," as a word in common usage. The word "placenta" was originally applicable only to the discoid type of organ characteristic of a few Mammalia including Primates (*placenta,* "a flat cake"). For reasons not evident here, Vesalius has described the zonary placenta found in Carnivora.

25. The (right) umbilical vein of the fetus; ligamentum teres of the adult.

26. The hypogastric arteries of the fetus (see Chap. IV, note 32).

27. The allantois ("sausage-like"). This is present in lower mammals but is not well developed in human beings; the error was corrected by Fallopius and acknowledged by Vesalius (see Cushing, pp. 186 and 190).

28. The urachus.

29. The amnion (ἀμνός, "lamb").

30. The amniotic fluid.

31. The vernix caseosa.

THE NAMES OF THE EXTERNAL REGIONS OR

PARTS OF THE HUMAN BODY VISIBLE WITHOUT DISSECTION

THE enumeration of the names indicating the external regions and places of man is here briefly indicated, and these may be entered with advantage in the margins of the plates showing the superficies of the male and female body. Their description, however, is concise, since my purpose is to furnish only an index to the figures presented on these plates. Almost the same names may be applied to the external regions as are used for the bones of the body and the parts lying beneath the exterior. Of these names, determined by those who more correctly employ the method of dissection,* we have already recounted the principal ones in the context of the discourse as far as our design in the *Epitome* requires.

It is the habit among teachers first to divide the entire surface of the body into large regions and then to give various names to the parts of those regions. So the Egyptian doctors used to divide the body into head (caput, κεφαλή), thorax (θῶραξ), arms (manus, χεῖρες), and legs (crura, σκέλη); just as Aristotle did, they gave the name thorax to the entire trunk (ὅλμος) of the body from the throat, neck, or clavicles to the groin and the pubis, or rather all the way to the upper part of the thighs. They did not mean by thorax, as Galen and some anatomists of the first rank did, merely the region of the body which was fenced off with ribs. Others of those who attribute the faculties of the entire body to certain regions and consider the intellect as the seat of the soul distinguish a fourfold division of the surface of the body just as did the Egyptians, but somewhat differently from the latter they first divide the trunk into two regions; they place the arms and legs in

* In writing this passage, Vesalius was upholding the more ancient, pre-Galenic anatomists who, in his opinion, derived their nomenclature from direct anatomical examination; the terminology of such observers as Galen (who, he contends, saw only the superficial aspect of the human body) is subject to criticism.

one division, those parts which, properly speaking, constitute the members (artus, κῶλα) or extremities. In the trunk of the body they make a division into two special regions, according to the two cavities therein which are obvious to dissectors. Of these, the lower one is cut off from the upper one by the intervention of the transverse septum; it contains the liver, which is the seat of the natural or nourishing faculty and the place where the blood is made, the organs which minister to the liver, and the parts which serve for the task of generation. The upper cavity holds the heart, the tinder of the agitative [pulsific] faculty, and the organs subserving the heart. The principal seat of the soul is assigned to the head; this third cavity of the body is the seat of the brain and the storehouse of the animal spirit.

Having thus cursorily divided the body, the teachers again divide the surface into separate parts as follows: the anterior part of the entire head above the eyebrows, free from hair (τρίχες) and showing certain furrows (στολίδες, ἀμαρυγαί), is called the forehead (frons, μέτωπον). Above this and verging toward the middle of the head is the sinciput (βρέγμα). On both sides of the sinciput and above the ear (οὖς), in which is the auditory meatus (ἀκουστικὸς πόρος), lies the temple (κρόταφος, κόρσος). The middle region of the head rising toward the posterior of the sinciput is called the vertex (κορυφή), like the center of a circle which circumscribes the hair margin (περίοδος, στεφάνη, περίδρομος). Near the highest region of the muscles called tendons (τένοντες) by many and behind the vertex, the occiput (ἰνίον) is seen. These muscles are prominent on either side of the neck and show a median hollow.

The front part of the head, from the forehead down to the chin, is the face (facies, πρόσωπον). The inferior part of the forehead is delimited by projecting eyebrows covered with hair (ὄφρυες) and by the interval between them (μεσόφρυον). Below these lie the eyes (oculi, ὀφθαλμοί), covered by the upper and lower eyelids (βλέφαρα); the regions where they come together mutually are furnished with eyelashes (cilia, βλεφαρίδες), a row of erect hairs like the oars we see on galleys; these regions are somewhat cartilaginous and contain the tarsi (τάρσοι). The termini of this commissure are the angles (anguli, κάνθοι); the greater one faces toward the nose, the lesser one toward the temple. Between the separated eyelids, in

91

addition to the caruncula (ἐγκανθίς) seen in the greater angle, there appears the "white" of the eyes (candidum, λευκόν), in the middle of which two circles present themselves. Of these the broader one is the iris (ἶρις, στεφάνη) or corona, the lesser is the pupil (κόρη). The nose (nasus, ῥίς) lies between the eyes; its apertures are called the nostrils (nares, μυκτῆρες, μυξωτῆρες). The external sides of these are fitted with the pinnulae or wings (alae, πτερύγια) of the nose; the inner aspect is made up of the septum (διάφραγμα). The regions at the sides of the nose, rather prominent and reddish like an apple, are called the malae (μῆλα); some call them the cheeks (genae). The regions midway between the nose and the cheeks are by some called the concava (κοῖλα), by which name others indicate the entire region of the eyes (γλήνη) extending from the eyelids to the cheeks. That part of the face which we inflate is the bucca (γνάθος). The entire region from the eyebrows to the upper row of teeth is the upper jaw (superior maxilla, ἡ ἄνω γένυς); the remaining part, which in men is adorned with the beard (barba, πώγων), is called the lower jaw (inferior, ἡ κάτω γένυς). The anterior extremity of this is led out into the chin (mentum, γένειον), sometimes provided with a hollow (fovea, τύπος, νύμφη) lying below the redness of the lower lip (τὸ κάτω χεῖλος). The region of the upper lip (τὸ ἄνω χεῖλος) lying below the nose is endowed with a little furrow (sulculus, φίλτρον); there the mustache is seen (mustax, μύσταξ, ὑπήνη). That which is circumscribed and contained by the lips is called the mouth (os, στόμα), in which when open we see the tongue (lingua, γλῶσσα), the palate (palatum, ὑπερῶα), the uvula (γιργαρεών, σταφυλή), the teeth (dentes, ὀδόντες), the gums (gingivae, οὖλα), and the internal aspect of the fauces (φάρυγξ).

That part of the body from the head to the clavicles or as far as the thorax is called the neck (collum, τράχηλος, αὐχήν) or cervix; if we restrict the latter name to the posterior part, just as the former is applied to the place where the rough artery (and especially its upper end) can be palpated (λάρυγξ), we should use the term throat (guttur).

The ancients called the joining of the armbone with the scapula the humerus (ὦμος), and from this they called that eminence at the root of the neck and to the sides of the thorax the summus humerus (ἀκρώμιον). That

92

part which turns directly away from it toward the throat (σφαγή) and the hollow at the root of the neck is the clavicle (κλείς). The region which extends from the humerus to the tips of the fingers is the arm (manus, χείρ). The first part of the arm extending to the nearest joint, the bend of the elbow (cubitus, ἀγκών), is called the brachium (βραχίων) and by some of the Latins* also the humerus. Under it lies the cavity called the axilla (μασχάλη) or wing, walled off with muscles which in that place many call tendons (τένοντες). The posterior region of the bend of the elbow is called the gibber (ὠλέκρανον, κορώνη). The part which extends from the gibber to the conterminous joint is the forearm (cubitus, πῆχυς), also by some of the Latins called brachium or ulna (ὠλένη). At the very end of the forearm begins the hand (summa manus, ἀκρόχειρ), of which a part extends from the forearm to the roots of the four fingers, divided into two regions; the region closer to the forearm is the wrist (brachial, κάρπος), the other is the postbrachial (μετακάρπος), which from the likeness of its construction to the chest is also called chest (pectus, στῆθος) and, by some, palm (palma). The inner aspect of the latter is hollowed, fenced off by various small mounds, and crisscrossed by many lines; this region is the vola (θέναρ). The remainder of the hand forms the fingers (digiti, δάκτυλοι), each one divided into three parts (σκυταλίδες, φάλαγγες) placed in series, the most external being equipped with nails (ungues, ὄνυχες). The largest of these digits is the thumb (pollex, ἀντίχειρ), which is opposable to the others by its action; the one next to it is the index (λίχανος), then the middle finger or impudicus (μέσος), next to which is the medicus or ring finger (παράμεσος, ἰατρικός). The last place is occupied by the little finger (μικρός) or ear finger (auricularis).

We here call the thorax (θῶραξ) that part of the trunk of the body which is fenced off with ribs (πλεύραι) and forms the greatest part of the sides (πλευρά). The anterior part of the thorax is the chest (στῆθος), occupied by the breasts (mamillae, μαστοί), with the nipples (papillae, θηλή) in the middle surrounded by a darkish circle (φῶς). The remaining anterior region of the trunk forms the abdomen (ὑπογάστριον); that portion

---

* While the apparent meaning is "Roman anatomists and physicians," the term probably refers to those who adhere to the Latin terminology rather than use the preferred Greek stem.

of it which is nearest the cartilage of the breastbone and the lower cartilages of the ribs is designated as subchondral (ὑποχόνδρια) as the viscera are surrounded by them. The place where the transverse septum is called the precordia is the region in which the septum inserts into these cartilages and thus obtains its name, although, again, others give this name also to the anterior region of the thorax. The region between the lowest ribs and the crest of the ilium (which projects more in the female than in the male) is free from bone and can be palpated; it is called the inania or flank (κενεῶνες, λαγόνες). In the middle of this region the umbilicus (ὄμφαλος) is seen, and immediately below it is the paunch (sumen, ἴτρον), the lowest region of which, nearest to the end of the trunk, is called the waterpot (aqualiculus, ἐφήβαιον, ἐπίσιον).

The pudenda or naturalia (αἰδοῖα) lie at the terminus of the trunk; this end is the pubes or pecten (ἥβη), at whose sides, in the flexures of the thigh, we place the groins (inguina, βουβῶνες). The part of the male pudenda visible without dissection is called the penis or prick (coles, ["stalk"], καυλός); the summit of it is thicker than the rest of its length and forms the glans (βάλανος), in the middle of which appears the channel common to the urine and the semen. The covering of the glans penis is the prepuce (praeputium, ποσθή), although others give this name to the entire summit of the penis. A prominent line in the semblance of a suture in the covering of the glans and in the rest of the skin to the anus we call the suture (ῥαφή); the entire part of the penis stretching prominently as far as the anus we call the taurus (ταῦρος). We call interfeminium (περιναῖον, διχάλα) the region between the anus and the covering of the testes (which, since it is composed of skin, is called scrotum, ὄσχεον). The opening of the female pudenda, which is the orifice of the neck of the uterus [vagina], is called the sinus (κόλπος, κτείς); on both sides of the sinus project wings and hillocks (πτερυγώματα), and on the summit of the sinus appears a fleshy skin (νυμφή). The orifice of the intestinum rectum which appears in the region is called annulus from its shape (δακτύλιος) and stricture (σφιγκτήρ) from its function.

The posterior part of the trunk of the body is called either back (dorsum, νῶτον) or tergum; its sides in the higher posterior aspect of the thorax are composed of the scapulae (ὠμοπλάται). The mid-region between them (μεσόφρενον) and the part of the back extending hence to the lowest ribs, or where the back protrudes most in flexion (ἄκνηστις), is ascribed to the thorax and is situated behind the transverse septum. The region extending as far as the buttocks comprises the loins (lumbi, ὀσφύς). The buttocks (nates, γλουτοί) are a rounded and fleshy region occupying the dorsal aspect of the iliac bones; in the midst of the buttocks the posterior processes of the os sacrum and the coccyx, subcutaneous, extend to the anus.

Where the joint of the femur appears, there protrudes the great rotator (τροχαντήρ); here is also the coxendix (ἴσχιον) or coxa, which name others assign to the femur (μῆρον), extending from the groin to the knee (γόνυ). The posterior region and the joint of the latter are called the ham (poples, ἰγνύς). The leg (κνήμη) follows from the knee to the next joint or the beginning of the foot; some call the leg the crus, while others use the same name to designate both leg and thigh. The anterior region of the leg (ἀντικνήμιον, κρέα) is bony to the touch; the posterior region of it, where the belly is seen, is fleshy and is called venter or the calf (sura, γαστροκνήμη). The tuberosities on either side at the end of the leg are, like bones, obvious and are called malleoli (σφυρά); not so is the talus (ἀστράγαλος) which, unlike these, is buried. The posterior region of the foot, projecting backward beyond the straight line of the tibia, is called the heel (calx, πτέρνα). The remaining regions of the surface of the foot take their names from the bones, especially the flat (tarsus, τάρσος) of the foot (πεδίον) or of the chest (pectus, στῆθος); the toes, furnished with nails, follow. However, when we speak of the entire foot, the lowest region on which we walk is usually called the sole (planta) or vestigium (τέλμα); its inner side is the hollow (concavum, κοῖλον), but the superior aspect is the tarsus.

THE GREEK MARGINAL NOTES OF VESALIUS
(218 ITEMS)

CHAPTER I

	MARGIN	TEXT	TRANSLATION
a	ὁμοιομερεῖς	similares	similar in temperament and elements
b	ὀστοῦν	os	bone
c	χόνδρος	cartilago	cartilage
d	σύνδεσμος	ligamentum	ligament
e	ἶνες	fibrae	fibers (muscle)
f	ὑμήν	membrana	membrane
g	σάρξ	caro	flesh
h	πιμελή	adeps	fat
i	ἀνομοιομερεῖς, uel ὀργανιχαί	dissimilares	dissimilar in temperament and elements
k	φλέψ	uena	vein
l	ἀρτηρία	arteria	artery
m	νεῦρος	neruus	nerve
n	μῦς	musculus	muscle
o	δάχτυλος	digitus	finger
p	χράνιον	calvaria cerebri	skull
q	ὀστοῦν μετώπου	in fronte . . . unum tantum (os)	frontal bone
r	ἰνίου	in occipitio unum os	occipital bone (inion)
s	βρέγματος, uel χορυφῆς	in uertice duo (ossa)	parietal bones
t	χροτάφου	tempus unum (os)	temporal bone
u	μαστοειδής	unus (processus) uberis	mastoid process
x	στυλοειδής, uel βελονοειδής, aut πλῆχτρον	stylum, aut acum, aut galli calcar	styloid process
y	ζύγωμα	iugale os	zygomatic processes
z	λιθοειδής	quam praeruptae rupi . . .	(see note 6)
a	σφηνοειδές, uel πολύμορφον	in capitis basi os	sphenoid bone

96

	MARGIN	TEXT	TRANSLATION
b	πτεριγοειδεῖς [sic]	processus uespertilionum alis simillimos	projections very much like the wings of a bat (pterygoid)
c	ἠθμειδές uel σφογγοειδές	os in narium summo	ethmoid bone
d	διάφραγμα	septum	septum
e	ἡ ἄνω γνάθος	superior maxilla	upper jaw
f	κόγχος	sedis oculi regione	orbit
g	πτερά	narium alae	wings of the nostrils
h	στεφανιαῖα	coronalis sutura	coronal suture
i	λαμϐδοειδής	sutura a Λ similitudine nomen. . . .	lambdoid suture
k	ὀϐολιαῖα [sic]	sagittalis sutura	sagittal suture
l	λεπιδοειδῆ προσκολλήματα	squamosae conglutinationes	squamous conglutinations
m	ἡ κάτω γνάθος	inferior maxilla	lower jaw
n	ὀδόντες	dentes	teeth
o	τέμνοντες	incisorios	incisors
p	κυνόδοντες	caninos	canines
q	μυλίται	molares	molars
r	φάτνια	praesepolis	tooth sockets
s	φάρυγγες	faucibus	pharynx
t	ὑοειδές	os υ imaginem exprimens	hyoid bone
u	λάρυγξ	laryngem	larynx
x	θυρεοειδής	scutum	thyroid cartilage
y	ἀνώνυμος	cartilago nomine destituitur, hinc . . . . id inueniens	cartilago innominata, the cricoid cartilage
z	ἀρηταινοειδής [sic]	vasorum orificio respondet	arytenoid cartilage
a	γλωττίς	lingulam	little reed: glottis or lingula; vocal apparatus
b	ἐπιγλωττίς	operculum	epiglottis
c	σιγμοειδεῖς	C imaginem exprimentibus	uncial capital sigma
d	ῥάχις	dorsum medulla	dorsal medulla, the spinal cord
e	αὐχήν, aut τράχηλος	collum	neck
f	θῶραξ	thoracem	thorax
g	ὀσφύς	lumbos	loins

97

MARGIN	TEXT	TRANSLATION
h ἱερὸν ὀστοῦν	sacrum os	sacrum os (holy bone), in the shape of a cross
i κόκκυξ	coccyx	coccyx or cuculus
k σπόνδυλος	uertebras	vertebrae
l ἀνάνθη	spina	spine
m ὀδοντοειδής	processus instar canini dentis	process like a canine tooth (see note 33)
n στέρνον	pectoris os	breastbone
o στῆθος	anteriorem sedem thoracis	anterior region of the thorax
p θῶραξ	thorax	thorax
q πλεῦραι	costis	ribs
r ἀληθεῖς	c. uerarum	true ribs
s νόθαι	c. spuriae	false ribs
t ξιφοειδής	manubrium cartilaginem	xiphoid process
u σφαγή	iugulum	throat, root of the neck
x κλείς	clauicula	clavicle
y ὠμοπλάτη	scapula	shoulder blade
z ἀκρώμιον	summus humerus	acromion process
a ἀγχυροειδής, uel σιγμοειδής	interior scapulae processus	coracoid or anchor process (see note 41)
b βραχίων	brachii os	bone of the arm, or humerus
c πῆχυς	duo inibi ossa	cubitus
d κερκίς	radius	radius
e πῆχυς uel ὠλένη	ulna	ulna
f ὠλέκρανον	gibberum	gibber, the olecranon process
g στυλοειδής	qui a styli forma nomen	styloid process
h κάρπος	brachiale	wrist, or carpus
i μετακάρπιον, aut στῆθος	postbrachialis	postbrachial, the metacarpals
k φάλαγγες, aut σκυταλίδες	tribus ossibus	phalanges of the digits, or three bones
l σησαμοειδῆ	ossicula	sesamoid bones
m λαγόνος ὀστοῦν	ilium os	hipbone
n ἰσχίου	coxendicis	os coxae
o ἥβης	pubis os	pubic bone
p μῆρον	femoris os	femur
q γλουτός, et μέγας τροχαντήρ	natem et magnum rotatorem	rump and great rotator, the greater trochanter
r μικρὸς τροχαντήρ	processum	minor or interior rotator, the lesser trochanter
s κνήμη	tibia	tibia

MARGIN	TEXT	TRANSLATION
t περόνη	exteriori interim osse	fibula

u μύλη,
    uel ἐπιγονατίς
	os rotundum. . . . mola
	    patellaue
		a round bone called mola
		    (millstone), or patella;
		    (kneecap)

x σφυρά	malleoli	malleoli
y ἀστράγαλος	talum	talus
z πτέρνη	calcis os	heel, especially the cal- caneum
a σκαφοειδές	ossis navicularis	navicular bone

b τάρσος	tarsi	tarsus, including the navicu-
		    lar, the three cuniforms,
		    and the cuboid bones

c χαλκοειδῆ	ossa tria	three bones
d κυβοειδές	os cubi et tesserae imaginem exprimens	cuboid bone
e πεδίου ὀστᾶ	ossa pedii	metatarsal bones
f ὄνυχες	ungues	nails
g τάρσοι	cartilagines	cartilages of the eyelids (the tarsal plates)

CHAPTER II

σύνδεσμος [extra ordinem]	ligamentum	ligament
a ἀπονευρώσεις	eneruationes	aponeuroses
b νεῦρος	nerui	nerves, often indicating sinews
c μῦς	musculus	muscle
d τένων	tendo musculi	tendon
e δέρμα	cutis	skin
f ἐπιδερμίς	cuticulam	epidermis
g ὑμὴν σαρκικός	membrana	membrane
h πιμελή	adeps	fat
i κροταφίτης	temporalis	temporal muscle of lower jaw
k μασσήτηρ	mansorius	masseter

i ἐπωμίς	humeri articulum
	    . . . . tegens
		covering the shoulder joint,
		    the first muscle of the arm

k δελτοειδής	Δ non absimilis	deltoid muscle (second), not unlike the Greek letter Δ
l μεσοπλεῦροι	exteriores musculi	intercostal muscles (see note 33)

99

MARGIN	TEXT	TRANSLATION
m διάφραγμα, et φρένες, et ἡ ἄνω κοιλία	septum transversum	diaphragm
n κρεμαστήρ	testi unus musculus	cremaster
o σφιγκτήρ	alius musculus	sphincter
p ἀντικνήμιον	musculus . . . . anteriori tibiae sedi inseritur	sartorius, the first muscle of the leg (see note 56)

CHAPTER III

a οἰσόφαγος aut στόμαχος	uiam, stomachus	esophagus
b κοιλία	uentriculus	stomach
c πύλωρος	inferius orificium	lower orifice of stomach (pylorus)
d ἔντερα	intestina	intestines
e ἔκφυσις	origo	origin (of the intestines)
f δωδεκαδάκτυλον	duodenum	duodenum
g νῆστις	ieiunum	jejunum
h ἴλεον	ilium	ilium
i τύφλον	caecum	appendix vermiformis
k κῶλον	colum	colon
l ἀπευθύσμενον, uel ἄρχον	recti ac principis intestini	straight intestine, the rectum
m ἀδῆνες [sic]	glandulis	glands
n μεσεντέριον uel μεσαραῖον [sic]	mesenterium	mesentery
o ἧπαρ	iecur	liver
p πύλης φλέψ	portae uenae	portal vein
q ἐπίπλοον, uel ἐπίπλουν	omentum	the omentum [caul]
r πάγκρεας, uel καλλίκρεον	glandulis	glands, fleshy in color (pancreas)
s σπλήν	lienem	spleen
t πόροι χολήδοχοι	meatus	bile ducts and hepatic duct
u κύστις χολήδοχος	uesiculam	gall bladder
x νεφροί	renes	kidneys
y πόρος οὐρητήρ	urinarius meatus	urinary passage
z κύστις	uesica	bladder
a περιτόναιον	peritonaeo	peritoneum
b κοίλη φλέψ	cauae	vena cava
c στεφανιαῖα	uena	cardiac vein

MARGIN	TEXT	TRANSLATION
d ἄζυγος	uenam paris expertem	azygous vein
e ὠμιαῖα, aut κεφαλική	humerariam [venam]	cephalic vein
f ἡ κατὰ βάθος σφαγίτις	internam iugularem	internal jugular
g ἡ ἐπιπολῆς σφαγίτις	superficiariam iugularem	superficial jugular
h μασχαλαῖα	axillaris uenae	axillary vein
i κοινή	communem	median antibrachial vein
k μέσαι	mediis uenis	middle veins (see note 74)

CHAPTER IV

a καρδία	cor	heart
b κόλποι, siue κοιλίαι	sinus seu uentriculos	sinuses or ventricles
c ἀρτηριώδης φλέψ	arterialis uena	arterial vein, or pulmonary artery
d ἀρτηρία φλεβώδης	uenalis arteria	venous artery, or pulmonary vein
e διάφραγμα τῆς καρδίας	septo	septum
f περικάρδιον	inuolucrum cordis	pericardium
g διαφράττοντες ὑμένες	membranis	mediastinal septum
h πνεῦμων	pulmo	lung
i τραχεῖα ἀρτηρία	asperae arteriae	rough artery, trachea
k παρίσθμιαι	tonsillae	tonsils
l ὑποζωκὼς [sic] χιτών	tunicae	tunic, pleura (see note 15)
m γαργαρεών	gargareonem	uvula
n καρδίας ὦτα	cordis aures	auricles, auricular appendages
o ἀορτή	magna arteria	great artery, or aorta
p καρῶτις	soporalem arteriam	carotid artery

CHAPTER V

a ἐγκέφαλος	animalis ac principis facultatum sedes	the seat of the animal and the principal faculty, the brain
b νωτιαῖος μελός	dorsalis medulla	dorsal medulla, spinal cord
c μυελός	ossium medulla	bone marrow
d παρεγκέφαλις	cerebellum	cerebellum
e παχεῖα μῆνιγξ	dura membrana	dura mater

101

MARGIN	TEXT	TRANSLATION
f περικράνιον	inuolucrum calvariae	pericranium (see note 3)
g λεπτὴ μῆνιγξ	tenui cerebri	pia (see notes 4, 8)
h διάφραγμα	septum	septum
i τυλλῶδες σῶμα	callosum corpus	corpus callosum
k ψαλλοειδές	parti quae instar fornicis testudinisue	fornix, arch, vault, or tortoise shell
l πύελος aut χοάνη nisi id hic descriptae glandi tribuere uisum sit	peluim	funnel or basin (infundibular recess), funnel, basin
m ὑπερῶον	palatum	palate
n ὀρχεῖς	testibus	testes
o γλουτοί	natibus	nates, buttocks
p σκωληκοειδής	processu	process, vermis
q χοροειδής	plexum	choroid plexus
r κωνάριον	glandis nucis pineae instar	pineal gland
s ληνός	torculari	wine press
t ἀμφιβληστροειδής	tunicam retis imagini similem	retina
u κρυσταλλοειδής, uel φακοειδής	crystallinum humorem	crystalline humor (lens)
x ἀραχνοειδής	tunica	capsule, lens
y ὑαλοειδὲς ὑγρόν	uitreo humore	vitreous humor
z ῥαγοειδής, aut ῥογοειδής	tunicam uuae folliculo similem	a tunic very similar to the skin of a grape, choroid tunic
a κόρη	pupillam	pupil
b σκληρότης aut στερεός	duram oculi tunicam	hard tunic, sclera
c κερατοειδής	pellucidam tunicam	transparent tunic, cornea
d ἴρις	iride	iris
e λευκός	alba tunica	"white" of the eye
f ὑδατώδες [sic]	aqueus humor	aqueous humor
g παλινδρομῶν	neruus recurrens	recurrent nerve

CHAPTER VI

a ὄρχεις	testes	testes
b ὄσχεον	scortum	scrotum
c ἐπιδιδυμίς	ualida membrana	a strong membrane, tunica albuginea

MARGIN	TEXT	TRANSLATION
d	ἐρυθροειδής, aliis δάρθος	alterum inuolucrum	another covering, tunica vaginalis proprius
e	κρεμαστήρ	testis musculum	testis muscle, cremaster
f	κιρσοειδὴς παραστάτης	corpus . . . . multas uarices exprimens	a body showing dilatations, pampiniform plexus
g	πόρος σπερματικός	uase instar uermis	a vessel like a worm, vas deferens
h	ἀδηνοειδὴς παραστάτης	glandulosum corpus	glandulous body, prostate gland
i	καυλός	penem	penis
k	βάλανος	glandis	acorn, glans
l	πόσθη	cute	skin (foreskin), prepuce
m	μήτρα	uterum	uterus
n	κέρατα	duos retusos angulos	two blunt angles, horns, cornua uteri
o	νύμφη	coriaceis carnibus	leathery pieces of flesh, labia minora
p	πτερυγώματα	colliculis alisue	wings or hills, labia majora
q	κτείς, uel κόλπος	orificium	orifice, vulva
r	χόριον	inuolucrum	envelope, afterbirth
s	ὄμφαλος	umbilicum	umbilicus (navel)
t	ἀλαντοειδής [sic]	secundum inuolucrum	second envelope, allantois (sausage-like membrane)
u	υὐραχύς	meatu	channel of urachus
x	ἄμνιος	tertium inuolucrum	third envelope, amnion
y	μαστός	mamillis	breasts
z	τιτθοί	papilla	nipple

THE EPITOME OF
ANDREAS
VESALIUS

(LATIN TEXT)

ANDREAE VESALII
BRVXELLENSIS, SCHOLAE
medicorum Patauinæ professoris, suorum de
Humani corporis fabrica librorum
EPITOME.

CVM CAESAREAE
Maiest. Galliarum Regis, ac Senatus Venti gratia & priuilegio, ut in diplomatis eorundem continetur.

LECTORI.

QVOD modò datum librorum de Humani corporis fabrica Compendium, in duas partes diffectum eft, quarum una fex capitibus complexa, fuccinctiffimam omnium partium hifto-
riam complectitur: altera in pluribus tabulis earundem delineationem fimul cum characterum quibus infigniuntur indice proponit. Quare tuo ipfius arbitratu noftrum ordinem (quem ex ua-
rio, dimpreffionis formam, compingendiq; rationem commodiffimum felegimus) tanti quanti uifum erit pendens, aut partium defcriptionem, aut defignationem, notarumq; indicem primum ag-
grediaris, quem omnino à figuris nudas mulieris imagines proponentibus aufpicabere, ubi externarum fedium appellationes, ceu illarum imaginum index, occurrent. Integram oftium
compagem offert figura à uiri tergo impreffa: quanquã & figuræ ad uiri illius proportionê delineatæ, ac uelut mufculorû tabulæ infcriptæ, externã fectionis ferie effa proponant & præcipuè
earum quarta & quinta. Mufculorum etenim ligamentorumq; delineatio petenda eft primùm ab illa quam è regione tabulæ omnia offa & experimentis locamus, obidq; prima mufculorum figuræ
infcribitur: cui fuccedit quæ tertia nominatur, dein quarta & quinta. Nutritionis quæ cibo potuiq; fit organa, & dein cor partes quæ ipfius munijs fubferuirent, fimul cum neruorum
ferie proponuntur figuris nudam mulieris imaginem fubfequentibus, ubi & mulierum generationis fpectantur inftrumenta, perinde ac uterum organa occurrunt n figuræ quintæ mufculorum tabulæ agglutinata. Eorum quæ caluaria complectuntur imaginem, præter tabulam neruis commonftrandis paratam, mufculorum figuræ fatis abfolutè refferunt, ac primùm quidem caput primæ figuræ, dein fecundæ, mox quartæ fimul cum imaginibus quas uis figuræ manus amplexantur, & has fi bequuntur quæ in finiftra quintæ
figuræ manu eft obuia, alæq; inibi præter oculi partium effigiem humi decumbens. Vale, &
noftris conatibus candidè (uti offeruntur) utere.

BASILEAE.

A

SERENISSIMO PRINCIPI PHI-
LIPPO, DIVI CAROLI QVINTI IMPERATORIS
MAXIMI INVICTISSIMIQVE FILIO HAEREDI.

Andreas Vesalius   S.

TENVI *hoc chartarum contextu, maxime Princeps* PHILIPPE, *qui immortalis tui no-*
minis splendore decoratus, in communem studiorum usum auspicatò emittitur, humani corporis
historiam enumerationis modo ita partitus sum, singulaq́; enumeraui, ut praecipua naturalis phi
losophiae pars creaturae omnium absolutißimae & iuxtà dignißimae fabricam pertractans, ima-
ginis cuiusdam uice operum Naturae studiosis ob oculos uersari poßit. quae quoad fieri licet suc
cinctè, ac minus operose ea exprimat, quae septem huius argumēti libris diffusè complexus sum,
quorum haec Epitome semita quaedam, aut appendix etiam iure habebitur, capita quae illis de-
monstrantur aceruatim comprehendens, omniaq́; sic semel proponens, ut augurer eam pro tua
incredibili humanitate, qua etiam tenuißimum quodq́; scripti genus alacriter amplecteris, è tuo
conspectu non reijciendam, quando ut hac ineunte adhuc aetate tam uarijs uirtutibus exornata,
omnium disciplinarū & artium miro amore teneris, ita quoq́; generosißimi, ac qui uniuerso orbi
aliquando praeficiatur digni prorsus animi tui domiciliū, uel obiter cognoscere iucūdum duces,
atq́; summorum Imperatorum, Regum, Consulum exemplo turpe miserumq́; esse arbitraberis,
nos adeò uaria sectantes studia, corporis quod perpetuò circunferimus harmoniā latere, ac hominem sibi ipsi penitus esse incognitum, neq́;
instrumentorū tam diuinè ab immenso rerum Opifice structorum compagem perscrutari: quorum munere ea quae potißimū, et sola prope
modum admiramur, alioquin conficiuntur. Verùm & si hac ratione conatus iste tuo omnibus admirabili iudicio forsitan non displicebit,
illum tamē medicis adeò nollem reddi familiarem, ut dum prodesse conor, ac in posterum quibusdam sordidorum typographorū mancipijs
ad aliorum labores ineptißimè in arctum contrahendos, suoq́; nomine emittendos ad rei literariae perniciem natis, occasionem praeripere
studeo, magnopere obsim. Nemo enim nescit, quantum dispendij in scientijs omnibus compendia conciliare soleant. Quandoquidem & si
illa ad perfectam absolutamq́; rerum cognitionem uiam quandam & ratione praefigere uideantur, ac latius prolixiusq́; alibi tradita, bre
uiter uniuersimq́; contineant , hocq́; in primis nomine instar indicis & memoriae sedis censeantur , in quam sparsim scripta ritè colloccen
tur , nihilo minus compendia ideo egregiè nocent , magnamq́; literis cladem adferunt , quod illis solummodo addicti , uix quicquam aliud
hodie perlegamus, etiā ijs qui se totos disciplinis manciparunt, duntaxat ad scientiarum umbram & superficiem aspirantibus, ac penitius
solidè ue nihil eruentibus. Huius mali quantumuis in omnibus propemodum studijs id latè uagari constet, medicorum uulgus grauissimè
insimulandum est, quod adeò ignauiter hominis partibus dignoscendis operam nauat, ut ne enumerationae quidē ad eas discendas utatur.
Quum enim praeter cuiusq́; partis functionem & usum, ipsius quoque situs, figura, magnitudo, color, substantiae natura, ad caeteras par
tes connexus ratio, ac eius generis permulta in partium examine medico nunquam satis perspecta esse queant, quotus quisque reperitur,
qui ossium, cartilaginum, ligamentorum, musculorum & uenarum, arteriarum neruorumq́; frequentißima per totum corpus serie excur
rentium, ac uiscerum, quae in corporis habentur cauitatibus, uel numerum modò tenet? Vt pestilentes praeter eam medicos, in communis
hominum uitae exitium grassantes, qui ne unquam quidem sectioni astitére, quum in corporis cognitione nemo aliquod operae precium prae
stiturus sit, qui non proprijs manibus, uti Aegyptiorum reges consueuerunt, sectiones obierit, & illas perinde ac simplicia medicami
na sedulò frequenterq́; uersauerit. Vnde etiam nunquam satis laudabuntur prudentißimae Asclepiadum familiae, liberos domi ut lectio
ne & scriptura, sic & cadauerum resectionibus exercentes, ut ita edocti, foelici Musarum omine studijs incumberent. Caeterùm hic no
stram in Anatome totius medicae artis basi ac fundamento perdiscenda oscitantiam, & quam nobis qui medicinae nomen dedimus, per
necessaria sit humanarum partium notitia, haud demonstrandum assumpsi: quum cuiusque conscientia abundè attestetur, in morbis curan
dis eorum cognitionem primas, secundas ac tertias partes meritò sibi uendicare, hanc que in primis ab affecta sede peti, debitum quoque
(praeter alia) auxiliorum usum commonstrante. Quinetiam qui ueteri medicinae nunc in plerisque gymnasijs pristino nitori propemo
dum restitutae dedicantur, assatim intelligere incipiunt, quàm parum frigidèq́; hactenus à Galeni temporibus in Anatome sudatum fue
rit : qui & si huius procerum facilè sit primarius , humanum tamen corpus nunquam aggressus est, & simiae potius quàm hominis ab illius
fabrica innumeris sedibus uariantis partes descripsisse (ne dicam, nobis imposuisse) modò colligitur.   Quòd autem ad meam attinet au
daciam, qua exiguum hoc tuaq́; indignum Maiestate munusculum, tanto patrocinio unicè commendatum, ancipitem iudiciorum aleam su
bit, nullam excusationem praetexurus sum, nisi quòd hanc salsam molam, qua maximè per studiorum rationem litare datur, tantisper meae
erga patriae Principem singularis obseruantiae pietatisq́; specimen esse uelim, dum thura quoq́; offerre
aliquando dabitur. Patauij, Idibus Augusti. Anno à Vir-
ginis partu M D X L I I.

ANDREAE VESALII BRVXEL-

LENSIS, SVORVM DE HVMANI CORPORIS
FABRICA LIBRORVM EPITOME.

DE OSSIBVS, ET CARTILAGINIBVS,
seu ijs quæ corpus suffulciunt partibus. Caput I.

OMNES humani corporis partes sunt aut similares, sensu've simplices, ut os, cartilago, ligamentum, fibræ, membrana, caro, adeps: aut dissimilares, instrumentariæ've, quemadmodum uena, arteria, neruus, musculus, digitus, & reliqua totius corporis organa: quæ eo magis instrumentaria fiunt, quo pluribus similaribus, ac dein instrumentariis etiam partibus (ut manus & caput) componuntur. Ossa durissimæ aridissimæq́ue totius corporis partes existunt. Cartilagines uerò ossibus molliores sunt, secundum ossa tamen durissimæ totius corporis partes censentur, atque his simul et illis uniuersum corporis sustinetur, omniaq́ue ipsis adnascuntur adstabiliunturq́ue. Caluaria cerebri ac sensus organorum sedes, multis constat ossibus: in fronte siquidem sæpius unum tantum, idq́ue præcipuè in mulieribus, conspicitur: in occipitio similiter unum, in uertice duo, ad utramq́ue aurem uel tempus unum, cui cauitas insculpitur, organo auditus reponendo adaptata: & duo complectens ossicula, quorum unum in cudi aut molari denti, alterum uerò malleo non ineptè assimilauris. Hoc quoque os, præterquàm quòd ipsi cartilago auris corpus erectum seruans continuatur, tres exigit processus: ac unus uberis papillam refert: alius stylum, aut acum, aut galli calcar: tertius antrorsum ductus, superiori's maxillæ ossi in externa oculi sede locatā ad serratā compage commissus, in altero latere portionem constituit eius sedis caluariæ, quam iugale os uocamus. Quin etiam temporis os posteriori's inferiori's ipsius parte simul cum occipitis ossis basi eam caluariæ regionem efformat, quam præruptæ rupi non duritia modò, uerùm & imagine conserimus. In capitis basi os insigne habetur, cuneo à Dissectionum professoribus comparatum, & forma impensè uarium, proq́ue educens uespertilionis alis similimos. Ad hæc, aliud os in narium summo reponitur, cribri aut potiùs spongiæ forma peruium, & cum septem enumeratis ossibus amplitudinem cerebro excipiendo paratam constituens, nariumq́ue septem efformans. In superiori maxilla, præter dentes duodecim ossa recensentur, unum utrinq́ue in exteriori sedis oculi regione, & duo utrinq́ue etiam in interiori, & unum utrobiq́ue in inferiori, quodq́ue maxillæ ossium longè maximum uisitur, superiorum alterius lateris dentium alueolos sibi insculptos obtinens. Ad palati finem, quà narium foramina in fauces pertinet, utrobiq́ue etiā unum eius maxillæ os consistit. & prominens denique nasi pars duobus extruitur ossibus, priuato nomine (ut & cetera maxillæ superioris ossa) destitutis, & nasi cartilagines producentibus, quibus cartilagineæ narium alæ stabiliuntur. Hactenus commemoratorum ossium plerarq́ue inuicem suturis committuntur, ex quibus transuersim in sincipite ducta coronalis dicitur: transuersim uerò in occipitio prorepens, à Λ similitudine nomen obtinuit. quæ autem ab huius uertice ad coronalis medium per capitis longitudinem incedit, sagittalis uocatur. at quæ ab hac æquè distant, & super aures feruntur, non suturarum speciem, sed ueluti duarum inuicem incumbentium squammarum imaginē exprimūt, inde etiam squamosæ conglutinationes appellatæ. Reliqui etiam dictorum ossium connexus nullibi adeò exquisitè, ac tres modò dicti, formam suturæ referūt: imò locis aliquot simplicis lineæ speciem commonstrantes, harmoniæ potiùs quàm suturæ nomen merentur. Inferior maxilla simplici constat osse, nisi fortè admodum pueruli in summo mento ex binis ossibus ita coalescat, quemadmodum plurima pueruli ossa multis ossibus componuntur, quæ aliàs illis, qui ad summum deuenere incrementū, simplicia occurrunt. Articulatur uerò inferior maxilla utrinq́ue ossi, quod ad aurem consistit, peculiari cartilagine hic præter illam interueniente, quæ ossium capita sinusq́ue ubi inuicem componuntur, crustæ modo oblinit, & articulum promptè uersatilem & ab iniurijs in continuo ossium affrictu liberum reddit. Vtraq́ue maxilla plurimùm sedecim dētes nanciscitur, quatuor nimirum incisorios, duos caninos, & decem molares, qui ut forma antequam eruantur apparente differunt, sic etiam impari radicum numero suis præpriolis infiguntur. In faucibus linguæ radici os præponitur imaginem uerius quàm Λ exprimens, & pluribus contextum ossiculis, ex quibus humiliora suis extremis asperæ arteriæ capiti (quod laryngem libentiùs quàm guttur nuncupamus) cartilagini committitur, quæ scutu refert, primaq́ue laryngis cartilago numeratur, ac tangentibus tota occurrit. Secunda enim magna ex parte posteriorem laryngis sedem constituit, & anulo quem Thraces dextro pollici sagittantes imponunt similis, nomine destituitur, hinc quodammodo id inueniens. Tertia, quæ duabus proprijs extruitur partibus, uasorum quibus aquam manus lauaturis affundimus orificio respondet, in laryngis medio rimam efformans tibiarū linguis, seu fistularum quas ori indimus rimis similem, lingulamq́ue ob id nuncupatam. His cartilaginibus operculum simul cartilagineum & pingue, ligamentiq́ue natura participāns insternit, reliquis interim aspеræ arteriæ cartilaginibus, quæ ipsius caudicē et ramos in pulmone digestos cōstituunt, uel C imagine exprimētibus. Dorsum medullæ dorsali iter potissimùm parās, ac corporis ueluti carina in collum ceruicemq́ue, thoracem, lumbos, sacrum os, & coccyx seu cuculus sic diuiditur, triginta quatuor ossibus (quas uertebras uocamus) efformatum. Ac ceruix septenas cōtinet, multis, & in omnibus non pari numero processibus ornatas, ad quarum primam (quæ sola inter reliquas uertebras spina destituitur, & transuersos processus egregiè protuberantes possidet) caput antrorsum retrorsumq́ue rectà ducimus. Secundæ uerò uertebræ (cui processus instar canini dentis prominens accidit) beneficio caput circumuertimus. Reliquarū autem opera in latus, sed tantùm secundariò, caput fertur. Thorax duodecim obtinet uertebras, costarum articulationes admittētes. acharum ferè infima suis ascendentibus & descendentibus processibus, quibus uertebræ præter ipsarum corporum connexum inuicem articulantur, à proximis uertebris suscipitur, uti prima ceruicis & suprà & infrà ipsi contermina ossa suscipitur: reliquis interim dorsi uertebris illi duodecimæ superioribus suprà quidem susceptis, infrà autem suscipientibus: & qui inferiùs consistunt, infrà susceptis, suprà suscipiētibus. Subsunt uerò illi duodecimæ, quinq́ue lumborū uertebræ, dein sacrū os, plurimùm sex proprijs compactum ossibus, inuicem ualidè exis. Coccyx uerò ab infima sede in cartilaginē desinens, crebrò quatuor exiguis constituitur ossiculis, nulli neruo iter præbentibus, ne que ullo donatis foramine, quò dorsalis medulla reponat. Pectoris os anteriorem thoracis (qui congruà cordi & ipsi subseruientium organorum sedem parat) regionem sibi uendicans, rarissimè septenis, uerùm paucioribus extruitur ossibus, septem costarum articulatione utrinq́ue excipientibus. Quippe ex duodecim costis utrobiq́ue positis, & in cartilaginem degenerantibus, septem elatiores suis cartilaginibus pectoris ossi coarctantur, hinc uerarum & legitimarū nomen sortitæ. Quæ autem pectoris os non contingunt, & tanto magis ab illo anteriori's abdominis regione deficiunt, quanto humiliorem sedem obtinent, spuriæ uocitantur. Inferior pectoris ossis sedes in cartilaginem cessat, obtuso ensis mucroni (perinde ac totum pectoris os ensi assimilatur) respondens. Superiori autem ossis sedi ubi latissimum & robustissimū est, iugulumq́ue consistit, utrobiq́ue una articulat clauicula, humeri articulum à thoracis latere remouens. Scapula etenim trianguli imaginem quodammodo exprimens, posteriorem thoracis sedem altera ex parte occupat, in ceruicem desinens, cui acetabulum insculpitur, brachij ossis capiti excipiendo conuenies: dein ex ipsius dorso processum educit, qui super humeri articulum pertingens, summus humerus appellatur: ac clauiculæ peculiaris cartilaginis interuentu (ut & in clauiculæ ad pectoris os nexu sit) articulatus, humeri articulum à thorace auxilio clauiculæ diducit: humeri etiam articulum superiùs perinde manies, ac interior scapulæ processus anchoræ, & C aut C comparatus. Brachij itaq́ue os, seu humerus, scapulæ articulatur, & huius inferiori sedi uarijs sinibus & tuberibus exornatæ, rursus duo inibi ossa iunguntur, radius nimirum & ulna, quæ totius membri nomine

B

mine etiam cubitus appellatur,pariꝗ́ue modo in homine ac in quadrupedibus ad brachij os flectitur,& extenditur, ac in superiori ipsius sede,qua posteriorem cubiti articuli regionem constituit, processum obtinet,quem ᵍ gibberum pleriꝗ̃ nominãt.Atꝗ̃ ita etiã inferior ulnæ pars alium gerit,ᵇ quia styli forma nomẽ nanciscitur. Cæte
rũm soli propemodum radio ᵇ brachiale articulatur, ac ueluti propria cartilagine ab ulna dirimitur,octo ossibus inter se forma & ma
gnitudine omnino differẽtibus extructu:cuius rursus inferiori sedi
quatuor postbrachialis ossa unã cũ primo pollicis esse coarticulãt.
Is nanꝗ̃,ut ᶜreliqui quatuor digiti,tribus ᵈossibus seriatim,ac uelu
ti in acie positis cõstituitur.Omniaꝗ̃ digitorũ ossa sunt quindecim.
quibus in secundo pollicis internodio duo parua accedunt ᵉossicu-
la, sesami semini collata:qualia etiam in primis quatuor digitorũ in
ternodijs(sed multo minora, impẽsiusꝗ̃ cartilaginea)interiori sede
habẽtur:& unum in pollicis tertio internodio, unumꝗ̃ ad exterius
latus connexus ossis postbrachialis paruum digitum sustinentias
brachiale secãtibus obseruatur.In reliquis uerò digitorum internodijs rariùs unum,nisi in ualde senibus uisitur. Vtriꝗ̃ sacri ossis la
teri grande os coarctatur:quod ubi amplum est,ilia,ꝗ̃ respicit," illiu
os dicitur:ubi uerò profundiori acetabulo femoris caput admittit,
ᵐcoxendicis: ubi autem cum alterius lateris osse pubem constituit,
insigniterꝗ̃ perforatum cernitur,ᵒpubis os appellatur:quamuis uni
uersum os subinde coxendicis ᵖnomine comprehendamus.ᵖ Femoris os suprà rotundo capite ceruici prolixæ, & introrsum obliqua-
tæ adnato , coxendicis ossi inarticulatur, infrà uerò duobus capitibus grandioris in ossis sinus subit,sinu quodam in eorum ca-
pitum medio existente, quo tuber dicti tibiæ ossis recipitur, pecu-
libus etiam cartilaginibus in hoc articulo quadrupedum & auium
ᵖᵠgenu similimo interuenietibus.Iuxta femoris ceruicis externã sedem grandis apparet processus,quemᑫ natem & magnum rotato.

rem appellamus. intus quoꝗ̃ alium obtinet processum ,sed multo ᵗ
minorem exteriori,quem hac occasione minorẽ seu interiorem ro-
tatorem uocamus.'In tibia,quemadmodum & in cubito , duo spe-
ctãtur ossa, quorũ internum crassitie exterius longè uincit,totiusꝗ̃
membri nomine comprehenditur, 'exteriori interim osse, quod femori nõ articulatur, fibula appellatur. Ante tibiæ cum semore articu
lum" os rotundum,& mola patellæ ue dictum,scuti instar prælocao
tur.Cæterùm imæ tibiæ & fibulæ partes externis ipsorum lateribus
prominentes ac excarnes,ˣmalleolũꝗ̃ appellatæ,ᵗ talum eadem sede
in homine ac in quadrupedibus repositum, & eundem in illo ac in
his usum subeunte apprehendunt:cui ᵃ calcis os subijcitur,tibiæ rectitudinem in posteriora longè excedens.Anteriori uerò tali sedes in
rotundum caput desinens, 'ossis nauicularis sinum subit, cui tria
ᵇtarsi ossa coarticulantur.ᶜ Quartum enim exteriusꝗ̃ tarsi os cubi
& tesseræ imaginem exprimens,calci iungitur.Porrò quatuor tarsi
ossibus quinꝗ̃ pedij ossa coarticulantur ,& in quinꝗ̃ pedis digiti
sustinẽtur, è quibus pollex duobus tantũ ossibus efformat,reliquis
interim tria internodia sibi uendicãtibus . Quinetiam in pede(quẽ
homo quadrupedibus multo breuiorem obtinet)totidem ac in ma
nu exigua occurrũt ossicula,quæ sesami semini comparamus:quan
quam primo pollicis internodio hìc duo longè grandiora quàm in
manu subijciantur,horumꝗ̃ interius illud sit,quod occultæ philo-
sophiæ sectatores corruptioni neutiquam obnoxium esse affirmãt,
& tantisper in terra asseruandum nugaciter contendunt,dum id re-
surrectionis tempore seminis modo hominem producat. Ad hæc,
in pede non minus quàm in manu 'ungues uisuntur, quos non in ᶠ
opportunæ substantiæ gratia huc reponimus : quemadmodum inter partes aliquid suffulcientes referimus palpebrarum ᵍcartilagi- ᵍ
nes,cilia quo minus flaccidè concidant erigentes.

DE OSSIVM AC CARTILAGINVM LIGAMEN-
tis,& musculis arbitrarij motus instrumentis.   Caput II.

LIGAMENTVM non minus quàm musculorum ᵃenaruationes, & organa quibus animalis spiritus à cerebro deducitur,'neruino-
mine uulgò donatu,corpus est simulare, ex osse aut cartilagine principium ducens,'sensu
propemodum omnis expers, durum, sed tamẽ
cartilagine mollius, album , & in colligando,
continendo,obtegendo,ac musculis constituendis usus in hominum fabrica usus præstans.ᶜMusculus enim motus ex nostro arbitratu pendentis instrumentum censetur, multis membraneis liga-
mentiꝗ̃ naturam possidentibus,& carne intertextis fibris formatũ,
ac ut in se contrahatur,mouendamꝗ̃ partem agat, neruorum à ce
bro animalem uim adferenti opem nõ secus quàm sensuũ organa
requirens:similiterꝗ̃ ut reliquæ quas enutriri oportuit partes, uenis ac arterijs irrigatũ.Cæterùm' tendo musculi quædã est eneruaᵈ
tio,ac ueluti illius librarum citra carnis interuentũ coalitus. Quippe
tendo à musculo tunc solùm producitur, quando ille adeò longam
sedem ab exortu(quem ab osse,aut cartilagine,aut membrana qua-
piam sumit)ad insertionem(quam in mouendam partem molitur)
obtinet,ut ipsius fibræ carneis primariæ musculorum partis implexu uniuerso ductu non indigeant. Adeò ut longiores musculi in
tendinem modò teretem,modò latum,& ueluti membraneum,mo
dò breuiorem, modò longiorem desinant : breues autem musculi
uniuerso progressu carnei permaneant, in nullam notatu dignam
eneruationem degenerantes . Porrò frontis cutem membrana ipsi ᵉ
substrata,& carneis fibris adauctã mouet.'Cutis namque natiuum
corporis tegumentum exteriùs tenuem admodum obnatam exigit
'cuticulam,ueluti ipsius uerę cutis efflorescentiam.Interiùs uerò per ᶠ
uniuersum corpus'membrana quædam cuti subducitur,quã quòd ᵍ
alicubi (quemadmodum hìc in fronte) carneis fibris adaugeatur,
carneam uocari uisum fuit.atque inter hanc membranam & cutem
"adeps plurimus homini asseruatur. Superior palpebra etiam de- ʰ
ctæ nuper membranæ beneficio mouetur:ea enim parte qua hæc ad
internam oculi sedis regionem carnea efficitur, palpebram attollit:
qua uerò ad externam oculi sedem carneis fibris ad C nostri imaginem ductis enutritur, palpebræ motus deorsum autor euadit.
Oculum septem agunt musculi,primus in latus introrsum,secudus
extrorsum,tertius sursum,quartus deorsum ducunt,quintus & sex
tus nonnihil oculum circumuertunt,primi & secundi musculorum

functionem parumper adiuuantes.Atꝗ̃ hi sex forma, quæ oblonga
& quasi teres uisitur,inuicem correspondent ,& à dura membrana
neruum usiorium inuestiente pronati,in anteriorem duræ oculi tunicæ sedem iuxta iridis latera orbiculatim membraneis tendinibus
inseruntur.Septimus uerò his occultus,& solus neruum usiorium
in orbem ita ambiens,ut sex dicti simul eunde unà cum septimo mu
sculo induebant,in posteriorem duræ oculi tunicæ sedem carneus
implatatur,& ijsdem ferè motibus cũ sex illis musculis preẽst. Al
terã nasi alam sursum extrorsumꝗ̃ ducit musculus,ab interiori male
latere pronatus,unaꝗ̃ parte in alam,altera in superius labrum, quã
id alæ subijciatur,insertus . Introrsum uerò alam contrahit membra
neus musculus,in narijs amplitudine sub tunica illas succingẽte latitans . Buccas & labra agunt musculi utrinꝗ̃ quatuor. ac primus
à carnea constituitur membrana , carneis fibris in anteriori potissimùm colli sede & facie ad malas usꝗ̃ enutrita , musculosaꝗ̃ facta.
Secundus à malis pronatus , superiori labro implantatur. Tertius
ab inferiori maxilla in humilius labrum pertinet:Quartus admodũ
uarius in ea buccarum parte consistit, quam inflamus:atꝗ̃ his accedit musculi illius portio,quem nasi alam extrorsum agere nouimus,
qui unà cum dictis mirificos illos uariosꝗ̃ buccarum & labrorum
motus effingit.   Maxillam inferiorem mouentium utrinꝗ̃ etiam
quatuor habentur.primus' temporalis est,à uerticis osse, & frontis ᶦ
quoꝗ̃,& cuneũ referente, & tẽporis ossibus amplo lato,ꝗ̃ principio
enatus ,ac maxillæ inferioris acuto processui insertur. Secundus à
mandendo ᵏmansorius dictus,ab ea capitis parte quę iugale,ꝗ̃ nun ᵏ
cupatur,procedit , externæ maxillæ sedi insertus . Tertius à capitis
processibus alarum imaginem exprimentibus, in internam maxillæ
sedem implantatur,unà cum dictis maxillam attollens , & in latera
prorsumꝗ̃ ac retrorsum agens.Quartus cum suo coniuge maxillã
deorsum trahit,& à stylum imitante capitis processu initiũ ducens,
duobusꝗ̃ uentribus priuatim donatus, ad summum mentum ma
xillæ inseritur.   Os ᵛ referens deorsum rectà trahunt duo musculi inuicẽ proximi,atꝗ̃ à pectoris ossis summo pronati. Sursum uerò
id ducit alij duo,à maxilla inferiori principiũ ducẽtes:in latera autẽ
id os sursum allicit uno utrinꝗ̃ musculo,quã à capitis processu stylũ
referẽte nasci . Deorsum quoꝗ̃ ad latera utrobiꝗ̃ unus mouet musculus,ab elatiori scapulæ costa principiũ obtinens. Octo presentes
musculi in anteriore ossis ᵛ imaginẽ exprimẽtis sedẽ implantantur.
Linguę radici à dicti iam ossis medio carnea moles implantatur,
qui

quæ

quæ duorum musculorum uice numerari posset, introrsùm'que &
deorsùm rectà linguã trahit. Ab eius ossis lateribus utrobiᵍ unus
etiam linguæ radici inseritur, introrsum, sed tamen magis ad latus lin
guæ agens. Quintus & sextus linguæ musculi in utroᵍ latere singu
li à capitis processibus stylum referentibus enati, linguæ radici im
plantantur, eam sursum, prout hic aut ille contrahitur, ad latus du
centes. Septimus & octauus utrinᵍ singuli à lateribus maxillæ infe
rioris iuxta molarium dentium radicem enati, linguæ longitudini
secundùm humiliora inseruntur, linguæ partem ante sectionem in
hiante ore conspicuam deorsum in latera mouentes. Nonus ab in
terna maxillæ inferioris sede iuxta summum mentum prodiens, eral
sus cernitur, & aliquot donatus in scriptionibus, linguæᵍ humilio
ri sedi insertus, eam extrorsum agit. quanquam præter hos muscu
los linguæ corpus ante sectionem apparens, talibus implicetur fibris,
ut magna Naturæ industria in omnem motus differentiam promp
tissimè feratur. Primam laryngis cartilaginem secundæ commit
tunt quatuor musculi, laryngis rimulam arctantes: & quatuor ter
tiam cartilaginem secundæ nectunt, rimulam aperientes: & duo ter
tiam primæ colligant, rimulam claudentes: alij duo in tertiæ cartila
ginis basi consistentes rimulam stringunt. Atᵍ hi duodecim musculi
h, laryngis proprij uocantur. Communiū uerò duo ab osse v simili
primæ cartilagini inseruntur, eamᵍ antrorsum attollentes, rimulam
laryngis reserant: & duo à pectoris osse pronati, in eandem quoque
cartalaginem pertinent. Dein duo à posteriori sede stomachi inuice
proximi principium ducentes, eius quoque cartilaginis lateribus to
ti carnei (ut omnes ferè laryngis) inseruntur, unà cum duobus po
stremò dictis laryngis arctantes. Alij duo ab osse v referente ena
ti, & in laryngis operculi radicem inserti, id sursum antrorsumᵍ uel
lunt. In caput mouentium classem illi quoque reijciuntur, qui pri
mam ceruicis uertebram mouent. sunt autem uniuersi sep
tem paria, quod scilicet utrobiᵍ totidem enumerentur musculi. Ac
primum par ex quinque superiorum thoracis uertebrarum spinis
pronatum, sensimᵍ extrorsum obliquè ascendens, occipitis ossi im
plantatur. Secundum par, quod non duobus, sed pluribus effor
mari uidetur musculis, admodumᵍ uarium cernitur, præcipua ip
sius portione ex transuersis quatuor superiorum thoracis, & quin
que humiliorum ceruicis uertebrarum processibus enatum, intror
sumᵍ noᵍnihil obliquè conscendens, occipitis ossi implantatur.
Tertium à spina secundæ ceruicis uertebræ enatum, & extrorsum
parumper obliquè repens, occipitis etiam ossi inseritur. Quartum
par similiter occipitis ossi insertum, à prima uertebra inibi prodit,
quà aliæ uertebræ in spinam desinunt. Quintum ab occipitis ossis
medio transuersim quodammodo ad laterales primæ uertebræ pro
cessus fertur. Sextum à spina secundæ uertebræ in eosdem proces
sus pertinet, similiter ac quinque nunc enumerata in posteriori cer
uicis sede consistens, ac pariter ut tertium, quartum & quintum, mu
sculis constit laryngis priuatim enatus carnis & teretibus & gracilibus. Septimum
par insignius est, atᵍ à pectoris ossis summo, clauiculisᵍ quà illi ar
ticulantur, utrinᵍ unus pronascitur musculus, qui sursum obliquè
ductus in mamillarem capitis processum insertionem tentat. Cæte
rùm primis quatuor paribus simul tensis caput rectà retrorsum du
citur: si uerò trium primorum parium musculi ex altero latere tan
tùm egerint, ad capitis circumuersionē auxiliabuntur, & in illo no
tu quintum & sextum par, primam ceruicis uertebram unà cum ca
pite in gyrum ducent. Septimi uerò paris musculis suum munus si
m il obcuntibus, caput rectà antrorsum flectitur: quū autem alter
natim laborant, circumuersionis autores efficiuntur. Verùm ad ca
pitis motum, quo id secundariò cum ceruice flectitur, & extenditur,
ac in latus ad humeros ducitur, ceruicis musculi famulantur, inter
o.to paria dorsum mouentia reponendi. Ac primum par à quintæ
thoracis uertebræ corporis lateribus incipiens, ad primam usᵍ cer
uicis uertebram pertingit, stomacho subiectū, superioremᵍ dorsi
partem flectens. Secundum à prima thoracis costa utrinque prona
tum, & internæ transuersorū ceruicis uertebrarum processuum
sedi insertum, ceruicem in latus, sed antrorsum magis, ducit. Tertiū
ex transuersis sex superiorum thoracis uertebrarum processibus o
riginem obtinens, externæ sedi transuersorum uertebrarum arcti
cis processuum implantatur, ceruicemᵍ retrorsum inclinantem
ad latus agit. Quartum par à septimæ thoracis uertebræ spina ad
secundam usque ceruicis uertebram pertinet, omnibus intermedijs
uertebris, uti & primum par, insertum, ac ex eisdem principijs ca
piens, superioremᵍ dorsi partem extendens. Quintum par u
trinque etiam habet musculum, ab ilium osse in transuersos lumbo
rum uertebrarum processus, & infimam thoracis costam insertum,
inferiorisᵍ dorsi partis flexus opificem. Sextum ab infima ossis sa

cri sede in dorso incipiens, ad ceruicem usque fertur, in transuersos
processus lumborum, sed manifestiùs adhuc thoracis uertebrarum
insertum. Huius paris ambobus musculis contractis, dorsum exten
ditur: altero autem tantū laborante (ut & in alijs paribus) hoc quo
que par obliqui seu in latera motus autor euadit. Septimum sub sex
to occultatum à posteriori sacri ossis sede principium ducens, ad un
decimæ usque thoracis uertebræ spinam consendit, omnibus in
termedijs spinis assertum, ac spinas inuicem colligendo, dorsum hic
extendens: uti & in sua sede octauum par, quod ab undecima thora
cis uertebra ad septimam usque ceruicis porrectum, ita prorsus in
termedijs spinis committitur, ut septimum illis quibus adnascitur
spinis. Scapulam ad pectus mouet musculus à thoracis secunda,
tertia, quarta & quinta costis anteaquam in cartilaginem illæ finiūt
enatus, & trianguli modo in internum scapulæ processum insertus.
Secundus scapulam mouentium ab occipitio pronatus, & dein se
cundùm ceruicis longitudinem ad octauæ usque thoracis uertebræ
spinam à uertebrarum apicibus principium sumens, in
scapulæ spinam summumᵍque humerum & clauiculæ portionem
inseritur, tota sui parte quæ in ceruice consistit scapulam sursum uel
lens: ea uerò quæ sub ceruice in posteriori thoracis sede habetur,
monachorumᵍque cucullis respondet, scapulam deorsum trahens.
Tertius à transuersis superiorum ceruicis uertebrarum processibus
enatus, ac elatiori scapulæ basis angulo insertus, illam quoᵍ attollit.
Quartus ex quintæ, sextæ & septimæ ceruicis, ac triū primarū tho
racis uertebrarum spinis præcipuè enascitur, scapulæᵍ basi inser
tus, eam ad dorsum nonnihil sursum contrahit. Primus brachij
motuum autor à media clauiculæ sede pectoris ossi proxima, & pe
ctoris ossæ pronatus, ac quodammodo in angulum arctatus, bra
chium pectori adducit. Secundus ab altera clauiculæ parte, & sum
mo humero, & scapulæ spina principium sumens, suoᵍ uertice bra
chij ossi transuersim insertus, id sursum uariè attollit, hunc humeri
articulum pulchrè tegens, & figuræ Δ non ᵇ absimilis. Tertius ab
humiliori scapulæ costa prodiens, brachium rectà ad dorsum alli
cit. Quartus à sextæ thoracis uertebræ spina ad humiliorem usᵍ
sacri ossis sedem ex intermediarum spinarum apicibus originem du
cens, & ueluti in trianguli uerticem coactus, in brachium inibi inse
ritur, ubi tres commemorati insertionem longè sub ossis capite sca
pulæ articulato moliuntur. atque hic musculus brachium uariè de
orsum trahit, uti ipsius principum perquam amplum est: neque ex
puncto ita ducitur, ut musculi simplicem prorsus motum obituri.
Quintus uniuersum scapulæ cauum costas respiciēs occupat. Sex
tus gibbam scapulæ sedem uniuersam sibi uendicat, sub ipsius spi
na consistentem. Septimus sinum implet inter scapulam spinam &
clatiorem ipsius costam conspicuum. Hi tres amplis implantationi
bus in ligamenta humeri articulum ambientia inseruntur, brachij
circumactus opifices, quamuis septimus & ad brachij eleuationem
aliquid auxiliari uideatur. Thoracem mouentium primus à
clauicula enatus, in primam thoracis costam inseritur, illam sursum
ducens, hacᵍque occasione ad thoracis dilatationem iuuans. Secun
dus à basi scapulæ pronatus, tanquam digitis quibusdam octo su
perioribus costis longè anteaquam in cartilaginem degenerent, in
seritur, eas'que extrorsum mouens, thoracem dilatat. Tertius ex a
picibus spinarum trium inferiorū ceruicis, & primæ thoracis uerte
brarum latum membraneum'que principium ducens, ternis ue
luti digitis, tribus quatuor superiorum costarum interuallis sub
scapulæ basi inseritur, hasᵍque costas sursum obliquè ducens, thora
cem ampliat. Quartus ab ilium osse incipiens, sursumᵍque ad ceruí
cem ductus, duodecim costis quà primūm à uertebris discedunt,
inseritur, thoracem arctans. Quintus ex spinarum apicibus dua
rum infimarum thoracis & aliquot lumborum uertebrarū mem
braneus enascitur, & transuersim ductus, ac nonæ, decimæ & un
decimæ costis ubi in interiora reflectuntur insertus, thoracem di
latat. Sextus in thoracis amplitudine repositus, uerarum costarum
cartilaginibus pectorisᵍque ossis lateri exporrigitur, thoracis con
strictioni præfectus. In duodecim costarum interuallis interiores
ac exteriores ¹ musculi reponuntur. qui exteriores in costarum
ossium interuallis consistunt, à superiori costa antrorsum obliquè
suas fibras in humiliorem mittunt: interiores uerò ab inferiori co
sta sursum obliquè in anteriora, ad superiorem costam fibras porri
gunt. In sex uerò cartilaginum quæ legitimis costis asscribuntur
interuallis, exteriorum musculorum fibræ ab humiliori cartilagine
in superiorem obliquè antrorsum repunt: interiores autem fibræ
à superiori cartilagine ad inferiorem antrorsum pertinent, ac proin
de in sex legitimarum costarum interuallis quaterni numerantur
musculi. in spuriarum autem costarum interuallis bini tantum, uni

C uersiᵍ

uersiʼq; unius lateris intercoſtales muſculi quatuor ſunt & triginta, ad unum omnes arctando thoraci præfecti. Atque numeratis hacte nus in uno latere thoracis quadraginta muſculis, alij totidem in altero latere congruunt. & his octuaginta unus accedit, utrique lateri communis, ipſum uidelicet * ſeptum tranſuerſum infimæ pectoris oſſis & ſpuriarum coſtarum cartilaginibus et uertebris lumborum ſuperioribus inſertum, ac in medio nerueum, in circuitu ueró ad inſertionem carneum, ut ſanguificationi generationiʼque ſubſeruientia organa à cordis & partium ipſi ſubminiſtrantium ſede dirimes, thoracemʼque proprio munere dilatans. His accedunt octo abdominis muſculi, utrinque nimirum quatuor. Primus ſeu extimus oblique deorſum in priora fibras porrigit, cum ſuo coniuge toti ab domini inuolucrum efformans. Secundus oblique ſurſum in anteriora fibras mittit, & cum ſuo pari inuolucrum quoque abdomini conſtituit. Tertius recta fibras ſurſum ducens, à pubis oſſe ad pectus conſcendit. Quartus tranſuerſim fibras digerit, ac cum ſuo pari etiam, ut & obliqui, inuolucrum abdomini extruit, ad thoracis conſtrictionem non minus quàm cæteri abdominis muſculi ſuppetias ferens. Cubitum duo flectunt, quorum anterior unum caput à ſcapulæ ceruicis elatiori ſede, alterum ab interno ſcapulæ proceſſu mutuatur, & illis efformatus capitibus in radium inſeritur. Poſterior à brachij oſſe enatus, in anteriorem cubiti articuli ſedem, potiſſimùm ueró in ulnam inſeritur. Extendunt autem cubitum tres, ac unus ab humiliori ſcapulæ coſta naſcitur, ſecundus à brachij oſſis ceruicis poſteriori ſede. hi in deſcenſu inuicem connaſcuntur, & ipſis tertius admiſcetur, à media ferè longitudine oſſis brachij enatus, & ſimul cum illis in poſteriorem ulnæ proceſſum inſertus. In interna cubiti ſede gracilis reponitur muſculus, qui ab interno oſſis brachij tubere pronatus, in latum degenerat tendinem, internæ ſummæ manus cuti magna ex parte ſubnatu: cuius beneficio ea cutis minus uerſatilis, & ad tangendu aptior reddi credit. Radius in pronu duobus muſculis ducitur. uno quideab interna cubiti articuli ſede enato, & in radiu oblique implatato: altero autè iuxta brachiale ab ulna in radiu tranſuerſim ducto. In ſupinu ueró radius alijs duobus ſer tur, uno quidem longo, & à brachij oſſe ad inferiore in radij partem, cui brachiale articulatur, pertinente: altero ab externa cubiti articuli regione ad mediam radij longitudinem oblique exporrecto, ibidemʼque inſerto. Brachiale quatuor præcipuis agitur muſculis, ac duo primi ab interno tubere brachij oſſis pronaſcuntur, & unus poſtbrachialis oſſi indicem ſuſtinenti, alter ueró brachialis minimo oſſi implantatur. tertius à brachij oſſe enatus, bifido tendine in poſtbrachialis oſſa indicem & medium ſuſtinentia inſeritur. quartus ab externo brachij oſſis tubere pronatus, ac ulnæ exporrectus, in poſtbrachialis os paruu ſuſtinens digitum inſertionem molitur. Duo primi ſimul brachiale flectunt: tertius ueró & quartus ſimul contracti, id extendunt. Verùm primo ſimul cum tertio tenſo, brachiale in internum latus agitur: ſecundo autem & quarto unà laborantibus, id in externum latus inclinatur. Digitos manus mouentium primus ab interna anterioriʼq; cubiti articuli ſede enatus, ante brachialis radice in quatuor diſcinditur tendines, ſecundis quatuor digitorum internodijs inſertos, illaʼq; flectentes. Secundus ab eadem ſede cu primo, ſed magis decliuè, origi nem ducens, primo ſubſternitur, in quatuor etiam diremptus tendines, qui primi tendinibus ſubiecti, ante ſecundi digitoru internodij radicem eos tendines perforã, tandemʼq; in tertia quatuor digitoru oſſa inſertionem molientes, ea flectunt. Tertius à radio iuxta cubiti articulum enatus, tertio pollicis articulo inſeritur, ipſiusʼque flexus autor euadit. Tertium muſculum, in ſerie alij tredecim numero ſub ſequuntur, in extrema manu repoſiti, quorum bini primo ſingulorum quinʼque digitorum oſſi inſeruntur, eius flexionis opifices, & tres ſecundo pollicis internodio potiſſimùm inſerti id quoque flectunt. Decimuſeptimus itaque digitos mouentium ab externo brachij oſſis tubere natus, & indici, medio ac anulari præcipuè implantatus, eos digitos extendit. Decimuſoctauus ab eadem qua nu per dictus ſede prodiens, parui digiti extenſionis primarius autor eſt, & uariè cum decimiſeptimi tendine tribus anularis digiti oſſibus inſerto commixtus, etiam abductioni uerſus exteriora nonnihil inibi ſubſeruit. Decimuſnonus cum illo qui uigeſimuſprimus erit, commune principium ab ulna, non procul à brachialis ſede nanciſcitur: & in duos ſerè diſſectus tendines, unum exteriori indicis, alterum medij lateri digerit, illorumʼque digitorum in externum latus abductionis autor cenſetur. Vigeſimus à brachiali pronatus, & externo poſtbrachialis oſſis paruum ſuſtinentis lateri exporrectus, primoʼque eius digiti oſſi inſerto, illum extrorſum in latus abducit. Vigeſimuſprimus externo lateri exterioris pollicis

regionis ad tertium uſque articulum implantatur, pollicis uerſus in dicem extenſionis autor. Vigeſimuſſecundus ab ulna paulo ſuperiùs quàm nuper dictus prodit: & mox bipartitò ſciſſus, una portione in tendinem ceſſat, brachialis oſſi pollicem ſuſtinenti inſertum, & ductum, quo manus radij motum in pronum ſequitur, adiuuantem. Altera autem pars in duas rurſus dirimitur, quæ ſingulæ unum efficiunt tendinem: & hæc quidem ſuum tendinem primi pollicis oſſis exterioris ſedis interno lateri inſerit: illius ueró partis tendo illi oſſi tantum obnaſcitur, in ſecundum & tertium pollicis os inſertus. Horum tendinum beneficio pollex introrſum uerſus extenditur. Vigeſimuſtertius ad internu primi pollicis oſſis latus ſedem obtinens, pollicè ab indice inſigniter abducit. Vigeſimuſquartus ab oſſe poſtbrachialis indicem ſuffulciente enatus, & primo pollicis oſſi præcipuè inſertus, pollicem indici proximè adducit. Superſunt adhuc quatuor graciles muſculi, quatuor tendinibus ſecundi digitos mouentium muſculi in uola attenſi, & in internum latus primi quatuor digitorum oſſis inſerti, eorumʼque digitorum ad pollicem in latus adductionis miniſtri. Reponuntur itaque in interna cubiti ſede muſculus, latum manus efficiens tendinem, primus & ſecundus brachialis motuum autores, primus ſecundus & tertius digitos mouentium, & duo radium in pronum ducentes. In externa autem ſede conſiſtunt decimuſeptimus, decimuſoctauus, decimuſnonus, uigeſimuſprimus, uigeſimuſſecundus digitos mouentium, & tertius & quartus brachialis motibus præfectorum, & duo radium in ſupinum agentes, ſuntʼque omnes numero nouem. Verùm decem conſurgent, ſi à uigeſimo ſecundo digitos mouentium illam portionem diſtinxeris, quæ brachialis oſſi pollicem ſuſtinenti tendinem offert. In extrema manu obſeruantur decem muſculi, primos articulos digitorum flectentes, & tres ſecundi pollicis internodij flexus autores, & dein digitos agentium uigeſimus, uigeſimuſtertius, uigeſimuſquartus, & quatuor muſculi quorum beneficio quatuor digiti pollici adducuntur. Singuli uirorum teſtes cum ſuis ſeminalibus uaſis tunica obducuntur à peritonæo pronata, & aliquot rectis carneiſʼq; fibris enutrita, infimæʼque ſemen deferentis uaſis ſedi inſerta. His fibris teſti * unus conſtituitur muſculus, cuius ope teſtis obſcurè ſurſum uellitur. Sic & membranæ uterum firmantes, utrinʼque carneis donantur fibris, hacʼque ratione uterus utrobique unum poſſidet muſculum, quo minus ille ad flexum occludatur, dilatantes. Veſicæ ceruici unus orbiculatim obnaſcitur muſculus, intempeſtiuam urinæ excretionem prohibens. Item alius quoʼque * muſculus, recti inteſtini finem circulatim ambit, immaturæ egeſtioni præfectus, & duo alij muſculi poſt egeſtionem rectum inteſtinum alacriter ſurſum attollunt. Penis radici utrinque à pubis oſſe gracilis inſeritur muſculus, nimis quàm ſegniter ad ipſius tentiginem iuuans. Quinetiam ab anteriori ſede muſculi rectum inteſtinum orbiculatim amplectentis, duo enaſcuntur muſculi, inuicem ſibi proximi, & urinæ meatui, quà is ſub pubis oſſibus ſurſum reflectitur, implantati, meatumʼque in ſeminis eiaculatione quo minus ille ad flexum occludatur, dilatantes. Primus femur mouentium ab ilium oſſis extima ſede, & coccygis oſſis poſteriori regione enatus, poſteriori magni femoris proceſſus ſedi, & eius quoque radici ampla inſertione innaſcitur. Secundus ſub primo magna ex parte reconditus, magiſ'que ab anteriori ilium oſſis ſede pronatus, etiam magno femoris proceſſui inſeritur. Tertius ſecundo longè minor, ipſoʼq; penitus occultatus, ab ilium oſſe iuxta poſteriorem coxendicis acetabuli ſedem enaſcitur, magno etiam femoris proceſſui inſertus, & ut duo priores femur extendens, extrorſumʼq; in latus agens. Quartus à tribus humilioribus oſſis ſacri oſſibus pronatus, etiam magno proceſſui inſeritur, femur extendens, & extrorſum non parum circumducens. Quintus omnium corporis muſculorum maximus, & pluribus partibus à coxendicis oſſe ac pubis principium ducens, poſterioriʼq; femoris ſedi ad humiliora ipſius uſque capita inſertus, extenſionis & rectæ ſtationis autor habetur, femur etiam introrſum agens, idʼq; ipſius potiſſimu portione à pubis oſſis humiliori ſede pronata. Sextus à duabus infimis thoracis & aliquot ſuperioribus lumboru uertebris initium capiès, minori femoris proceſſui inſeritur, femoris flexus unà cum ſeptimo autor: qui à tota interiori oſſis ilium ſede enatus, minori quoque proceſſui elatiùs ſexto implantatur. Octauus à pubis oſſe pronatus, ſub minori proceſſu femori longa inſertione implantatur, id quidem flectens, uerùm etiam impenſe introrſum mouens. Nonus anteriorem pubis oſſis foraminis ſedem occupans, maioriʼque femoris proceſſui inſertus, introrſum femur circumuertit. Decimus poſteriorem interioremʼue dicti iam foraminis ſedem ſibi

bi

bi uendicans, & secundùm coxendicis ossis posteriora tutissimè reflexus, ac ueluti alijs musculis hîc pronascentibus adauctus, maioríque femoris processui implantatus, femur extrorsum circumuertit. Tibiam agentium primus ab ilium ossis spinæ antica sede enatus, & admodùm oblique secundùm femoris internam sedem ductus, anteriori tibiæ sedi inseritur, totiúsque corporis gracilimus, & simul longissimus musculus efficitur. Secundus à pubis ossis commissura enatus, in eandem cum primo sedem inseritur. Tertius à coxendicis ossis appendice principium obtinens, in eam quoque sedem tibiæ implantatur. Quartus ab eadem sede coxendicis ossis pronatus, & portionem sui à femoris osse in descensu assumēs, tibiæ cum fibula articulo, sed potissimùm fibulæ inseritur. Quintus ab eadem etiam regione principium adeptus, in anteriorem tibiæ sedem cum tribus primis, uerùm minus decliuis, implantatur. Sextus ab ilium ossis spina pronatus, membranæ modo musculis os femoris amplex ntibus obducitur, & potissimū ad exterius latus genu articuli inseritur. Septimus à radice magni femoris processus enatus, & externum femoris latus occupas, cum octauo & nono tendinem efformat, cui patella innascitur. Octauus enim à ceruice femoris & radice maioris ipsius processus originem ducēs, quasi totum femoris os proximè ambit. Nonus à coxendicis ossis tubere supra ipsius cum femore articulum, anteriori in parte cōspicuo originem sumens, & septimo & octauo instratus musculis, ad anteriorem genu regionem fertur: ac in tendinem degenerans, cum duobus nuper dictis unum constituit tendinem, anteriori tibiæ sedi ualidissimè implantatum. atque ita primus, sextus, septimus, octauus & nonus tibiæ extensionis opifices habentur, secundo interim, tertio, quarto & quinto tibiam liquidè extendentibus. Qui in poplite latitat musculus, & ab externo genu articuli ligamento in tibiæ os obliquè pertinet, tibiam non flectit, & si quid agit, obscurè motum imitatur primi radium in pronum mouentis musculi. Eorum qui pedem mouent, primus ab interno femoris capite iuxta genu articulum incipit, uti & secundus ab externo capite principium nasciscitur, ambo posteriorem suræ partem constituentes, & cum quarti pedem mouentis musculi tendine congredientes, in calcem inseruntur. Tertius exiguus est musculus, ab externo quoque femoris capite pronatus, & in poplitis regione adhuc in tenuissimum tendinem desinens, calcis ossis interno lateri insertum. Quartus, pedem mouentium maximus est, a cà fibulæ cum tibia coarticulatione incipiens, in ualidissimum desinit tendinem, cui duorum primorum tendo unitur, simul cum ipso calci insertus. Quintus musculus tibiæ ac fibulæ posteriori sedi proximè allocatus, ab ijsdem pronascitur ossibus, ubi illæ primùm dehiscunt, & iuxta interioris malleoli posteriora tendinem educit in tarsi, quod tesseram imitati ossi conterminum est, insertum. Sextus in anteriori tibiæ sede positus, à tibiæ osse quà illi fibula superiùs coarticulatur pronatus, tēdinem in radicem pedij ossis pollicem sustinentis inserit. Septimus à fibula principiū ducens, externum tibiæ latus occupat, ac tendinem sub pedis inferiora reflexum, pedij ossi pollicem suffulcienti inserit. Octauus septimo occultior, atque à fibula etiam enatus, tendinē inserit radici pedij paruum digitum sustinentis. Nonus pars est eius quem quatuor pedis digitos extenderem mox dicturus sum: inseritur ueró ad m dium ferè longitudinis ossis pedij, antè paruum digitum pedij. Primis quinque musculis pes extenditur, seu fortiter terræ admouetur, quamuis tertius musculus id inualidè præstet: & si quid ad pedis motum facit, eum in obliquum uersus interiora agit: sexto autē, septimo, octauo & nono pes flectitur, horumq́ musculorum beneficio pes laterales motus, prout singuli agunt musculi, experitur. Pedis digitos mouentium primus in planta musculo collocatur, & in fima parte membranam impensè crassam, & lato in manu tendini non absimilem pertinaciter obnatam possidet: & à calcis osse pronatus, secundis quatuor digitorum internodijs singulos tendines offert, eorum flexus autores. Secundus & tertius posteriorem tibiæ sedem perreptant, & secundus tibiæ ossi magis quàm fibulæ exporrectus, ab illóq́ pronatus, tendinem in plantam mittit, qui in quatuor dissectus tendines, singulos quatuor digitorum tertijs ossibus inserit, primi musculi tendines, perinde ac in manu sit, perforantes, eáq́ ossa flectentes. Tertius à fibulæ ad tibiam nexu enatus, & etiā fibulæ multum exporrectus, tendinem in plantam profert: à quo exigua portio tendinibus commiscetur, indicis & medij tertium internodium flectentibus: reliquus autem totus in secundum pollicis os inseritur, illius flexionis autor. Decem musculi his succedunt, qui insigniter mutuó implexi, ac pedij ossibus adnati, prima digitorum ossa flectunt, duobus musculis ad singulos digitos pertinentibus. Decimusquartus igitur, cuius pars nonus pedem mouentium

censebatur, à tibiæ anteriori sede pronatus, in quatuor dirimitur tendines, qui quatuor digitis inserti, eorum extensionis autores cen sentur. Decimusquintus ab anteriori tibiæ sede etiā procedens, pollici inseritur, ipsius extensionis opifex. Decimussextus in superiori pedis sede reponitur, carneáq́ est moles in quatuor diuisa tendines, quorum unus pollicis superioris sedis externo lateri implantatur, se cundus indicis, tertius medij, quartus anularis: atque hi tendines eorum digitorum, in externum latus abductionis opifices sunt. Decimusseptimus externum pedis latus occupans, & parui digiti primo ossi insertus, illum à cæteris remouet. Decimusoctauus interno pedis lateri exporrectus, pollicem à cæteris digitis abducit. Dein in pedis planta carnea consistit substantia, in quatuor graciles dissecta portiones tendinibus adhærentes, quorum ministerio tertia quatuor digitorum ossa flectuntur. Hæ portiones interno quatuor digitorum lateri ad primum articulum insertæ, eorum ad pollicem ad ductionis autores habentur. ac proinde si istas quatuor portiones quatuor musculorum uice enumeraueris, in tibiæ posteriori sede obseruabis primum, secundum, tertium, quartum pedem mouentium, secundum & tertium digitos mouentium, et sub illis quintum pedem mouentium. In anteriori sextum, septimum, octauum, decimumquartum digitos mouentium: in pede autem habueris primum digitos agentem, & decem prima digitorum ossa flectentes, & decimumsextum, decimumseptimum, decimumoctauum digitos quoque mouentium, nisi decimumsextum in plures diuidere propositū esset. Porró in musculorum enarratione passim ligamentorum non memini, quòd magna ex parte articuli inuicem respondeant. Omnibus enim articulis orbiculatim ligamentum ab uno osse in aliud, aut in cartilaginem, uel à cartilagine in os, aut cartilaginem in sertum priuatim obducitur, paucis'que articulis ligamenta accessere peculiaria. Vt in capitis articulo teres quoddam à dente secundæ ceruicis uertebræ in occipitis os ducitur, & secundùm dentis posteriorem sedem in prima uertebra unum transuersim fertur. Vertebrarum corpora ligamentis admodùm cartilagineis committuntur, ascendentes uero & descendentes eorundem processus ualidis quoque, sed tantùm ambientibus colligantur: dein in spinarum interuallis membraneum cōsistit ligamentum, sicut in cubito & tibia, ubi ossa hîc inuicem dehiscunt: insuper in pubis ossium foraminibus huius generis occurrit ligamentum, seu membrana potiùs. In humeri articulo tria peculiaria uisuntur, quorum primum teres est, & ab interno scapulæ processu enatum, in externum humeri caput fertur, alia duo ab elatiori ceruicis scapulæ sede enata, in idem caput pertinēt, & unū quoq́ hîc ab interno scapulæ processu in summum humerū ducitur. In brachialis ossium inter se & cum postbrachialis ossibus connexu, ut & in pede, passim cartilaginea ligamenta interueniunt. A' sacro osse duo teretia in coxendicis os pertinent. Ex femoris superiori capite teres ligamentum in coxendicis acetabulum inseritur. In genu articuli medio cartilagineum consistit ligamentum, & dein in posteriori ipsius sede, & utrinque ad latera unum peculiare secantibus obuium est. Ex ligamentorum uerò transuersim tendinibus obductorum, tendinesq́ue nè sua sede declinent, continentium numero, in interna brachialis sede unum consistit, & secundùm uniuersam internam cuiusq́ue digiti sedem unum continuum habetur, iuxta brachialis radicem in externa radij & ulnæ sede sex occurrunt. In anteriori tibiæ sede iuxta talum unum quoque obseruatur, & tria inter calcem internum'que malleolum, dein unum inter calcem & externum malleolum. Sic & in interna inferiori'ue pedis digitorum sede, huius quoque generis ligamenta spectantur.

DE ORGANIS NVTRITIONI,
quæ ex cibo potúq́; fit, famulantibus.
Caput III.

QVANDOQVIDEM homo propter semen genitale sanguinemq́ menstruum, generationis nostræ primordia, & eorum quibus constamus materiam immortalis fieri nequiuit, immensus rerum Opifex, ut is quàm diutissimè uiuat, & species ipsius nunquam deficiens semper immortalis perseueret, solicitè machinatur. Vt enim ad debitum incrementum homo attingeret, ac illa quæ insitus calor perpetuò depascitur, quàm fieri posset proximè restituerentur, organa

D   gana

gâha nutritioni multifariam famulantia obtinuimus. Cibus namꝗ
dentibus, quò poſtmodum leuiori opera conficiatur, effractus, per
inde ac potus ab ore in uentriculum, tanquam in promptuarium,
per *a* uiam ducitur, quæ duabus proprijs tunicis tendi, atque in ſe
concidere aptis formata, ex faucibus ſub aſpera arteria, ac dein ſe
cundùm thoracis uertebras per ſeptum tranſuerſum in ſuperius, ſi
niſtrum *ue* uentriculi orificium pertinet, & ſtomachus aut gula uo
catur. *b* Ventriculus uerò inter iecur & lienem ſub ſepto repoſitus,
& inſigniter capax, & ſecundùm tranſuerſum obẃgus, in ſiniſtraꝗ
corporis ſede quàm in dextra amplior, & duabus demum tunicis
diſtendi contrahiꝗue idoneis, & tertio quodam inuolucro quod
peritonæum educit intectis, efformatus : & compluribus uenis, ar
terijs ac neruis implexus, quod ab ore illi delatum eſt concoquit, ac
uelut in lacteum cremorem inſita ui emutat, quem per ſuum *c* inſe
rius orificium ex clatiori ſede dextri ipſius lateris exortum, in *d* inte
ſtina propellit. quæ corpora ſunt teretia uno continuoꝗ ac innu
meris orbibus gyris que tortuoſo ductu à uentriculo ad podicem
pertinentia, & ſimiliter ac uentriculus duabus proprijs tunicis ex
tructa. quibus tertia à peritonæo accedit, non minus quàm duæ
propriæ, laxari contrahiꝗue apta, non tamen undique pariter am
pla. Inteſtinorum ſiquidem à uentriculo procedens *e* origo, ſecun
dùm uentriculi poſteriora ad dorſum uſque reflexa, & *f* duodenum
nobis appellata, ac dein huic ſuccedens inteſtinorum pars, quam
g ieiunum dicimus, & ea quæ *h* ilium ſeu uoluulus nûcupatur, ſuiſꝗ
orbibus ilia & ſedem undique umbilico ſubiectam & contermi
nam implet, pari quodammodo conſtat amplitudine, quæ quum
arcta ſit, ut dictis nuper inteſtinorum partibus gracilium nomen in
deretur, in cauſa fuit. Porrò inteſtinorum pars in quam ilei termi
nus ceſſat, impenſe craſſa & ampla uiſitur, ipſiꝗ appendiculum con
tinuatur, inſtar lumbrici inuolutum anguſtumꝗue, & uno ore do
natum, ideoꝗ *i* cæcù diſſectionis proceribus appellatum. Ipſa uerò
craſſa inteſtinorû pars à dextri renis ſede ad iecoris cauũ aſcendens,
hinc ſecundùm uentriculi fundum ad lienis ſedem, & illinc ſecun
dùm ſiniſtri renis ſedem deuoluitur, & gyro quodam in ſiniſtra pu
bis ſede reflexa, totoꝗue illo ductu *k* colum conſtituens, ſuper oſſis
ſacri initium rectà deorſum ad anum fertur, *l* recti ac principis inte
ſtini nomen inibi nanciſcitur. In hæc itaque inteſtina quicquid uen
triculi conſecit, depellitur, per uarios illorum gyros deuoluen
dum: uenæ autem quæ innumera ſerie à iecoris cauo unà cum arte
rijs à magna arteria depromptis, inter duas membranas inteſtina
dorſo colligantes, multaꝗue pinguedine ac *m* glandulis abundan
tes, & *n* meſenterium uocatas, in inteſtina pertingunt, ex ipſis (ſed
potiſſimùm gracilibus) inteſtinis, quicquid ſanguini efficiendo ido
neum eſt, ſimul cum aqueo tenuiꝗue concoctionis uentriculi recre
mento exugunt, id iecori ſanguificationis officinæ deferentes. Ip
ſum autem craſſius & ineptum ſuctioni recrementũ ſenſim in craſſa
colligitur inteſtina, illic tantiſper aſſeruandum, donec hominem
moleſtans, recluſo rectù inteſtinũ orbiculatim ambiente muſculo,
ſemel uniuerſim que hominis arbitratu egeratur. *o* Iecur in nullas di
remptum fibras lobosue, ipſi ſubminiſtrantium organorum elatiſ
ſimam ſedem occupat, ac uentriculo magna ex parte incumbens,
ſepto que tranſuerſo proxime ſubditum, & magis dextram quàm
ſiniſtram corporis ſedem implens, ſuprà gibbum, infrà cauum uiſi
tur, accumbentium illi partium formæ ad amuſſim congruens, &
multarum uenarum implexu, quibus propria iecoris ſubſtãtia con
creto nuper ſanguini ſimilis circunfunditur, efformatum, tenuiꝗue
inuolucro ab ipſius ligamentis quibus peritonæum firmatur proce
dente obtectum, neruulos que duos & arteriam item unam admit
tens, & naturalis ſeu altricis, aut, ut Plato dicebat, uenereorum cibo
rum & potuum concupiſcibilis animæ fomes. Cæterùm uenarum
per iecur diffuſarum una ſeries in gibbo ipſius conſiſtit, ad cauam
p pertinens uenam, altera in iecoris cauo reponitur, *q* portæ uenæ cau
dicem conſtituens: quæ primum ueſiculæ bilem flauam recipientis
ſurculos duos promit, dein uentriculi poſteriori ſedi iuxta inferius
ipſius orificium: inde uentriculi fundi dextræ parti ramus offertur,
à quo ramuli in uentriculum & ſuperiorem *q* omenti membranam
ſparguntur, quod membraneum eſt corpus ſacculi modo extru
ctum, & uaſis tutò deducendis præcipue adaptatum : quanquam
quum uenis arterijs que & pinguedine illis affuſa ſcateat, inteſtino
rum quoque calori fouendo auxilietur. Inſtar circuli enim à dorſi
medio ſub uentriculi poſteriori ſede in cipiens, per iecoris cauum ad
fundum uentriculi (à cuius tertio inuolucro inibi pronaſcitur) ad lie
nis cauum, & hinc ad dorſi medium ſuo uelut initio defertur. Hinc
uerò ſacculi inſtar deorſum protenſum, anteriori inteſtinorum ſedi
obuoluitur, innataꝗue, colum inteſtinũ quà uentriculo exporrigi

tur, meſenterij uice dorſo committens. Cæterùm portæ caudex
poſtquã omento ſuffultus, dictas nuper depromptã propagines, in
duos partitur truncos, ac dextrum qui grandior eſt, per meſenteriũ
uariè digeſtum, inteſtinis offert, prius duodeno inteſtino, & ieiuni
initio ramum exhibens, glanduloſo corpore huic inteſtinorum ſedi
exporrecto ſuffultum. Siniſter truncus inferiori membrana omenti
intextus, uentriculi poſteriori ſedi quà dextram dorſi partem reſpi
cit, paruam offert propaginem, dein etiam omenti inferiori mem
branæ, mox *r* glandulis hic uaſorum tutæ diſtributioni præfectis,
& colore carneis: dein ſecundùm poſteriora uentriculi ramus ab il
lo aſcendit, uentriculi dorſi medium ſpectãti ſedi ſurculos primùm
exporrigens, & coronæ ritu ſuperius uentriculi orificium ample
ctens, à quo præter ſurculos deorſum ſurſumꝗ depromptos, unus
ſecundùm uentriculi poſteriora ad inferius uentriculi orificiũ pro
repit. Ipſe autem ſiniſter portæ caudicis truncus ſiniſtrorſum ſem
per tendens, inſignem hic quoꝗ promit uenam, omento & colo
inteſtino implicitam: ille uerò in uarias ſectus propagines, & ſobo
lem adhuc humiliori omenti membranæ ſpargens, lienis cauo inſe
ritur, ab ipſius propaginibus, anteaquam lienem ſubeant, uentricu
li ſiniſtro lateri ramulos offerens: inter quos inſignis occurrit, qui
fundum uentriculi in ſiniſtra ſede perreptans, uentriculo & ſuperio
ri membranæ omenti ſoboles deriuat. Venæ portæ autem ſoboles
per iecoris ſubſtantiam diſtributæ, quicquid ab inteſtinis & nonni
hil à uentriculo quoque iecori detulerunt, in ſe continent : ac iecur
cius cremoris optimum concoquens, in ſanguinem id emutat, ſuæ
etiam concoctionis duplex recrementum, uti in uini omni que con
coctione alia fieri cernimus, obtinens: unum quidem craſſius, quod
ueluti ſanguinis fæx & lutu cenſetur, atra que bilis uulgò ſerè dicitur:
& per portæ uenã in *s* lienem ablegatur, qui ad ſiniſtrum uentriculi
latus ad inferiora poſterioraꝗ repoſitus, linguæ craſſioris imagi
nem exprimit, accumbentium organorum formæ iecoris ritu con
gruens, & multis uenis ac item arterijs intertextus, quibus propria
lienis caro lutoſo ſanguini ſimilis, & tenui tunica, quam omentum
porrigit, intecta obnaſcitur. Lien itaque craſſius iecoris recremen
tum ad ſe allicere, atꝗ in ipſius nutrimentum conuertere, & ſi quid
ſibi adaptare nequit, in uentriculum id eructare credimus. Tenuius
autem iecoris recrementum, quod ueluti flos uini habetur, bilis fla
ua eſt, quam *t* meatus inter portæ & cauæ propagines per iecoris
ſubſtantiam digeſti in ſe alliciunt, & ſenſim collecti in unum mea
tum ceſſant: qui ex iecoris cauo eductus in bilis *u* ueſiculam pertinet,
cauæ iecoris ſedi inſtar oblongioris piri media ipſius amplitudine
innatam, & corpore conſtantem diſtendi laxariꝗ apto. In hac ue
ſicula bilem aſſeruari diſſectionis profeſſoribus perſuaſum eſt, do
nec ipſa meatus peculiaris beneficio illam in duodenũ inteſtinum
protrudat: ſimul cum ſiccis uentriculi recrementis egerendam, ac
inteſtina ſua mordaci facultate ad propellendum irritaturam, atque
à pituita illis inſidenti liberaturam. Cæterùm ſanguis dictis nuper
excrementis repurgatus, ex anguſtiſſimis uenæ portæ ramis in ar
ctiſſimas cauæ uenæ propagines contendit, tenui aqueoꝗ recremen
to, quod ex inteſtinis in iecur aſſumptum fuit, uehiculi loco utens.
Id namque hactenus ſanguinem concomitans, & ſimul cum ſangui
ne in cauam uenam conſcendens, ſui in his angiportis inſignem u
ſum præſtat. Quum uerò huc uſque ſanguini promptæ digeſtionis
nomine aſtitit, & ſanguis tantam ipſius copiam inſuper non requi
rit, conſonum fuit, ut id à ſanguine alioquin onuſt ipſi futurum ex
purgaretur: cui muneri *x* renes appoſitiſſimè famulantur, utrinque
ſinguli ad uenæ cauæ latera, & iecori proxime allocati, ac maximam
ſeroſi illius humoris portionem ſtrenuè ad ſe allicientes, illamꝗue à
ſanguine excolentes. Quod quo opportunius moliantur, inſignis
uena & item arteria reni tranſuerſim exporriguntur, ac ren in ſinum
membraneum & ampliter cauum, in multas que diſſectum propa
gines, ſeroſum ſanguinem excipit, & ſubſtantiæ renis illi ſinui obna
tæ, & duplici tunica obtectæ beneficio urinam expurgat, illam in a
lium deducens ſinum, quem *y* urinarius meatus uenæ modo con
ſtrictus excipit, hanc in ueſicam delaturus. *z* Veſica etenim rotun
dæ lagenæ quodammodo ritu urinam ſenſim admittentis, ad poſte
riorem pubis oſſis ſedem poſita, peculiari conſtat tunica ſimplici &
neruea, triplici que fibrarum genere intertexta, & contrahi ac di
ſtendi prompta, cui à *á* peritonæo abdominis ue membrana, quæ
hactenus dictorum organorum eſt inuolucrum & firmamentum,
alia obducitur. In poſteriorem ueſicæ ſedem haud procul ab ipſius
ceruice, à ſingulis renibus ſinguli meatus admodum induſtriè inſe
runtur, ipſaꝗue tantiſper urinam colligit, donec illa aut copia aut
qualitate hominem moleſtans, recluſo orbiculatim ueſicæ ceruicem
ambiente muſculo, uniuerſim excernatur. Sanguis hac induſtria
repurga

repurgatus per cauæ uenæ ramos, ceu riuulos quosdam uniuerso corpori digeritur, ut singulæ partes sibi familiare ex sanguine emulgeant, id que emutantes, & sibi apponentes, in proprium nutrimentum conuertant: ac demum huius concoctionis quoque recrementa à se proprijs functionibus abigant. Porrò cauæ series eiusmo di plurimum obseruatur, ubi ea in posteriori iecoris sede consist t, ex anteriori ipsius regione ramos promit, in iecoris gibbum numerosa serie digestos: sursum autem ascendens, ac septum transuersum cum cordis inuolucro perforans, duas propagines septo largitur. Ad dextram cordis aurem caua ampliori orificio in dextrum cordis uentriculum dehiscit, quàm cauæ orbicularis amplitudo uspiam uistitur. A' posteriori eius implantationis (nisi mauis dicere exortus) sede, uena prodit, cordis basim coronæ modo cingens, & deorsum per cordis superficiem ramulos digerens. Caua à corde sursum conscendens, ac cordis inuolucrum inibi prætergressa, uenam paris expertem, & octo frequentius inferiora costarum interualla utrinque enutrientem, à dextro latere promunt. In iugulo autem tota bipartitò scinditur, ab ipsius anteriori sede pectoris ossi & intersepientibus thoracem membranis uenas offerens, abdominis superiora perreptantes. A' radice verò alterius trunci factæ modo in iugulo bipartitionis insignis promitur uena, super primam costam in axillam procurrens, sed priùs in thoracis cauitate ramum promès, in tria superiora sui lateris costarum interualla absumendum, & alium per transuersos ceruicis uertebrarum processus in caluariam usque porrigendum, & alium in posteriora thoracis iuxta ceruicis radicem sparsum. Præsens uena thoracē egressa, interdum hic humerariam promit uenam, & ramum musculis anteriori thoracis sedi instratis: alium posteriori sedi thoracis, & cauo scapulæ: & lateri thoracis alium digerit, in axillam festinans. Trunci autem in iugulo factæ bipartitionis reliquum in duos impares ramos disciditur, & horum interior gracilior internam iugularem constitues uenam, duabus propaginibus duram cerebri membranam adeuntibus, caluariã subit. Exterior verò as interiori latere propaginem, ex qua humeralis uena constituitur, deducens, sursum conscendit, superficiariam efformans iugularem uariè ad fauces usque excurrentem, & in linguam, laryngem, palatum, faciem, tempora & uerticem distributam, tribusque uenis caluariam ingredientem. Humeralis verò priusquam sub clauicula & summo humero in brachium fertur, ramum posteriori ceruicis sedi, & alium scapulæ gibbo, & alium summi humeri superiori sedi exporrigit, & secundum exterius latus musculi cubitum flectentium anterioris sub cute prorepens, surculosque graciles euui depromens, supra cubiti articulum dissecta, aliquando unum ramum penitius latentem, & mox assumptum, ad cubiti articulum defert. alium sub cute obliquè ad cubiti flexus medium cum axillaris uenæ ramo coiturum, communemque uenam constituturum. tertium sub cute secundum radium in posteriora cubiti, ac tandem ad brachialis radicem iuxta ulnæ extremum mittit, qui axillaris propagini inibi commixtus, parui & anularis digitorū exteriora scandit. Axillaris in axilla latitans, & cuti anteriorem brachij sedem uersus interiora inuestienti ramum offerens, surculum præbet capitibus musculorum cubitum extendentium, & alium illorum mediæ propemodum longitudini, dein aliam propaginem cum quarto brachium petente neruo secundùm brachij posteriori ad cubiti usque exteriora ablegat. Mox in duas secta uenas, unam prorsus toto ductu in profundo submersam, ac arteria semper concomitatam, per cubiti articuli flexus medium deducit, quæ ante cubiti longitudinis medium in duas secta propagines, unam secundū radium, alteram secundùm ulnam uersus brachiale porrigat. & hic rursus in surculos dirempta, in internam digitorum sedem ita digeritur, ut singulis digitis duæ offerantur soboles, & surculus quidam inter pollicis primum internodium & postbrachialis os indicem sustinens, ad manus externam sedem pertingat. Altera autem uena sub cute semper exporrecta, iuxta cubiti articulum in duos partitur ramos: quorum alter obliquè uersus cubiti articuli flexum contendens, cum humeralis ramo cōmisceatur, simul cum illo communem efformans uenam, quæ duabus illis medijs uenis constituta, ac obliquè deorsum repens, radium que tandem conscendens, in externa cubiti sede instar Y in duas disciditur soboles, quarum altera medij digiti potissimùm externam sedem petit, altera verò pollici & indici offertur; surculum in internã manus sedem spargens, ramulis montem Veneri sacrum implicantibus commiscendum. At alter axillaris iuxta cubiti articulum factæ diuisionis ramus, uarias propagines in cubiti internam sedem depromit: quibus crebrò uena accedit, ab altero uenam communem constituentium ramo, quem axillaris porrigebat, enata. Hæ propagines admodum

uariè modò coëuntes, modò rursus inuicem diremptæ, ac internam cubiti sedis cutem implicantes, tandem in internam manus cutem prorepunt. Cæterùm insignior eius rami propago ulnæ exporrecta, & in cubiti exteriora etiam surculos promens, iuxta brachialis radicem humerariæ ramo commiscetur, ad anularis digitum & anularem contendenti. Cauæ uenæ pars sub iecore deorsum repens, à sinistro latere ramum offert pingui renis sinistri tunicæ & locis reni contentminis. Dein singulis renibus magna depromitur uena. Ab elatiori sede uenæ dextrum renem petentis, quæ frequenter altiùs uena sinistro reni propria initiū sumit, propago pingue dextri renis tunicam accedit. Ab illius verò quæ ad sinistrum proficiscitur renem, humiliori sede sinistra seminalis uena exoritur, dextra interim à cauæ caudice demissiùs multo principiū ducente. Porrò ubi caua uertebris lumborū innititur, geniculatim illis propagines dat, in musculos proximos et ad abdominis usque latera absumendas. Atque harū illæ sunt præcipuæ, quæ à caua inibi pronascuntur, quã supra ossis sacri ad lumborum uertebras nexum in duos pares dissciditur trúcos, quorū sinister perinde ac dexter surculos quosdam ossis sacri foraminibus offert: & in duos partitur ramos, quorum interior propaginem mittit in musculos exhauriendam, qui ossis ilium & sacri posteriorem sedem occupant, & aliam deriuat in uesicam, & penem, & mulieribus in uterū multiplici sobole pertinentem. Quod reliquum rami est, ab externo ramo portiunculam assumens, per pubis ossis foramen in femur ducitur, cuti & musculis internam femoris sedem occupantibus surculos exhibens, & ante genu articulum cessans, suoque termino cum alterius crus petentis uenæ ramo, ut mox dicam, coiens. Exterior namque ramus sinistri cauæ trunci per inguina femur aditurus peritongo propaginē offert, in inferiorem abdominis sedem ad umbilicum usque absumendam: in femur uerò procidens, pubis cuti & pudendi muliebris colliculis sobolem porrigit. Verùm insignem uenam per femoris & genu & tibiæ interiora, sub cute ad pedis usque digitorum summū diffundit, in progressu sparsim cuti ramusculos depromentem. Aliam quoque sub cute ad coxendicis articuli anteriora deriuat. ipse autem penitùs inter musculos submersus, propaginem communicat musculis, & cuti in externa femoris sede locatis, & aliam offert musculis internã anterioremque femoris sedem sibi uendicantibus. Atque cum hac propagine extremū uenæ eius coit, quæ per pubis ossis foramen descenderat. Hinc grandis uena secundùm femoris posteriora retorqueatur, propagines eius sedis musculis communicans, à quibus ramuli in cutem pertinent, tum sursum, tum deorsum ad suram usque excurrentes. Inter anteriora uerò femoris capita grandis hæc uena in dues scissa truncos, minorem exterioremque uersus fibulam deriuat, à quo præter soboles anteriorem genu sedem petentes ramus disscinditur, sub cute externam tibiæ sedem uersus posteriora obtegente, ad digitorum usque superiora uariè disscisus. Quod uerò reliquum est, altius inter musculos externæ fibulæ sedi attensos occultatum, ultra tibiæ longitudinis medium properat. Interior autem truncus inibi igniter amplus, ramum dispensat secundùm internam tibiæ sedem uersus posteriora sub cute ad pedis usque digitos dispersum. Deinde alium depromit, per suram nonnihil reconditum, & ad calcem usque pertingentem. Quod uerò huius trunci præcipuum est, musculos posteriorem tibiæ sedem occupantes subit, & ab anteriori ipsius regione ramum per ligamentum membranam demittit, fibulam tibiæ alligans: atque is sub anterioribus tibiam integentibus musculis absconditus, ad pedis usque superiora pertingit. Ipsa autem uena secundùm posteriora descendis, & hinc inde cuti & conterminis musculis ramulos offerens, tandem inter calcem & tibiam pedis inferiora subit, inibi in musculos & digitos in eum modum distributa, ut duæ soboles singulis offerantur.

DE CORDE, AC ORGANIS
ipsius functioni subministrantibus.
Caput IIII.

ORGANORVM, quæ insito nobis calori recreando, & spiritibus restituendis enutriendisque fabricantur, cor irascibilis animæ sedes facile præcipuum censetur, instar nucis pineæ anteriùs ac posteriùs compressæ effigiatum, et sua basi sub pectoris ossis medio collocatum, suoque mucrone in sinistrum latus impensè antrorsum uergens, substantiaque constans carnea, sed quàm musculorum
E

rum est substantia duriori & triplici fibrarum genere intertexta, ac uenis arterijsq́ue proprijs donata. Dein cor duos sinus seu uentriculos possidet, quorum alter in dextro consistens latere, amplior ac rariori tenuioriq́ue cordis substantia obductus cernitur, & cauæ uenæ orificium ad hunc pertinet, cui tres membranæ introrsum ductæ præficiuntur. Quinetiam uas arteriæ constans corpore, sed uenarum munere fungens, ac proinde arterialis uena appellatum, ab illo uentriculo egreditur, in ipsius orificio tres quoq́ue exigens membranulas extrorsum spectantes. Alter autem uentriculus in sinistro repositus latere, & crassa præcipuáq́ue cordis substantia circundatus, etiam duobus donatur orificijs, quorum humilius cui cuiusq́uam est, arteriæ, quod ad aërem attinet, usum præstantis, at uenæ corpore efformati: & proinde uenalis arteria appellati, & in ipsius orificio duas membranas introrsum conniuentes exigentis. Elatius uerò orificiú arteriæ magnæ dedicatur principio, cui etiam tres membranas Natura elargitur extrorsum respiciétes. Atq́; hi sinus septo interstinguuntur impensè crasso, & comprimi distendíq́ue apto, & in tus foueis plurimis (ut & cordis uentriculi) abundanti corpore extructo. Totum uerò cor membraneo quodam inuolucro tegitur, ipsi nulla ex parte connatum, & corde multo ampliori aqueóq́ue humore intus rorato. Hoc exterius inferiori sua sede septo transuerso non mediocri amplitudine connascitur, in lateribus autem duabus continetur membranis cauitaté thoracis intersepientibus, & inuolucrum hoc, ut cor in sua sede seruaretur, suffulcientibus. Pulmo autem reliquam thoracis cauitatem, quam cor & dictæ nuper mem brangæ & stomachus deorsum descendens non occuparunt, implet, undiq́; sese accumbentium partium formæ iecoris modo adaptans, ac proinde bubulo, aut alioquin bisulco pedi admodum similis, & primum dextra parte & sinistra conformatus: quæ rursus singulæ in duas fibras lobos ue diremptæ, multis uasorum implexibus extruuntur. Asperæ namq́; arteriæ à faucibus (ubi etiam tonsillæ & alia duo glandularum genera consistunt) in thoracem deductæ, & ut uoci famularetur partim cartilagineæ: ut uerò concidere distédíq́ue apta efficeretur, ac respirationi subseruiret, partim membraneæ, rami pulmonè passim implent: & arterialis uena à dextro cordis uentriculo familiarem sanguini pulmoni præparate, procedens, eumq́; sanguinem pulmoni offerens, innumera serie in pulmonem distribuitur, similiter ac uenalis arteria frequenti serie pulmonem implicans. Atq́; his uasis fungosa, mollis, spumea & admodü sequax propriáq́; pulmonis substantia circunfunditur, quam tenuis admodum & pulmonis dilatationem compressionemq́; haud prohibens tunicula proximè ambit, tunicæ costas succingenti semper attigua. Cæterum quia pulmo thoracis motum è nostro pendentium arbitratu, uacui beneficio sequens dilatatur, uacui etiam ratione extrinsecus nos ambiens aër per nares secundùm gargareonem: & quum uehementiùs aërem ducimus, is per os etiam ueluti in follem attrahitur, ipsius portiuncula per caluariæ foramina cerebrum petens, & reliqua portione per fauces in asperam arteriam subintrans, & pulmonis cauitatem ex ipsius dilatatione factá ad amussim implens. Hunc aërem pulmonis substantia insita ui alterat, cordísq́; usibus aptans, optimam sui portionem à uenalis arteriæ ramis undiq́; asperæ propaginibus attensis assumi permittit, ut eius arteriæ interuentu aër in sinistrum cordis sinum deferatur, spiritus uitalis idonea futurus materia. Cor enim hunc aërem attrahens, & in sinistrum ipsius uentriculum magnam sanguinis copiam à dextro alliciens, ex halituoso eius sanguinis uapore, & illo aëre, propria uirtute ipsius substantiæ insita spiritum conficit, quem sanguine impetu ruente, concomitatum forumq́; per magnam arteriam uniuerso corpori distribuit, & nasium cuiusq́; partis calorem ita temperat, quemadmodum respiratio cor insiti caloris fomitem recreat: itaq́; idem usus sit respirationis & pulsus, quo arteria magna cordis rhythmo dilatatur & cóstringitur. Ad spiritum igitur conficiendum cor aere utitur, ipsóq́; illius feruidus calor temperatur. Verùm quicquid in hac spiritus cósectióne fuliginosum spiritúsq́; efficiendo ineptú est, per uenalem arteriá in pulmonè reduci, atq́; hinc cú aere qui in pulmone reliquus erat, compresso thorace excerni, dissectionis professoribus est concessum. Adeò sanè ut cor indefessa ipsius dilatatione sanguinem in dextrum ipsius uentriculum à caua attrahat, ut is partim in sinistrú uentriculum ducatur, partim uerò in aptum pulmonis nutrimentum ab ipso amicé præparetur, & contracto corde per arterialem uenam pulmoni offeratur. Cor uerò dilatatum in sinistrum uétriculum ex pulmone aerem assumit, constrictú uerò spiritum uitalem unà cum sanguine impetu ruente in magná arteriá propellit. Quò minus autem rapida cordis attractio uenæ cauæ & uenali arteriæ noxam inferret, Natura cordi aures creauit, uelut promptuaria cordi apposita. Quatuor autem cordis uasorum orificijs membranæ arbitramur præfectas, ne irritus cordis labor fiat. Membranæ enim cauæ & uenalis arteriæ orificijs præfectæ, impediút quo minus in cordis contractione sanguis in cauam, & spiritus uitalis in uenalem arteriá refluant, illæ uerò quæ in arterialis uenæ & magnæ arteriæ orificijs habentur, obstant quo minus in cordis dilatatione sanguis pulmoni oblatus, & spiritus uitalis iam emissus, in cor denuò regurgitent. Porrò magna arteria simulatque è corde pronascitur, duas educis propagines cordis basim cingentes, deorsum ramulos per cordis substantiam spargentes. ipse autem arteriæ caudex paulo supra cor in duos sectus truncos, grandiorem sinistrorsum ad spinam detorquet, à quo utrinq́; ramiad octo humiliores costas exporriguntur. Quum uerò is sub septo deorsum fertur, huic quoq́; propagines offert, mox ab una radice omento, uentriculo, iecori, bilis uesiculæ, colo intestino, & demúlieni soboles offerens, uenæ portæ ramis concomitatas. Dein aliam radicem truncus hic in mesenterium dispensat, & utrinq́; renibus unam deriuat nonnihil inferius, ab ipsius anteriori sede seminales producens arterias, & dein adhuc demissius mesenterio alium ramú exhibens, & in progressu uertebris lumborum ipsísq́; accumbentibus musculis surculos depromens. Ad sacri ossis initium, & si arteria prius cauæ in sinistro latere subijciatur, eá quo rutior prorepat cóscendit, & eodem cum caua modo hic bipartitó scinditur, parem cum illa ad extremum usq́; pedis distributionem in profundo faciens. quippe nullus huius arteriæ magnæ trunci ramus cutem subit. Verùm id priuatim huius trúci propagini per pubis ossis foramen procedenti accidit, quod illi arteria committitur, quæ ab umbilico secundùm uesicæ latus descendens, foetui propria censetur. Arteriæ magnæ caudicis truncus superiora petens, statim à sinistro ipsius latere ramum promit, obliquè ad elatissimá thoracis sui lateris costam protensam, à quo primùm propago superioribus costis offertur, & dein alia transuersis processibus uertebrarú ceruicis, quæ postmodum in duram cerebri membranam exhauritur. dein alia sinistro pectoris ossis lateri exhiberur, quæ in alto sem per condita, ad umbilicum usq́; pertingit. Vbi uerò ramus ille thoracis cauitatem superauit, surculum posteriorem ceruicis sedem occupantibus musculis transmittit, & similiter ut axillaris uena ad digitorum usq́; extrema digeritur, si axillaris ramos cutem subeuntes exceperis, ac in alto latitantes solùm hic intellexeris. Cæterùm insignior portio dictinuper magnæ arteriæ trunci ad iugulú ascendés, in duos impares ramos partitur. Sinister, qui & gracilior est, sinistri lateris soporalem constituit arteriam: dexter uerò, ab ipsius dextro latere ad primam costam propaginem deriuat, eodem prorsus modo ab sumendam, quo ramus ille qui obliquè primam sinistri lateris costam adire dicebatur. Verùm dextri rami reliquum, huius lateris soporalem efformat arteriam, quæ similiter atq́; sinistra secundùm asperæ arteriæ latus fauces petens, ramum porrigit in faciem penitiùs & in temporum cutem ad uerticem usq́; absorbendam. ipsa autè laryngi & linguæ & triplici hic reposito glandularum generi soboles offerens, caluariam adit, & in duas diuisa propagines, minorem in primum dextrum ue durgmembranæ sinum exhauriendam mittit. grandior absq́; uenæ coniugio per proprium foramen in caluariam mergitur, atq́; hic mox in duræ membranæ latus soboles ab ipsa deriuantur, & alia per peculiare foramen ad narium amplitudinè uersus nasi extremum contendit: ipsa autem propagata caluariæ basi instrata, & in nullum tamen plexum reticularè digesta, antrorsum fertur, & ramum cum secundo pari neruorum cerebri ad oculum depromens, sursum ascendit, duram cerebri membraná perforans, & partim in tenuem membraná hic absumpta, partim uerò in dextrum cerebri uentriculum repens, plexus eius in hoc uentriculo repositi, ac extimo foetus inuolucro comparati portionem efformat, uitaleméq́; spiritum cerebro offert, ut ex illo cerebri beneficio animalis spiritus, uti nunc dicam, præparetur.

DE CEREBRO, ET ORGANIS
cerebri officiorum nomine extructis.
Caput V.

EREBRVM animalis ac principis facultatum sedes in caluaria reponitur, formam cauitatis quam occupat concinnè referens, ac superiori sede secundùm capitis longitudinem, ac anterius posteriúsq́; in dextram partem & sinistram diremptum, in ipsius autem basis medio continuum. Vbi dorsalis medullæ ab ossium medulla plurimùm differentis producit initium. exirúrsus cerebellum

bellum unitur, decuplo ferè minus cerebro, ac posteriori illius parti omnino subiectum, neque magis retrorsum quàm cerebrum ipsum uergens. Atque hæc uniuersa cerebri dura amplectitur membrana caluariam proximè succingēs, & per suturas caluariæ fibras porrigens, quæ in peculiare ' inuolucrum caluariæ degenerant. Hæc membrana tantùm à ᵉ tenui cerebri membrana distat, ut uasorum ipsius motum non præpediat, processum mittens inter dextram cerebri partē & sinistrā, & item aliū inter sedem cerebelli elatiorem & cerebrum quà cerebello innititur. Huic membranæ quatuor præcipui insunt sinus, uenarum arteriarum'que usum simul subeuntes, & uariam uasorum seriem in tenuem cerebri membranam digerentes. Cerebri enim substantiæ, quæ continua, alba, & nullis uenis intertexta est, tenuis quædam membrana uicinissimè obducitur, quæ passim in cerebri reuolutiones intestinorum anfractibus similimas se implicans, uasa cerebri continet. Cerebrum uerò tribus insignibus et impensè amplis donatur cauitatibus seu uentriculis, quorum unus secundùm cerebri longitudinem in dextra cerebri parte consistit, qui ex posteriori sede deorsum per cerebri substantiam reflexus, ad medium usque basis cerebri perfertur. Secundus huic prorsus respondens, in sinistra cerebri parte collocatur, & ambo quà internis lateribus se inuicem spectant, superiori sede tenui quadam cerebri substantia mutuò distinguuntur, quam ᵇ septum nuncupamus, & quæ superius continuatur cerebri portioni, quæ quòd cæterarum cerebri partium in superficie positarum subdurior & magis candicans sit, ᶜ callosum corpus appellatur. Humilior autem septi sedes unitur continua'que est cerebri ᵈ parti quæ instar fornicis ᵉ testudinis'ue extructa, utrinque ex posteriori duorum primorum cerebri uentriculorum sede, ampla basi pronascitur, & sensim antrorsum procedens, ueluti in acutum trianguli uerticem coarctatur, humiliori sua sede quamodò recensendæ cauitati incumbit, instar fornicis cauata. Humiliores enim dictorum uentriculorum sedes inuicem septo non interstinguuntur, uerùm in communem sinum conueniunt, sub corpore instar fornicis formato repositum, & uno insigni meatu rectà deorsum per cerebri substantiam pertinentem in infundibulum seu ' peluim à tenui membrana instar infundibuli extructam: quà cerebri pituita per illum meatum descendens, glandi quadratæ & ossi cuneum imitanti superstratæ instillatur, illinc ad ʰ palatum & narium amplitudinem per insignia, non autem congiæ modo pertusa, foramina defluens. Ista communis dextri & sinistri uentriculorum cauitas tertius cerebri est uentriculus, posteriori sua sede in meatum desinens, qui per cerebri corpora ' testibus aut ' naribus non absimilia, in quartum uentriculum contendit, qui communis est cerebello & dorsalis medullæ initio, anteriori ac posteriori sede cerebelli ' processu ornatus, quem ex anfractuum imagine uermi in lignis nato comparamus. Verùm in hoc uentriculo, quemadmodum in tribus uentriculis prioribus, nullum peculiare corpus secantibus occurrit. In dextrum namque uentriculum (similiter ac in sinistrum) per ipsius inferiorem posteriorem'que sedem soporalis arteriæ insignior ramus conscendit, ᵏ plexum efformaturus, quem extimo foetus inuolucro comparamus. Is enim ab illo arteriæ ramo & eius uasis portione constituitur, quod ' glandulæ nucis pineæ instar effigiate, & cerebri testibus incumbenti suffultum, ab extremo quarti duræ membranæ sinus secundùm cerebelli longitudinem exporrecti, per tertium cerebri uentriculum ducitur, & ab eo sinu tanquam à ' torculari, uenæ arteriæ'que materiam suscipit. deinceps in duas portiones dissectum, una in dextrum uentriculum, altera in sinistrum pertinet, ac cum arteriarum ramis eò peruenientibus, dictum nuper plexum in utroque uentriculo constituit. Ex hoc uitali spiritu in illo plexu cerebri munijs adaptato, ac ex aere quem inspirantes in cerebri uentriculos allicimus, cerebri substantiæ insita uis spiritu animalem conficit, quo cerebrum ad principis animæ functiones partim utitur: partim uerò per neruos ab ipso pronatos, ad organa spiritu animali indigentia (quæ potissimùm sensus ac motus uoluntarij sunt instrumenta) transmittit, non mediocrem ipsius portionem à tertio uentriculo sub testibus cerebri in uentriculum cerebello, & dorsali medullæ communem diffundens, quæ postmodum neruis omnibus à dorsali medulla ortum ducentibus digeritur. A'cerebri enim basis medio utrinque unus nascitur processus longus & teres, & secundùm cerebri basim antrorsum ductus, & altero sinui caluarii capitis ossis incumbens, & olfactus organo proprius: uerùm quoniam ex caluariæ amplitudine non procidit, nerui nomine à Dissectionum professoribus non donatur. Primum enim septem quæ cerebro ascribuntur pariū paulo posteriùs quàm dicti modò processus neruorū substantiæ respondentes, initium à cerebri basi ducit, uisorios constituens neruos, qui in oculi

'tunicam retis imagini similem degenerant. Oculus namque in centro habet ᵃ crystallinum humorem, cuius anteriori sedi ᵇ tunica tenuissimæ ceparum pelliculæ correspondens obnascitur. Posterior eius humoris regio à ᶜ uitreo humore continetur, cuius posteriorem ambit sedem inuolucrum cerebri substantiæ respondens, in quod uisorij nerui substantia dissoluitur. Tenuis autē cerebri membrana neruum uisorium inuestiens, in ᵈ tunicam dilatescit uuæ folliculo perquàm similem: quippe ipsa uniuersum oculum amplectens, anteriori sedi foramine eò peruia cernitur, quod ' pupillam dicimus. Dura autem cerebri membrana neruum uisorium circundata, in ᵉ duram oculi tunicam finitur, toti oculo obductam, & in anteriori sede oculi cornu modo ᶠ pellucidam, quæ ' iride seu maiori oculi circulo circumscribitur, ad quem ᵍ alba adhærens'ue oculi tunica anteriori oculi sedi obnata definit. Porrò inter corneã hanc & anteriorem crystallini humoris sedem ʰ aqueus habetur humor, qui à uitreo tunica quadam tenui & ciliorum imaginem exprimenti, & orbiculatim crystallino humori adnata, atque ab uuea principium obtinente distinguitur. Secundum neruorum par mouendis oculorum musculis seruit. Tertium duabus radicibus inuicem distantibus utrinque enascens, minorem digerit quadam portiuncula ad frontis cutem, & quadam ad superiorem maxillam superius'que labrum, & quadam in narium amplitudinem, & quadā ad musculos maxillam inferiorem attollentes. Maiorem uerò radicem tertium hoc par linguæ exporrigit, hæc'que illius beneficio gustus instrumentum efficitur. Verùm ab hac etiam radice ramus capreoli modo intortus dictis nuper offertur musculis, & alius superioribus dentibus, alius'que inferiori maxillæ ac dentibus illi infixis, & inferiori tandem labro. Quartum par in palati cessat tunicam. Quintum duplici quoque radice, ut & tertium par, prodiens, minorem musculis maxillam inferiorem attollentibus dispensat, crassiorem uerò auditus organo offert, quamuis & ab hac binas dispergit soboles per diuersa foramina in commemoratos modò musculos etiam pertinentes. Sextum par præter ramusculos ab ipso quibusdam in ceruice musculis & laryngi in descensu oblatos, septimi paris portione adaugetur, atque iuxta pectoris ossis summum soboles quasdam illinc prodeuntibus musculis præbens, ramum costarum radicibus deducit, in organa sanguificationi subministrantia pulchrè digerendum. Ita hactenus uterque sexti pāris neruus pariter distribuitur. Dexter uerò priuatim sui portionem ad arteriam dextro brachio exporrectam retorquet, à quo neruus consurgit secundùm asperæ arteriæ dextrum latus ad laryngem proficiscens, ob id'que neruus ᵉ recurrens nuncupatus. Quod autem reliquum ab hoc dextro neruo descendit, pulmonis dextræ parti & cordis inuolucro ramusculos offert, ac stomacho tandem commissum, septum'que permeans, uentriculi superioris orificij sinistram sedem multis propaginibus donat. Sinister autem neruus ad arteriæ magnæ truncum dorso explicatur, portiones suas reuersium sinistri lateris neruum constituentes retorquet. Ab huius lateris neruo peculiariter cordi gracilis propago digeritur: quod autem eius adhuc restat, dextram superioris orificij uentriculi sedem intertexit, secundum uentriculi superiora ramulum ad iecur usque mittens. Septimum par præterquàm quod sextum impensè auget, præcipuè in laryngis & linguæ musculos absumitur. Nerui à dorsali medulla in uertebris conclusa principium ducentes, triginta complectuntur paribus: quorum septem ceruicis dedicantur uertebris, duodecim thoracis, quinque lumborum, sex sacro ossi, nullo interim neruo à coccygæ osse profiliente. Quæ à ceruicis labuntur uertebris, in musculos ipsis adnatos proximos'que digeruntur: & à quarto, quinto & sexto parium surculis utrinque unus efficitur neruus, septo transuerso proprius: dein à quinto, sexto, septimo, & dein ab octauo ac nono, seu primo secundo'que thoracis paribus, uarius neruorum consurgit textus, à quo in brachium sex nerui pullulant, præter uarias soboles scapulæ cauo & gibbo dispersas. At primus brachium petens neruus ab ipsius propaginibus, quas brachium attollens offert musculo, sobolem impensè gracilem in cutem brachij externæ sedi obductam digerit. Secundus per axillam brachium ingrediens, ramulos'que priori cubitum flectentium musculo præbens, insignem ipsius portionem tertio brachium accedenti neruo impartitur. ipse uerò in cubitum festinans, & ramulum primo radium in supinum ducenti musculo exhibens, cutem subit: ac in uarias dissectus propagines, superioris interioris'que cubiti sedis cutem ad extremam usque manum implicat. Tertius per axillam quoque dissectus, & anterioris brachij sedis cuti ramulos deprimens, ac secundi nerui portione adauctus, propaginem'que communicans, posteriori cubitum flectentium musculo per anterio-

F rem

rem fedem interioris tuberculi offis brachij in cubitum properat,
mufculis hinc principiū ducentibus furculos unà cum quinto neruo fpargens,& fecundùm radium exporrectus,atque in manus uolam ductus,duas foboles pollicis internæ fedi,& totidē indici quoque,& unā tantū externo lateri interioris fedis medij clargitur,non
infrequenter etiam medio binos ramulos & unū anulari offerens.
Quartus brachij neruus cæteris multo craffior per axillam ingrediens,& ramos mufculis cubitum extendentibus difseminans,fe-
cundùm brachij pofteriora ad externum offis brachij tuberculum
contendit,in cutem prius duas diffundens foboles. Neruus ad hāc
externam articuli cubiti fedem pofitus,ramum in cutem externæ cu
biti fedis ad brachiale ufqȝ fpargens, & mox in duos ueluti truncos
diuifus,mufculis'que ab externo brachij offis tubere pronatis foboles dans, unum truncum ulnæ exporrigit, à quo ramuli in mufculos ab externa ipfius fede pronatos digeruntur:ipfe autem truncus iuxta brachialis radicem ceffat.Superior uerò truncus radio exporrigitur, & præter furculos graciles, quos accumbentibus præbet mufculis,brachiale petit,& duos ramulos externæ pollicis fedi,
ac duos item indicis,et unum medij digiti interno lateri impartitur.
Quintus neruus arteriæ brachij proximus in axilla latitat,& nullas
foboles in brachio à fe deducés,in cubitum per pofteriorem interio
ris tuberculi offis brachij fedem pertingit, ac mufculis hinc prona-
fcentibus unà cum tertio neruo ramos communicans, fecundùm
ulnam ad brachiale excurrit, in medio ductu ramum diffundens,
qui duobus furculis in externam parui digiti fedem,& duobus item
in anularis, & uno in medij exterioris fedis externum latus abfumi-
tur.Quicquid uerò quinti nerui internam brachialis fedem adit, interiori parui digiti fedi , & anularis & medij ramulos offert. Sextus neruus infigniter gracilis,fecundùm internam brachij fedem fub
cute deducitur,& in progreffu ramulos quofdam in cutem diffundens ad cubitum pertingit,in cuius cutem fecundùm ulnam ad brachiale ufque frequentibus furculis difseminatur.   A' neruis è tho
racis uertebris profilientibus , præter ramos qui retrorfum ad fpi-
nas uertebrarum, & dehinc in mufculos ab illis principium ducen-
tés porriguntur , fingula coftarum interualla fingulos ramos fibi
uendicant , ad pectoris & abdominis ufque medium orbiculatim
pertinentes,& mufculis thoraci inftratis, abdominis quà mufculis,
& demum cuti furculos difpergentes. Ad hæc ab intercoftalibus
neruis portiunculæ digeruntur, quæ fexti paris neruorum cerebri
propagines coftarum radicibus exporrectas adaugent. Cæterùm
diftributio neruorum è lumborum uertebris progredientium thoracis neruis magna ex parte refpondet:illi nanque retrorfum ramos
diffeminant,& fecundū ilia ad abdominis mediū circulatim afcen-
dunt,ramulos cöterminis mufculis & cuti elargiétes. Verū à primo
horū pari ad teftes cum feminalibus arterijs propagines quàm mini
mæ pertingunt, à quatuor autem humillimis paribus nerui in femur procidentes principium fumunt, quanquam omnium maximus à quatuor primis facri offis neruorum paribus pronafcatur.
Primum facri offis neruorum par, fimiliter ac thoracis & lumborum paria,è uertebris labitur. Quinqȝ autem humiliora facri offis
paria non à lateribus profiliunt,uerùm una radice antrorfum,alte-
ra retrorfum egrediuntur,& pofterioribus radicibus in mufculos
facro offi & ilium offibus adnatos & cuti fparguntur.Anterior uerò primi paris ramus unà cum anterioribus triū fuccedentiū pariū
radicibus dictům nuper neruū cöftituit. Humiliorum autem pariū
radices in ueficam , anum & penem,aut mulieribus in uteri ceruicē
& pudendi colliculos deperduntur . Porrò quatuor neruorum in
femur progredientium primus fecundùm fextum femur mouentē
mufculū deducitur,ac in externā femoris cutē diffeminans,in
mufculos abfumitur exterius femoris latus occupantes. Secundus
fimul cum grandiori femoris uena & arteria femur fubit, mox ramum depromens per internam femoris & genu & tibiæ fedem ad
fummum ufque pedis digitorum'que extrema fub cute fimul cum
uena ,quam hàc proreperc dictum eft,defcendens : hucȝque ac illuc
ramulos digerens . Quod uerò fecundi nerui eft reliquum , in mufculos ceffat anteriorem femoris fedem contegentes . Tertius neruus pubis offis foramen perreptans, & mufculis id occupantibus
ramulos offerens,fobolem deriuat in internam femoris cutem ali-
quoufqȝ fparfam:reliquū autē eius nerui in mufculos difcinditur,
in interna femoris fede inibi locatos . Quartus omniū corporis ner
uorum,qui ex pluribus neruis conftruuntur,facilè craffiffimus,ubi
coxendicis os à facro dehifcit,in pofteriora femoris ducitur, ramū
in cutem femoris pofteriorē fpargens, qui paulo fub media femoris longitudine ceffat.Humiliori etenim fedi alius offertur ramus,à
quarto propagatus neruo,qui etiā mufculis à coxēdicis offis infima

pofteriotiqȝ fede pronatis,foboles exhibet , uti & mufculis ab inferioribus femoris capitibus pronatis. Dein in poplitis regione in
duos diffectus truncos,graciliorem exteriorem'que ad fibulam defert,à quo ramus ad externam tibiæ cutem ad paruum ufqȝ digitum repit,& alius in anteriorem tibiæ cutem difpergitur : cius uerò
trunci reliquum fibulæ exporrigitur, ubi feptimi & octauipedem
mouentium mufculorum pendet origo . Cæterùm grandior inte-
riorēȝ truncus ramum in internam tibiæ cutem,& in furæ pariter
cutem ad calcem ufqȝ porrigit:ipfe uerò in mufculis furam confti
tuentibus occultatus,ramum per ligamentum membraneum mittit,quo fibula tibiæ alligatur.hic ramus mufculis anteriorem tibiæ
fedem obtinentibus recönditus,tandem in pedis fuperiora contendit,inibi digitis oblatus.Præcipua eius grandioris trunci portio fecundùm tibiæ pofteriora deorfum properans , & nonnullas foboles huc illuc mufculis exhibens,inter calcem interioremȝȝ malleoli
pedis humiliora adit,& exiguas admodum foboles mufculis inibi
repofitis offerens,inferiori fingulorū digitorū fedi duas propagines
cömunicat.Atqȝ ad hunc fanè modū immēfus rerum Opifex non
ad uiuendū modò,fed etiam ad cömodè uiuendū corpus noftrum
corruptioni obnoxium condidit.quæ autem ad fpeciei fucceffionē
fabrefecerit,quiȝȝ hæc.nutritionis organis procul à fenfibus & ra
tionis fede fubiunxerit,nunc obiter & quantum hæc humanæ fabri
cæ partium enumeratio admittit,fubrjciam.

DE ORGANIS SPECIEI
propagandæ famulantibus.
Caput VI.

INITIO ad fpeciei confervationem humanæ
fabricæ autor duos homines ita extruxit, ut uir
quidem infantis primarium porrigeret principium, mulier uerè id aptè conciperet, infantu-
lum'que ex hoc pronatum principio tantifper nö
fecus quàm aliquod fui corporis membrū enu-
triret, quoufque is ualidior redditus, in aërem
nos ambiente produci poffet. Atqȝ his munijs idonea peculiariaȝȝ
inftrumenta uir ac mulier obtinuit,quibus tanta ad generationem
delectationis uis & illecebra inditur,ut animalia hac incitata,fiue iu
uenilia, fiue ftulta & rationis experti a fint,haud aliter fpeciei propa
gandæ incumbant, quàm fi effent fapientiffima. Vir quidem duos.
adipifcitur teftes,cute quæ hic fcortum dicitur,carneaȝȝ que membrana obductos,& alba ac continua peculiari'que prorfus fubftan
tia extructos:quam ualida continet membrana , orbiculatim fub-
ftantiæ huic proximè adnata,ac eorum quæ tefti applantantur infertionem connexumȝȝ excipiens, fingulis'que teftibus peculiare in-
uolucrium conftituens. cui alterum quoȝȝue proprium accedit à
peritonæo inibi pronatum,ubi id uafis feminalibus uiam offert.Il
linc namque membrana pronafcitur, ea uafa cum tefte continens,
& tefti nufquam,neque etiam feminalibus uafis(nifi quà ex magna
peritonei amplitudine excidunt)neque pronafcitur conexa.Ad humilio
rem enim teftis fedem hæc tunica ipfius carnea parte tantum adna-
fcitur , quam teftis muſculum cenfemus . Vafa autem feminalia
funt,una utrinque uena,una'que arteria. Vena dextrum teftem petens à cauæ caudicis anteriori fede fub uenarum in renes pertinentium exortu pronafcitur: quæ uerò finiftro tefti offertur, ab humiliori fede ueneȝ finiftrū renem adeuntis ob hoc principiū fumere cre
ditur,ut non purū fanguinem dextræ ueneȝ modo tefti perferat,fed
ferofum,qui ipfius falfa & acri qualitate in feminis eiectione pruri-
tum conciliet.Ambæ arteriæ à grandi arteria paulo inferiùs quàm
dextra feminalis uena initium ducant,& dextra cauȝȝ caudicem con
fcendens ad dextram fertur uenam,fimul cum hac uaricofa accedens: & cum uena anteaquam teftem attingat,uariè perplexa, corpusȝȝ
efformans multas uarices exprimens,fua'que bafi elatiori teftis fedi
infertũ,& ramulos intimo teftis inuolucro offerens, multifariamȝȝ
per teftis fubftantiam digeftum, quæ fanguinem hunc benignum,
& fpiritum ingenita ipfi facultate in femē haud fecus emutat,quàm
iecoris fubftātia cremorem ab inteftinis ei delatum, in fanguinem
alterat.Confectum femen à ualido uafe inftar uermis teftis pofte-
riori fedi adnato,uariè'que capreoli ritu implexo excipitur.hoc uas
furfum ad magnam peritonæi cauitatem ab uia confcendens,qua feminalis uena & arteria defcendēre,nerui cuiufdam modo teres efficitur:& deorfum ad pubis os reflexum, pofteriorem ueficæ fedem
accedit,ad quam uas à finiftro tefte femen deferens etiam properat,
quod

a fcortū.
b fubftaip.

c carnea tunica.

*d fubftan-
tiæ ueste*

*e fpermae-
tici*

f tunica

g uerpes

quod dextro uafi unicum, fimul cum illo in ueficæ ceruicis radicem inter glandulofum corpus ceruici hic obnatum inferitur, communiſq; femini ac urinæ meatus confurgit, qui deorfum modicè ductus, denuò furfum ad pubis offium commiffuram foris reflectitur, corporibus penem efformantibus fubnatus. Prodit enim utrinq; à pubis offe unum nerueum teresq; corpus, quod intus impenfe fungofum ac craffo fanguine plenum cernitur. utrumq; fimul connatum unitumq; penem conftituit, eius fubftantiç beneficio, quum is femen in uterum miffurus eft, erigi augeriq; aptum: et aliàs quum nullus fuæ proceritatis ufus eft, flaccidum & gracilem, qui etiam ad commodum Veneris ufum fuo apice glandis modo tumet, ac cute qua tegi & retegi queat decoratur. Mulier uterum fibi uendicat, femini excipiendo foetuiq; continendo dedicatum: qui inter ueficam & rectum inteftinum repofitus, ueficæ que inftar fundo ac ceruice utrifque tendi ac in fe concidere aptis formatus, membranis laxis & carneis aliquot fibris (quorum auxilio uterus uoluntarie nonnihil agitur) intertextis, ita fuis lateribus ad peritonæum alligatur, ut mefenterium inteftina continet. Fundi forma non prorfus rotunda exiftit, uerum anterius pofteriufq; depreffa: fuperius obtufa, & duos (utrinque uidelicet unum) retufos oftendens angulos, qui uitulum fronti cornua producturæ affimilantur. Fundo fimplex adeft finus, fundi formæ ad amuffim refpondens, & in orificium definens, glandis penis modo in uteri ceruicis amplitudinê prominens, & naturali tantum ui, non autem mulieris arbitratu fefe conftringens & referans. Fundus fimplici propriaq; conftat tunica, non prægnantibus infigniter craffa, ut utero gerentibus in miram amplitudinem extendi ualeat. Huic alia obducitur, à peritonæo initium fumens. Ceruix uteri teres eft, & in utero non gerentibus aliàs non diftenfa, haud multo minus ipfo fundo ampla, & ueficæ ceruicis infertionem excipiens, coriaceis que carnibus &

colliculis alis ue ad fuum orificiû ornata. Quinetiam utero utrinq; unus accumbit teftis, ad quem uafa eodem prorfus modo atque in uiris pertingunt. Verùm hîc id priuatim accidit, quod media tantû feminalis uenæ arteriæq; pars tefti offeratur, altera uteri fundum implicante. Vas femen tenue & impenfe aquofum paucûq; à muliebri tefte deferens, in obtufum fui lateris uteri inferitur angulû. Venæ & item arteriæ frequentiffima ferie, præter antea dictas, uterum implicantes, ab illis prodeunt uaforû diftributionibus, quæ poft facri offis ad infimam lumborum uertebram nexum perficitur. Atq; hæc uafa enutriêdo foetui, & ipfius infito calori recreando fubferuiunt. Foetus autem in utero complexus tribus inuolucris integitur, uno quidem uulgò fecundæ uocato, quod inftar latioris tantum cinguli ipfum ambit, infigniter que craffum & lienis modo nigricans eft: quod utero connatum, uafa in uterum pertinentia excipit : quo illa in ipfo poftmodû collecta, duabus uenis & totidem arterijs in umbilicum inferantur, & una tandem uena iecori, duæ autem arteriæ grandis arteriç propagationis per pubis offiû foramina defcenfuris offerantur. Secundum inuolucrû membrana eft, foetû uniuerfum amplectens, farciminiſq; imagini affimilatum, inter ipfum & tertiû inuolucrum foetus urinam colligens, quæ peculiari meatu ex ueficæ elatiori fede in hanc amplitudinem perfertur, quo minus urina foetus cuti circumfufa, ipfius acrimonia obfit. Tertium inuolucrû tenuiffima eft membrana, hinc etiam agnina diffectionis proceribus appellata, foetuiq; proximè obducta, ac demum foetus fudorê inter fe & foetus cutem fubflauo quafi luto oblitam afferuans. Foetus uerò in lucem editus, lac familiare ipfius alimentum è mamillis à nemine edoctus fugit: quæ in pectore fedem uendicantes, & papilla ornatæ, glandulofo corpore infita ui fanguinem per uenas ipfi adductum in lac conuertente extruuntur.

ENVMERATIONIS OMNIVM HVMANI CORPORIS FABRI=
cam fubeuntium partium finis: quem quoad fieri potuit, collectiffima integriſq; earundem delineatio in fubfe=
quentibus paginis excipit, ea ferie intuenda, quam mox initio præfcripfimus.

G

ANDREAE VESALII.

FORMATS PARTIBVS AGGLVTINATVR, ORDINE FIGVRARVM MVSCVLOS OSTENDENTIVM
quinta numerari potest. eos enim proponit, qui ex omnibus in anterio
mi sint, non mirum est, praesentem figuram magna ex parte, uti &
quae sinistra continetur manu, illi succedit quae quartae figurae sini-
media occurrit pars) iacet. quod uerò in caluariae amplitudine spe-
ri subijciuntur. Vbi etiam figura cum suis partibus explicatur, quae
uiris peculiaria exceperis, praesenti pagina etiam indicanda.

ri facie uidendi sunt reliqui. Verùm quum hi paucißi-
praecedentem, nuda ossa proponere. Cerebri figura,
stra amplectitur, & praesenti illa quae humi (ubi oculi
clandũ est reliqui, illis uidendum est figuris, quae mulie-
praesenti figurae agglutinatam cernis, si modò organa

FIGVRAE HVIC CHARTAE IM-
pressa characterum Index, una cum eorum characterum explicatione, qui organis generationi famulantibus in figura praesenti chartae
agglutinata inscribuntur.

A Frontis ossis portio.
B Verticis ossis dextri portio.
C Dextri temporis os.
D Cuneum imitans os.
E Iugale os.
F Occipitij os.
G Primum superioris maxillae os.
H Quartum maxillae superioris os. Verùm
haec, ut neq; foramina in hac caluaria no-
tanda ueniunt prolixius, sed magis in fi-
guris sunt spectanda, omnia simul ossa ex-
primente.
I Alter primi paris musculorum dorsum
mouentium.
K Alter secundi paris dorsum mo-
uentium.
L,L Costarum sunt ossa.
M,M Intercostalium musculorum in costa-
rum ossibus repositorum, interiorumq;
species. atque ijdem inferiorum costa-
rum cartilaginem notantur interuallis.
N,N Costarum uerarum cartilagines.
O,O Musculorum intercostalium in dictis
nuper cartilaginibus positorum, eorũ
dermq; interiorum imago.
P Pectoris ossis inferior posterior ue superficies. est enim in una cum cartilaginibus huc in dextrũ reflexum, quasi illo cor
& pulmonem apte integere posses.
Q Sextus thoracae mouentium.
R Summus humerus.
S Interior scapulae processus.
T Brachij os.
V Vlna.
X Stylum referens processus.
Y Radius.
Z,Z Octo postbrachialis ossa.
a,a Quatuor postbrachialis ossa.
b,b,b Quindecim digitorum ossa.
c,c,c Ossicula sesamo comparata
notantur.
d Dorsum mouentium quinti
paris alter.
e Sextus femur mouentium.
f Septimus femur mouentium.
g Prime thoracis uertebrae
corpus.
h Prime lumborum uertebrae corpus.
i Primum os sacri ossis.
k Primum os ossis coccygis: atque hic etiam
radices anteriorum neruorum e sacro osse
prosilientium notantur.
l Ilium os.
m Coxendicis os.
n in agglutinata ad extendis os chartula, ut o o obiuim, pubis os indicatur.
o Cartilago pubis ossium commissuram inte, ueniens.
p Femoris os.
q Supremum femoris caput.
r Maior exterior ue femoris rotator.
s Interior rotator.
t,u Duo inferiora femoris capita.
x Patella.
y Tibiae os.
z Fibula.
& Talus.
q Calcis ossis portio.
ɣ Nauiforme os.
d,d Quatuor tarsi ossa, quorum extimum cu-
bum refert.
e,e Quinque pedij ossa.
i,i Quatuordecim pedis digitorum ossa.
CEREBRI figurae, quae sinistra
manu continetur, cerebellum à sua sede deorsum habet inuolutum, ac que modò subiungam,
propensè.
A,A Sedes caluariae quae cerebellum retine-
tur, adhuc dura membrana succincta.
B,B Primus durae membrane sinus ade-
pertus.
C,C Secundus durae membrane sinus.
D Foramen occipitij ossis, quo dorsalis
medulla elabitur.

E Dorsalis medulla.
F Sinus dorsalis medullae cum cerebelli sinu, quartum
constituens cerebri uentriculum.
G,G Venae cerebelli tenuem membranam petentes.
H Quinti neruorum cerebri paris alter.
I Sexti paris alter.
K Septim paris alter.
L,L Cerebellum tenui adhuc inuestitum membrana. Ve-
M rùm M mediam ipsius sedem uermis modo inuolu-
tam indicat.
N,N Cerebri adhuc relicta portio.
ſ HIC humi decumbens figurae inferiorem cerebel-
li sedem commonstrat, quae dorsali medullae commit-
tebatur initio.
O,O Sedes quibus cerebellum dorsali continuabatur
medulla.
P Sinus cerebelli cum sinu dorsalis medullae, quarti
cerebri efformans uentriculum.
Q,R Apices mediae partis cerebelli, quae uermis modo
inuoluuntur. atque hos apices priuatim à cerebello resectos, hic humi prostratos effinximus,
S,T. S&T insignitos.
PORRO figurae humi ad-
huc reliqua, ac Δ notata, median
oculi partem à priori in posteriori transuersim alia diuisam oculis subijcis, ad hunc modum oculi
partes indicatura.
a Crystallinus humor.
b Tunica cepe pelliculae non
abfimilis, ac anteriori crystallini humoris sedi obuo-
luta.
c Vitreus humor.
d Visorij nerui substantia.
e Tenuis cerebri membrana
portio, uisorium induens.
f Durae cerebri mem-
brana portio, ui-
soriorum quoq; ui-
urestiens.
g Tunica reti assi-
milata.
h Tunica uuea foll-
iculo comparata.
i Pupilla.
k Tunica palpebra-
rum pilos seu ci-
lia imagine refe-
rens.
l Dura oculi tunica.
m' Cornea oculi tunica.
n,n Aqueus humor.
o,o Musculi durae oculi tunicae inserti.
p Adhaerens oculi tunica.
CAETERVM notae in figura huic basi affixa
apparentes inter mulieris tabularũ notas explicabuntur: si modò
eas exceperis, quibus organa uiuo ad generationem peculiaria
indicantur quae habent ferè in hunc modum.
u,u Meatus urinam è renibus in uesicam deducentes.
x Sinistra seminalis uena.
y Dextra seminalis uena.
z Arteriarum seminalium ortus.
& Sinistrae seminalis uenae cum sinistra arteria congressus.
q Ramuli ad membranas deducti, uenam seminalem & arteriam peritonaeo nectentes.
Sinistrum testem cum tunica adhuc ipsi propria, atque à
peritonaeo pronata, & s,s notata delineauimus: ita tamen
hic est dissecta apertaq;, ut nihil quominus apte cernatur
impediat. imò etiam musculum illi innatum commonstrat,
u. indicatum.
λ Hàc uena & arteria peritonaei amplitudine egreditur.
μ Varicosum corpus, itsaq; adeò uenae arteriae uariaq; mi-
rabilis implicatio.
ν Sinister testis tunica ipsi proxima obtectus.
ξ,ξ Vasis semen deferentis ad testem reuolutio.
π Vasis semen deferentis ascensus ad pubis os.
ρ Sinistri uasis semen deferentis ad pubis ossis posteriora
inflexus.
σ Dextri uasis semen deferentis reflexus.
τ Dextri sinistriq; uasorum semen deferentium coitus.
φ Vasorum semen deferentium insertio.
χ,χ Glandulosum corpus uasorum semen deferentium insertionem excipiens.
ψ,ψ Meatus urinae seminiq; communis.
ω Musculus orbiculatim à ducto ei meatui obductus.
æ,æ Penis, atq; adeò ipsius ipsius corpora.

RI CORPORIS SEDE SVB ILLIS QVI SECVNDAE FIGVRAE SINISTRO LATERE EXPRIMVNTVR
reconditos proponit musculos, dextro quidē latere eos qui primū occur runt, sinistro autē qui sub ipsis adhuc cōduntur, quibus ostendendis
pes & caput humi collocata pariter iuuant. Tres uerò in hac figurae conspicuae cerebri partium imagines inuicē sectionis ordine sub
sequuntur, ac harum prima in integri hominis consistens capite, sinistro lateri secundae figurae capitis succedit, primam autem excipit quae
dextra manu hic cōtinetur: illa quae sinistra complectitur, ultimū locum sibi uendicante.

H TERTIA

TERTIA MVSCVLOS OSTENDENTIVM FIGVRA, PRIMAM ET SECVNDAM SE

QVITVR, MVSCVLOS ILLIS QVOS IPSAE SINISTRIS LATERIBVS REFEREBANT PROXIME
succumbentes, dextro latere in anteriori facie proponens, dein sinistro atere illos referens qui dextri lateris subsunt musculis. praeter linguae & laryngis musculos, & cartilagines hic humi repositas. Cerebri uero partium hic nihil propter capitis in posteriori
reflexum occurrit.

DEXTRI LATERIS CHARActerum Index.

A Palatum sua adhuc obductum tunica.
B Gargareo.
C Tertius inferiorem maxillam mouentium. est enim hic maxil-la ad summum mentum dissecta, & utrinque ad latera ducta.
D Dextra pars inferioris maxillae.
E, F Duo quarti maxillam mouentium musculi uen-tres.
G. G Neruae sedes inter eos uentres consi-stens.
H Laryngis operculum.
I Altera tonsilla.
K Lingua.
L Quintus linguae musculus.
N,N Dexter u referens os ad latera trahentiu.
O Dexter duorum à pectoris osse in scuti imagi-nem exprimentium laryngis cart. lag. nem inser-torum.
P Asperae arteriae caudex.
Q Dexter primi paris dorsum agentium.
R Dexter secundi paris dorsum agentium.
S Portio secundi paris caput mouentium.
T V Portio tertij scapulam mouent:um.
V Series neruorum axillam petentium.
X Pectoris os.
Y, Y Costarum ossa.
g.g Costarum cartilagines.
b,b Intercostalium exteriorum series in ossium interuallis.
i,i Intercostalium exteriorum series in cartila-ginum interuallis.
k,k Secundus thoracem mouentium.
l Cartilaginis in quam pectoris os exacuitur sedes.
m Rectus abdominis musculus a,b,c,d circum-scriptus.
n Vmbilici relicta portio.
o Transuersi abdominis musculi magna portio.
p Seminalia uasa hic iam praesecta.
q Penis corporum hic conspicitur substantia.
r Meatus urinae ac semini communis.
s Septimi brachium mouentium.
t Quintus brachium mouentium.
u Interior scapulae pro-cessus.
x Brachij os.
y Tertius brachium mouentium.
a Quarti brachium mo-uentium insertionis portio.
ß Primus cubitum extendentium.
γ Posterior cubitum flectentium.
δ Primus radium in pronum agentium.
ε Insertio anterioris cubitum extendentium.
ζ Primus radium in supinum ducentium.
η Secundus digitos mouentium, a,b,c circumscriptus.
θ Tertius digitos manus mouentiu, cuius tendo à indicatur.
ι Minor primorum duorum pollicis os flectentium.
λ,μ,ν,ξ Quatuor musculi quatuor digitos pollici adducentes.
π Exterior duorum primum paruu digiti os flectentium.
ρ Ilium ossis spina hic excarnis modo usitur.
σ Portio tertij femur mouentium.
τ Septimi femur mouentium portio.
υ Sexti femur mouentium portio.
φ Octauus femur mouentium.
χ Quinti femur mouentium portio.
ψ Maior exterior ue femoris processus.
ω Septimus tibiam mouentium, d,e,f circumscriptus.
℥ Octauus tibiam mouentiu, d,e,f etiam insignius, magnaq; adhuc portione sub septimo latitans.
ᴦ Tendo noni tibiam mouentium.
Δ,Δ Tibiae ossis excarnis pars.
Θ Decimusquintus digitos pedis mouentium.
Λ Portio septimi pedem mouentium.
Ξ Decimussextus digitos mouentium.
Π Tendo tertij pedem mouentium.
Σ,Σ Quintus pedem mouentium.
Υ Hic tendo primi & secundi pedem mouentium quarto con-nascitur unituraq; musculo, estq; hic praesectus.
Ω Portio secundi pedis digitos mouentium.
ᴣ,ᴣ Portiones sunt transuersorum baru sedium ligamentoru.

SINISTRI LATERIS CHARActerum Index.

A Propago minoris radicis tertij paris neruorum cere-bri, quae cuti frontis offertur.
B Dicta radicis propago, narium amplitudine petens.
C Propago dictae radicis, superiorie accedens maxillae.
D Quarti paris neruorum cerebri series in palatii tunica.
E Maioris tertij paris radicis propago, instar capreoli sinuolata.
F Dictae radicis portio linguam petens.

G Dictae radicis portio inferiori maxillae distributa.
H Dictae iam portionis soboles inferiori labro deprompta. atq; hic notatus sinistru inferioris maxillae pars.
I Portio secundi paris caput mouentium.
K Glandula sinistro lateri laryngis subnata.
L Sinister primi paris caput mouentium.
M Sinister secundi paris caput mouentium.
N Tertius scapulam mouentium.
O Clauicula sinistri lateris.
P Summus humerus.
Q Interior scapulae processus.
R S T Secundus thoracem mouentium.
R Vena ac arteria sinistro pectoris ossi exporrecta.
S Sinistri lateris transuersus abdominis musculus, a,b,c circumscriptus.
V Brachij os hic prorsus nudum conspicitur.
X Primus cubitum extendentium.
Y Primus radium in pronum ducentium.
ſ Secundus radium in pronum agentium.
g Radius.
h Vlna.
i Ligamentum radium ulnae in ibi committens, ubi haec ossa inuicem dehiscunt.
k Tendo primi brachiale mouentium.
l,m,n Tres secundum pollicis internodium flectentes. Qui au-tem hic in uole sunt reliqui, octo illi censentur, quibus pri-ma quatuor digitorum ossa flectuntur.

o,o Transuersa digitorum li-gamenta indicantur, qui-bus primi & secundi digi-tos mouentium tendines ob-ducebantur.
p Septimi femur mouentis porti o.
q Sexti femur mouentis portio.
r,r Pubis os sinistrum.
ſ Nonus femur mouen-tium.
t Exterior maior ue femo-ris processus.
u Octauus tibiam mouen-tium, qui uniuersum quan-si femoris os proxime ambit.
x Portio tendinis septimi femur mouentium.
y Tendo noni tibiam mo-uentium.
z,z Tibiae os.
ᴣ,ᴣ Fibula.
Λ Ligamentum membra-neum fibulam tibiae colli-gans.
ᴥ Septimus pedem mouen-tium.
Ω Octauus pedem mouen-tium. Superior autem pedis sedes omnino iam excarnis est, ipsius q; ossa ligamentis adhuc obducta conspiciuntur.
Posterior tibiae sedes hic dextro cruri respondet.

EORVM QVAE HVMI IACENT characterum Index.

ᴣ Hic linguam cum suis dextri lateris musculis delineauimus, ac & & ſ primum notat, u tertium, ß quintum, s septimum, u nonum.
λ Hic dextrum laryngis latus cum osse u referente, & u notato de-lineatur, & stomachi portione u indicata. ſ musculi ab osse u refe-rente in laryngis operculum inserti.
t Dexter ab osse u referente in primam cartilaginem insertorum.
τ Portio dexter à pectoris osse in primam cartilaginem insertorum.
ε Dexter à stomacho ad primam cartilaginem pertinentium.
ϑ Anterior laryngis sedes, ipsius q; primae cartilaginis imago.
ϕ Laryngis operculum.
x,ϟ x exterior dextri lateris, & interior sinistri lateris quatuor secun-dam cartilaginem primae iungentium.
w,w Posterior facies primae cartilaginis.
2,3 Duo dextri lateris tertiam secundae iungentium.
4 Dexter duorum in basi tertiae cartilaginis positorum.
5 Dexter duorum tertiam primae nectentium. sinistri autem portio
6. 6 insignitur.
7 Hae sigura laryngem totã prostratam, atque à reliquo asperae ar-teriae caudice obstellam ostendit, ut ipsius rimula seu lingula in con-spectum hic ueniat, & notata 8.
9 Secunda laryngis cartilago, ex latere dextro expressa.
10 Tertia cartilago, ex latere quoque dextro delineata.

SECVNDA

REM CORPORIS SEDEM ITA PROPONIT, VT PRIMA ANTERIOREM. IN DEXTRO ENIM LA
tere musculos ostendit cuti subtensos, in sinistro autem latere eos qui   illis sectionis serie subijciuntur. Praeterea caput etiam sectionis ordi
ne primae figurae capiti pulchre succedit.

SINISTRI LATERIS CHARA-
cterum Index.

τ,τ Hic sinistrae cerebri tanta portio ablata est, ut si-
     nistra callosi corporis relicta portione, sinister cerebri
     uentriculus appareat: notatus enim τ & τ cerebri sub-
     stantia.
Δ   Callosi corporis sinistra pars.
•   Sinister cerebri uentriculus dextro omni ex parte re-
     spondens.
Λ   Sinistri uentriculi plexus, extimo foetus inuolucro
     comparatus.
A B Temporalis musculi portio.
C   Masseter, seu maxillam mouentis in altero latere secundus.
D   Iugalis ossis sedes.
E   Portio alterius musculi septimi paris caput mouentium.
F   Alter primi paris caput mouentium.
F,F Alterius secundi paris caput mouentium portio.
G   Scapulam mouentium tertius.
H   Alterius os u referens deorsum ad latera uellentium portio.
I   Clauicula.
K   Alterius secundi paris dorsum mouentium portio.
L   Portio tertij thoracem mouentium, qui figura quinto tho-
     racem mouentium, ac Y notando respondet.
M   Septimus brachium mouentium.
N   Sextus brachium mouentium, a, b, c circumscriptus.
O   Scapulam mouentium quartus, d, e, d, e circumscriptus.
P   Brachium mouentium tertius.
Q   Secundi thoracem mouentium portio.
R   Quarti thoracem mouentium portio.
S   Sexti paris dorsum mouentium alte-
     rius portio.
T   Octaui paris dorsum mouentium al-
     terius portio.
V,V Costarum ossa.
X,X Costarum interualla.
Y   Quintus thoracem mouentium.
f,g Hic portio conspicitur abdominis mu-
     sculi suas fibras oblique sursum exporri-
     gentis, & interdi à transuersis lumborum
     uertebrarum processibus in it unsunctis.
h   Primi cubitum extendentium origo.
i   Secundi cubitum exten-
     dentium origo.
k   Sedis qua duo primi cubi-
     tum extendentium muscu-
     li coëunt.
l   Brachij os.
m   Caput exterius anterio-
     ris cubitum flectentium.
n   Posterioris cubitum fle-
     ctentium portio.
o   Portio primi radium in
     supinum agentium.
p   Tertius brachiale mouen-
     tium, cuius tend nij inser-
     tionem a & b indicant.
q   Secundus radium in supinum agentium.
τ,τ Vlnae os hic nudum conspicitur.
f   Musculus digitos mouentium uigesimus secundus, cuius pars tendinë
     ossi brachialis pollicem sustinenti inserens à insignitur, reliquae ipsius
     partes b & c indicantur.
t   Musculus digitos mouentium uigesimus primus.
u   Digitos mouentium decimusnonus.
x,x Hic brachialis ossa ligamentis obducta oculis subijciuntur, una cum
     postbrachialis ossibus & musculis illorum interualla opplentibus.
     Secundus femur mouentium, a, b, c circumscriptus.
β   Quartus femur mouentium.
γ   Decimus femur mouentium.
δ,ε Duo carneae partes seu musculi, decimum qua hic ad coxendicis os re-
     flectuntur concomitantes.
ζ   Ligamentij ab osse sacro in coxendicis ossis accupuli processij pertinës.
η   Ligamentum ab osse sacro in coxendicis ossis appendicem insertum.
θ   Magnus seu exterior femoris processus.
ι,κ Quintus femur mouentium portio.
λ   Secundus tibiam mouentium.
μ   Tertius tibiam mouentium.
ρ,ρ Quintus tibiam mouentium.
ς   Quartus tibiam mouentium.
σ   Septimus tibiam mouentium.
ω   Primi tibiam mouentium portio.
ϛ   Octaui tibiam mouentium portio.
τ   Tertius pedem mouentium.
υ,υ Musculi in poplite latitantis portio.
φ   Quartus pedem mouentium.
ψ   Hic primi & secundi pedem mouentiü ten-
     do à quarto pedë mouentiij resectus est.
χ   Interior malleolus.
ψ   Septimi pedem mouentium portio.
ω   Octaui pedem mouentium portio.
ϰ   Exterior malleolus.
     I N pedis hic humi prostrato pedis miscetur planta, æ
     x musculum primum notans pedis digitos mouentium.
     n uerò tendinem secundam pollicis os flectentem.

DEXTRI LATERIS CHARA-
cterum Index.

A,A,B Cerebrum sectionis serie à tenui ipsius membrana
       detectum: ac A & A dextrae cerebri partis superfi-
       ciem notans, quae caluariam spectat. B uero eam quae
       sinistram cerebri parte sectionis ordine abscissam re-
       spiciebat.
C   Durae membranae pars, dextram & sinistram cere-
       bri partes mercedens, & ab osseo caluariae osse hic
       dirempta, sursumq; reflexa.
D   Tenuis membrana à cerebro diuulsa.
E,F   Secundus scapulam mouentium, a, b, c, d, e circum-
       scriptus.
G   Secundus brachium mouentium, posteriori sua sede
       hic apparens, & a, b,c circumscriptus.
H   Portio sexti brachium mouentium.
I   Tertij brachium mouentium portio.
K   Quartus brachium mouentium, hic a, b, c circumscriptus.
L   Musculi abdominis oblique deorsum suas exporri-
       gentis fibras portio.
M   Primi cubitum extendentium portio.
N   Secundi cubitum extendentium portio.
O   Posterioris cubitum flectentium portio.
P   Intertium radium in supinum mouentium.
Q   Brachiale mouentium tertius, a, b, c etiam notatus.
R   Excarnis ulnae pars.
S   Decimusseptimus digitos mouentium.
T   Decimusoctauus digitos mouentium.
V,V   Notatur uaria tendinum commixtio ad quatuor di-
       gitorum radices.
X   Quartus brachiale mouentium.
Y   Secundus brachiale mouentium.
f,g,h Musculus digitos mouentium uiges. in musculo-
       rum uetruni f partem notans tendinem ossi; officium
       sustinet in inserentem: g uerò & h partes sunt, ten-
       dines pollici efferentes.
i   Vigesimiprimi digitos mouentium portio.
k   Vigesimus digitos mouentium.
l   Vigesimus quartus digitos mouentium.
m   Secundus femur motorum portio.
       Sextus tibiam mouen-
n   tium, cuius tendo tam te-
       nuis est, ut subiectorum
       musculorum inspectionë
       non praepedias. est enim
       hic a, b sextus tibiam
       mouentium.
o   Primus femur mouen-
       tium, a, b, c, d circum-
       scriptus.
p   Secundi tibiam mouen-
       tium portio.
q   Testis sua obductus tu-
       nica hic propendet.
r   Tertius tibiam mouen-
       tium.
ſ   Quartus tibiam mouentium.
t,t   Quintus tibiam mouentium.
u   Primus pedem mouentium.
x   Secundus pedem mouentium.
y   Tertij pedë mouentiü carnea pars.
z   Septimus pedem mouentium.
ʒ   Octaui pedem mouentium pars.
ꝝ   Excarnis fibulae pars exterior ue
       malleolus.
ɑ   Tendo noni pedem mouentium.
e   Aliquot tendines decimiquarti
       digitos pedis mouentium.
ʒ   Decimusseptimus pedis digitos
       mouentium.

I   PRIMA

PRIMA FIGVRA EARVM QVAS OSTENDENDIS MVSCVLIS POTISSIMVM PA

RAVIMVS, IN CVIVS DEXTRO LATERE MVSCVLI MOX SVB CVTE RECONDITI, ANTERIORI
facie conspiciuntur: in sinistro autem illis resectis obuij sunt, qui in
figura redderetur copiosior, eorum quæ caluaria complectitur ima
characterum index docebit, delineantes.

ginem sectionis ordine proponere incepimus, humi oculi musculos, uti

DEXTRI LATERIS CHARActerum Index.

A,A Dura cerebri membrana ita apparens, uti inter secandum caluariæ superiori parte sectionis ordine ablata, occurrit.

B,B Duræ membranæ uasa secundum ipsius latera uenarum arteriarumque modo digesta.

C,C Tenuis duræ membranæ sinus hic secundum longitudinem adapertus cernitur.

D Circulus iste os est caluariæ.

E Musculosa substantia frontis cutem mouens.

F Palpebram superiorem attollens musculus.

G Musculus eandem palpebram deorsum ducens.

H Hic duo musculi nuper dictis sese contingunt.

I Temporalis musculi sedes.

K Musculus una portione & insignia in nasi alam, altera uerò b indicata in superius labrum insertus.

L Cartilago ab altero nasi osse producta.

M Dextra nasi ala.

N Musculus à malis in superius labrum insertus.

O Musculus ex carnea constitutus membrana, & labra & buccas mouens, et a,b,c,d circumscriptus. uerùm d priuatim sede notæ in altero latere secundi maxillam inferiorem mouentium musculi.

P Brachium mouentium secundus hic anteriori suæ sede a,b,c circumscriptus.

Q Brachij motorum primus, a,b,c,d circumscriptus.

R Portio est quarti brachium mouentii.

S,S Sedes S,S insignita, et inter illos characteres media musculi thoracem mouentium secundi est portio.

T Deorsum oblique in anteriora fibras suas ducens abdominis musculus, a,b,c,d,e circumscriptus.

V Testis una cum seminalibus uasis tunica, quam ipsi peritonæum offert, adhuc obductus.

X Prior cubitum flectentium.

Y,Y Posterior cubitum flectentium.

& Cubiti extendentii primi portio.

b Radium in pronum agentium primus.

i Radium in supinum agentium primus.

h Portio tertij brachiale mouentium.

l Brachiale mouentium primus.

m Latum tendinem sub interna manus cute producens, ac a,b circumscriptus.

n Brachiale mouentium secundus.

o,o,o His interuallis primus digitos mouentiû se offert.

p Digitos mouentium uigesimustertius.

q Portio maioris primum pollicis os flectentium.

r Digitos mouentium uigesimus.

s Penis cute ipsius ut inuolucro circumcisus.

t Primus tibiam mouentium, a,b circumscriptus.

u,x Sextus tibiam mouentium, a,b,c,d circumscriptus.

y Glandulæ in inguine uasorû distributioni præsectæ.

z,a Portio septimi femur mouentium.

a Portio quinti femur mouentium, cui octauus committitur.

b Portio secundi tibiam mouentium, cuius insersio & insignitur tertij autem tibiam agentis insertio d notatur.

y Portio noni tibiam mouentium.

λ Portio octaui tibiæ motorum.

μ,μ Nuda excarniq; tibiæ ossis sedes.

ν Sextus pedem mouentium, a,b circumscriptus.

ξ Portio decimiquinti digitos pedis mouentium.

ο Portio & tendines decimiquarti digitos pedis mouentium.

π Tendo noni pedem mouentis.

ρ,ρ Hæc oblique prorepunt tendines decimisexti digitos mouentium.

σ,σ Ligamentum transuersum in tibiæ anteriori sede positum hic dissectum cernitur: uti & ligamenta internum malleolum & calcem conspicua, & μ notata.

τ Primus pedem mouentium.

υ Tendo tertij pedem mouentium.

φ Portio quarti pedem mouentium.

χ Secundi digitos pedis mouentium portio.

ψ Quinti pedem mouentium portio.

ω Decimusoctauus digitos mouentium.

SINISTRI LATERIS CHARActerum Index.

A,A In hac capitis parte sectionis ordine duram cerebri membranam à tenui remouimus, hicq; tenuis cerebri notatur membrana.

B,B Vasa in tenui membrana ex tertio duræ membranæ sinu depropta.

C Duræ membranæ pars deorsum à tenui reflexa.

D Ductuum instar uenæ ex nasis per duræ membranæ latera excurrentibus in tenuem membranam pertinentium unus.

E Neruus superioris oblatus maxillæ, à minore tertij paris neruorum cerebri radice.

F Musculus in buccis posteus, ac buccas labraq; mouentium in altero latere quartus.

G Labra mouentium tertius.

H Primus ossi u referenti propriorum.

I Septimi paris caput mouentium alter.

K Portio secundi scapulam mouentium.

L Portio tertij scapulam mouentium.

M Alterius, os u referens deorsum in latera trahentium portio.

N Clauicula.

O Primus thoracis motorum.

P,Q Hæc uasorum neruorumq; copia axillam petit.

R,R Pectoris ossis anterior sedes hoc latere detecta cernitur.

R,R Costarum ossa hic quoq; aliqua ex parte nuda usuntur.

S,S Costarum cartilagines.

T,T Intercostalium musculorum exteriorum inter ossa costarum sedem obeuntium imago.

V,V Intercostalium musculorum exteriorum in cartilaginum uterarum costarum interuallis consistentium forma.

X Primus scapulam mouentium, a,b,c circumscriptus.

Y Secundi thoracem mouentis uan portio.

ſ Recti abdominis musculi sursum portio.

g Oblique sursum suas fibras ex dirigens abdominis musculus, a,b,c circumscriptus.

h Vmbilici pars.

i Testis intimo ipsius inuolucro obductus.

k Venæ arteriæq; seminalium antequam testi inseruntur impliciius.

l Vas semen à teste deferens.

m Testis musculus.

n Ligamentum ab interno scapulæ processu ad scapulam pertinens humerum.

o Interior scapulæ processus.

p Primum ligamentum humeri articulo propriorum.

q Brachij os.

r Cubitum flectentium anterior, cuius capita a d b notantur: tendo autem c.

ſ,ſ Cubitum flectentium posterior.

t Cubitum extendentiû primi portio.

u Radium in pronum ducentium primus.

x Radij in supinum motus autorum primus.

y Portio tertij brachiale mouentium.

& Primus digitos manus mouentium, a,b,c,d quatuor ipsius indicantur tendines.

β Secundi digitos mouentium portio.

γ Vlnæ portio.

γ,δ Tertij digitos mouentium portio.

ε Pars uigesimisecundi digitos mouentium, quæ tendinem inserit brachialis ossi pollicem sustinenti.

ζ,κ Duæ portiones sunt alterius uigesimisecundi musculi partis, quæ singule tendinem pollici offerunt.

ζ,θ Ligamentum transuersum in brachialis interna sede positum, hic dissectum uisitur.

ι Maior duorum qui primum pollicis os flectent.

κ,κ Tendines secundi digitos mouentium musculi.

λ Alter est musculus parui digiti primum os flectentium.

μ Ilium os hic excarne est propter oblique descendentem abdominis musculum inibi resectum.

ξ Secundi femur mouentium portio.

ο Septimi femur mouentium portio.

π Sexti femur scapulam mouentium.

ρ Nonus tibiæ motorum.

ς Septimi tibiæ mouentium portio.

τ Quinti femur mouentium portio, cui octauus committitur.

υ Secundus tibiam mouentium, cuius insertionem a notat.

φ Octaui tibiam mouentium portio.

χ Quarti tibiam mouentium portio.

ψ,ψ Excarnis tibiæ ossis pars.

ω Hic sextus pedem mouentium musculus à tibiæ osse est resectus.

α Decimusquartus digitos mouentium, cuius aliquot tendines a,b insigniuntur.

β Digitos mouentium decimusquintus.

γ Nonus pedem mouentium.

δ Sextus pedem mouentium. Reliqua in hoc crure cum dextro construit.

ε Oculus simul cum ipsius musculis adhuc integris à sua sede erutus, hic humi iacet.

ζ Sex primi oculi musculi hic ab exortu ad insertionem usq; sunt liberati.

η septimo in suo loco relicto, es netuo uisorio n in utroq; oculo insignito.

OMNIVM

CHARACTERVM HVIVS OMNIVN
oſsium imaginem oſtendentis figuræ Index.

ETSI in figuris ad præſentem de humani corporis fabrica Epitomen paratis, & ad proportionem uiri mulierisﬃ, quæ modò ſubſequitur, imaginum delineatis, oſſa occurrunt: quum tamen id paſſim fiat, neﬃ eadem figura ſimul omnia commiſſis illis partibus nuda detectaﬃ ſpectentur, non abs re fuerit, in hanc paginam alioqui uacantem, ex primo libro huc imaginem rejicere, quæ ex tribus illic omnia oſſa ſimul exprimentibus figuris, hæc magis & anteriori ac poſteriori ſede proponit. Præterquam quod hæc figura etiam caluariæ, cui ſiniſtra manus incumbit, baſim una eiuſ oſſe u imaginem referente & audius organi oſſiculis ſpectandum offerat. Vti characterum Index modò enarrabit.

A   Suturarum capitis quæ tranſuerſim feruntur anterior, coronalisﬃ dicta.

B   Sedes alterius tranſuerſæ ſuturæ, quæ A imaginem proponit, & à cuius uertice alia ad coronidem, & uerò hinc ad naſi ſummum fertur, quam à recto ductu ſagittalem nuncupamus.

D   In temporibus obuiæ inſtar duæ-um ſquamarum quæ inuicem incumbunt, commiſſuræ, cui ab imagine nomen ind tum eſt. Reliquis uerò caluariæ ſuperioriſﬃ maxillæ ſuturis, quæ nominibus proprijs deſtituuntur, nullus adhibitus eſt character.

ß   Alterum uerticis os.

ß   Frontis os nunquam geminum, niſi quam rariſſimè à coronali ſutuæ medio ad ſummum uſﬃ naſi ſuturæ quæpiam pertingit. In huius baſi in interna caluariæ amplitudine oſſ ſpectabitur, quod capitis octauum appello.

ɣ   Occipitis os, in grandioribus natu ſimiliter unum.

Λ   Dextri temporis os, cuius proceſſus ſtyli aut acus aut galli calcarei imagini comparatus, & inſignitur: is uerò qui uberis papillæ conſertur, ſ inſcriptum oſtendit.

e,n   Hæc caluariæ ſedes ab imagine & duritie quam cum prærupta rupe ſimilem gerit, nomen obtinet, quod permultis temporum duntaxat oſſibus aſcribitur.

E   Os cuneo à diſſectionis proceribus comparatum. Huius proceſſus,
e.   quos alis aſſimilamus, ß inſigniuntur.

F   Hæc caluariæ ſedes duorum oſſium efformatæ proceſſibus, perinde ac ſi peculiare os eſſet, iugale os nominatur. Superioris autem maxillæ oſſa mihi duodenario numero comprehenſa, quin nominibus careat, hæc exigua tabella characteribus non obruenda putaui.

G   Inferior maxilla ſimiliter ac ſuperior ſedecim dentibus ut plurimum decorata.

H   Os u imaginem exprimens, unitatisﬃ nomine, & ſi pluribus conſtet oſſiculis, donatum.

g.ﬆ   E regione dicti oſſis hic iuxta caluariæ baſim duo occurrunt auh'rua organi oſſicula, quorum alterum ﬃ & inſignitum: molari denti duabus talli radicibus donato, uno intendi comparamus: alterum ac'd * radi' catum, malleo cuipiam, aut magna ex parte femoris oſſi.

I,K,L,M,N   Hs characteribus dorſi oſſium ſeu uertebrarum notatur ſeries, quorum ſeptem ab I ad K pertinens collum efformant. duodecim à K ad L numeratæ, thoracem. quinque ab L ad regionem M ſuccedentes, lumbos. à regione M, quo oſſis ſacri in quinta muſculorum tabula apparentis, ſedes indicatur, & N ſacrum os ſex extructum oſſibus conſiſtit, cui coccyx oſ ſubijcitur.

O   Pectoris os pluribus conformatum oſſibus.

P   Mucronata cartilago, in quam pectoris os gladij modo exacuitur.

1,2,3.4.5.6,7,8,9,10,11,12   Numeri characteribus duodecim coſtæ indicantur, quarum ſeptem ſuperiores & uertebris & pectoris oſſi articulantur, hinc ueræ nuncupatæ: inferiores autem quinque ſpuriæ dictæ, ad ſolas uertebras articulationem moliuntur.

Q   Clauicula.

R   Scapula, cuius ſuperior proceſſus, quem ſummum humerum dicimus,
λ,μ.   λ inſignitur: interior autem, qui anchoræ imagini conſertur, μ.

S   Brachij os, multis humerus appellatum.

T,V   AT ad V ſedes metitur, quam cub tum uocamus, duabus conſtructæ oſſibus, quorum longius inferiusﬃ. ac V inſignitum, cubitus priuatim & ulna appellantur. Huius poſterior, iuxta illius cum brachij oſſe articulatione proceſſus u inſignitur. Proceſſus autem illius
ﬅ.   acutus iuxta brachiale conſpicuus, ﬅ inſcribitur. Porrò ſuperius in cu
X.   bto os, radius appellatum, X notatur.

Z   Octo brachialis oſſa, duplici ordine digeſta.

Γ   Quatuor poſtbrachialis oſſa.

Δ   Quindecim digitorum oſſa.

   Hoc charactere ſiniſtrum os totum aut ſacri oſſis lateribus com mittitur obuiam eſt: quod in tres ſedes, perinde ac ſi tribus pecu
e,m.   liaribus oſſibus conſtitueretur, nomine diuidimus, quæ dextrum os
r,t.   characteribus notata refert. e nanﬃ ilium os, n coxendicis, ﬃ pu his indicat, t uerò cartilaginem pub: oſſi coaliti interuenientem.

Λ   Femur, cuius exterior maior'ﬃ rotator τ indicatur, interiori &
τ.   minori interim hic nuſﬃ conſpicuo.

   Os ſcuti patellæﬃ inſtar, genu articulo præpoſitum.

ιι,Σ   Λ ιι ad Σ ſedes metitur, quam tibiam nuncupamus, quæﬃ duobus
ﬁ.   conſtat oſſibus, uno interiori & craſſiori, ac tibia appellato, ac ﬁ in
τ.   ſigno: altero graciliori exteriori, quod τ inſcriptum fibulæ nomen obtinuit.

ﬆ.λ   Inferiorum appendicum oſſium quæ tibiam conſtituunt proceſſus, quos malleolos appellare conſueuimus.

ā   Talus tibiæ ſubditus, calci'ﬃ inſtratus.

ā   Calcis os, tibiæ rectitudinem longè excedens.

b   Os cymbæ imagini à diſſectionum peritis comparatum.

c,c   Quatuor tarſi oſſa, quæ ſingulis characteribus d, e, f, & g in
d,e.   dicentur. ut ſic interiora trìa quæ nominibus carent, ab extimo,
f.g.   quod g inſignitur, & teſſeræ & cubo conſertur, diſtingui queas.

ß   Quinque oſſa tarſum ſequentia, pedionﬃ conſtituentia.

ī   Quatuordecim pedis digitorum oſſa.

Δ   Pluribus locis hæc figura & occurrit, oſſicula indicaturum quæ à ſeſami ſemine nomen inuenerunt.

K   EXTERNA

SOLVITVR OMNE DECVS
LETO, NIVEOSQVE
PER ARTVS
IT STYGIVS COLOR, ET
FORMAE POPVLA-
TVR HONO-
RES.

HIC NON prolixior nominum externas hominis sedes loca'ue indicantium enumeratio inftituitur, quàm cõmodè imaginũ uirilis muliebrisq́ corporis fuperficiè exprimentiũ marginibus adhiberi poteſt. Quanquam fuccinctam eorum deſcriptionem, ac uelut præfentium figurarum indicem duntaxat proponere nihil obſtet, quum eadem ferè nomina externis corporis fedibus ac oſſibus, partibus'que externæ fedi fubditis, accommodentur, quorum præcipua, ab ijsq́ qui rectiùs diſſecandi rationem aggreſſi fuerunt inſtituta, iam prius in orationis contextu, quantum propoſita nobis Epitome requirit, recenſuimus. Solet itaque uniuerſa corporis fuperficies ab illius nominum inſtitutoribus primùm in magnas fedes diuidi, ac dein illarum partes rurſus uarijs nomenclaturis donari. Atque ita Ægyptij medici corpus in ᵃ Caput, ᵇ Thoracem, ᶜ Manus, & ᵈ Crura diuidebant: Thoracem, perinde ac Ariſtoteles, nominantes, uniuerſum corporis truncum, à iugulo aut collo clauiculis ue ad inguina & pubem, aut magis ad femorum uſque fuperiora pertinentem: non autem tantum, ut Galenus, nonnulliſq́ Anatomicorum primarij, corporis fedem coſtis fcptam. Alij facultatum corpus uniuerſum diſpenſantium, animarumq́ fedibus mentem adhibentes, quadrifariam quidem fimiliter ac Ægyptij corporis fuperficiem diſcernunt, uerùm fecus quàm illi corporis truncum in duas fedes primùm diſtinguetes, manus & crura unius partis loco prima hac diuiſione enumerãt, illa quæ ᶠ Artus propriè uocatos conſtituunt, extremorũ nomine complectêtes. Ac in corporis trunco duas præcipuas locant fedes, fecundùm duas cauitates fecantibus inibi obuias: quarum inferior ab elatiori, interuentu fepti tranſuerfi feiũcta, iecur naturalis altricis'ue animæ fedem fanguificationiſq́ officinã, ac inſuper huic fubminiſtrantia organa complectitur, partibus quoque generationi famulantibus parata. Superior cauitas cordi iraſcibilis animæ fomiti uitaliſq́ ſpiritus fonti, illiq́ fubferuientibus organis aſcribitur. Cæterùm tertia corporis cauitas capiti tribuitur, cerebro'que potiſſimùm principis animæ fedi, animaliſ'que ſpiritus promptuario facratur. Corpore in hunc modum obiter diuifo, fingularum partium fuperficies ita rurſus diſtinguĩtur, ut capitis totius pars anterior fupercilijs fuperpoſita, ac ᵍ crinibus nuda, "lineas'que quaſdam proponens, ⁱ Frons nominetur. Hac ſuperior & uerſus capitis medium uergens, ᵏ Sinciput. Vtrinque ad ſincipitis latus, ſupra'que ˡ Aurem, cui ᵐ Auditorius meatus ineſt, conſiſtens, ⁿ Tempus. Media capitis fedes ſinciput uerſus poſteriora fuperans, ⁰ Vertex, qui ueluti centrum eſt ᵖ circuli crinium originem circunſcribentis. Poſt uerticem uſque ad muſculorum qui utrinque in ceruicis ſummo prominentes, in medio foueam oſtendunt, ac pleriſq́ ᑫ Tendines dicuntur, elatiſſimam fedem ʳ Occiput fpectatur. Prior autê capitis pars à frõte ad mentũ uſque protenſa, ˢ Facies. Inferior enim frõtis pars, ᵗ Supercilijs ueluti eminêtibus, piliſq́ cõſitis terminis, eorundemq́ ᵘ medio circunſcribitur. His fubſunt ˣ Oculi, inferiùs & ſuperiùs ʸ Palpebris intecti: quarum fedes ubi inuicem conniuent, & erectis ordinata'que, ut in nauibus remos fpectamus, ſerie poſitis pilis, quos ᶻ Cilia nuncupamus, ornatur, quodammodo'que cartilagineæ ſunt, ᵃ Tarſi habentur. Commiſſionis huius termini, ᵇ Anguli funt: quorum maior naſum, minor tempus fpectat. In diſiunctarum palpebrarum medio præter ᶜ Carunculam in maiori angulo conſpicuam, ᵈ Album candidum'ue oculorum apparet: in cuius medio duo ſe offerunt circuli, quorum amplior ᵉ Iris & Corona eſt, minor ᶠ Pupilla. ᵍ Naſus oculos interiacet, cuius foramina ʰ Nares uocantur: quarum externa latera naſi ⁱ Pinnulis ſeu Alis, interna uerò ᵏ Interfepto naſi conſtituuntur. Sedes ad naſi latera mali in modum prominulæ

minulæ ac rubentes, Malæ, & quibusdam Genæ uocantur. Sedes inter nasum & malas mediæ nonnullis Concaua dicuntur, quo nomine alij totam oculorum sedem à palpebris ad malas metitam uocarunt. Faciei pars quam inflamus Bucca est. tota uerò ipsius pars à superciljs ad elatiorem usque dentium seriem pertinens, Superior maxilla nominatur, reliqua autem quæ in uiris Barba decoratur, Inferior. cuius anterius extremum, Mentum nonnunquam foueâ ornatum educit, sub Labri inferioris rubore consistens. Elatioris labri sedes naso subdita, Sulculoque donata, Mustax censetur. Quod labris circunscribitur & continetur, Os, quo hiante Lingua, Palatū, Gargareon, Dentes, Gingiuæ, internaque Faucium sedes occurrit. Quod caput ad dauiculas usque aut thoracem excipit, Collum & Ceruix est, & si posterius nomen magis posteriori parti accommodetur, uti & anteriorem qua aspera arteria, & potissimùm ipsius caput tangentibus occurrit, Guttur dictam legimus. Humerus ueteribus uocabatur brachij ossis cum scapula articulus, unde & partem maximè ad colli radicem thoracisque latera eminentem, Summum humerum dixerunt. Quod ab illo prorsum uersus Iugulum foueamue in colli radice obuium uergit, Clauicula est. Quod autem ab ipso ad extremā digitorum aciem protenditur, Manus: cuius prima pars (sub qua cauitas Axilla aut Ala appellata, & musculis quos Tendines permulti illic uocant septa, consistit) ad proximum usque articulum Cubitiue flexum producta, Brachium & Latinorum quibusdam Humerus dicitur. Posterior flexus illius sedes Gibberus est. Pars ab hoc ad conterminum articulum ducta, Cubitus, & Latinorum quibusdam Brachium & Vlna. Ad cubiti extremum Summa manus incipit, cuius pars à cubito ad quatuor digitorum radices porrecta, in duas sedes partitur: ac cubito propinquior Brachiale, quæ à constructionis specie cum pectore etiam Pectis, à quibusdam Palma nuncupatur. Huius interior sedes caua ac uarijs monticulis septa, multisque lineis interstincta, Volam efficit. Reliqua summæ manus pars, Digiti sunt, singuli ternis partibus tanquam in acie locatis efformati, & exteriùs Vnguibus ornati. Horum maior alijsque actione oppositus Pollex est, illi proximus Index, dein Medius seu Impudicus, cui proximus est Medicus & Anularis. Extimam uerò sedem occupat Paruus, Auricularis ue. Thoracem hic nominamus corporis trunci partem Costis septam, maximamque sedem Laterum efformantem: cuius anterior sedes Pectus est, quam Mamillæ, atque in illarum medio Papillæ cum obfusco ipsas ambiente circulo occupant. Reliqua anterior trunci sedes Abdomen constituit, cuius regio pectoris ossis cartilagini & costarū cartilaginibus illa humilioribus proxima, perinde Subcartilaginea nuncupatur, ac uiscera cartilaginibus illis complexa. Sic quibus septū transuer-

sum præcordia appellatur, sedes in quam id cartilaginibus inseritur, Præcordiorum nomen obtinuit. quanquam rursus alij ita etiam thoracis anteriorem sedem nuncupent. Quod sub infimis costis & ilium ossis spina (quæ mulieribus multo magis quàm uiris educitur) ossibus destituitur, tangentibusque cedit, Inania sunt & Ilia. in quorū ueluti medio Vmbilicus cernitur, sub quo mox Sumen, cuius infima sedes trunci termino proxima, Aqualiculus nuncupatur. Terminus autem ubi hic Pudenda & Naturalia consistunt, Pubes est & Pecten, ad cuius latera in femorum flexu Inguina recensemus. Maris pudendi pars citra sectionem conspicua, Penis & Coles uocatur: cuius summitas magis quàm reliqua longitudo crassesces, Glandem efformat, in cuius medio meatus urinæ seminique conspicitur. Huius inuolucrum Præputium est, licet alijs tota penis summitas ita nuncupatur. In inuolucro reliquaque ad anum cute protuberante suturæ modo lineam uocamus Suturam, & totam hāc exporrectam extuberantemque ad anum usque penis partem Taurum. Vti & sedem inter testium inuolucrum (quod ex cute paratum Scortum dicitur) & anum conspicuam, Interfeminium nuncupamus. Muliebris pudendi rima, quæ uteri ceruicis est orificium, Sinus uocatur, quem Alæ & Colles utrinque prominentes, & cuticularis in ipsius summo apparens caro ornant. Recti intestini orificium per sedem prodiens, à figura Anulus, & ab officio Strictior appellatur. Posterior trunci corporis pars, Dorsum aut Tergum ferè nuncupatur, cuius latera in elatiori posteriori que thoracis sede Scapulis constituunt. Inter ipsas uerò mediū & dorsi sedes hinc ad infimas usque costas, aut ubi id maximè in flexu protuberat, pertinens, thoraci ascribit, ac post septum transuersum consistit. Sedes uerò hanc à nates usque sequens, Lumbos complectitur. Sunt autē Nates carneæ & globosæ sedes, iliū ossiū occupātes dorsum, in quarum medio sacri ossis & coccygis posteriores processus uelut excarnes ad anū usque occurrunt. Vbi articulus femoris percipitur, magnusque Rotator extuberat, Coxendix est, aut Coxa, quod nomen alij Femorique ascribunt, ab inguinibus ad Genu pertinenti: cuius posterior sedes & flexus Poples nuncupatur. Genu ad proximum usque articulum pedis ue initiū Tibia subsequitur, quæ nōnullis Crus nominatur, & si plures ad nomen simul tibiæ femorisque uelint esse cōmune. Anterior tibiæ sedes ossea tangētibus occurrit, posterior autē ubi ipsius Venter seu Sura cernitur, carneā. Tubera ad tibiæ imū utrinque uelut ossea tangētibus obuia, Malleoli, neutiquā uerò Talus illis exceptus reconditusque nominatur. Postica pedis pars extra tibię rectitudinem retrorsum prominens, Calx appellatur. Reliquæ uerò pedis superficiariæ sedes prorsus ossium nomenclatura assumunt, potissimū autē Tarsi, Pedij seu Pectoris, quod

digiti hic etiam unguibus ornati sequuntur. Quanquā ubi de integro pede sermo instituitur, infima sedes qua calcamus plerunque Planta, & Vestigium, ipsiusque internū latus Concauū, superior uerò Tarsus nuncupetur.

L   FIGVRAE

FIGVRAE AD PROXIMAM PAGINAM AGGLVTINATAE,

MVLTISQVE PARTIBVS EXTRVCTAE,

characterum Index.

QVONIAM figura hic è regione à capite ad proximã paginam glutinata, ac omnẽ uenarum arteriarumq́ seriem una cum organis tunica costas succingente & peritonæo obductis cõmonstrans, pluribus insignienda uenis characteribus, non abs re fuerit, primùm præcipuas ipsius partes maiusculis Latinis literis indicare, ac deinsingula uti casus offeret, alijs characteribus exprimere.

A,A,A Septum transuersum hic conspicitur, quà à costarum et pectoris ossi cartilaginibus rescissum est, & in qua à liceris & lienis posteriora subit.

B Cordis inuoluori est portio inibi relicta, quà id se pro magna amplitudine continuabat.

C Cor tam aptè atq́ hac simplici figura licuit in sua sede expressum, & sua uasa aures quæ ostendens. Huic cordis figuræ aliæ subiectissimu, quæ ipsius uentriculos, orificia, & ipsis præsecta ostendissent membranas, si modò id una atq́ altera chartula fieri potuisset.

D,D,D,D Pulmonis quatuor notentur lobi seu fibræ. Verùm ut cor manifestius unica hac figura pingeretur, thoracem interseptentes membranas emisimus, ac pulmonem uelut in latera recidentem delineauimus.

E Asperæ arteriæ caudex simul cum larynge, ipsíq́ annexis glandibus.

F,F Iecoris gibbi magna superficies, tota enim caua iecoris sedes sub hac, atque adeò uentriculo delineatur.

G,G,G G priuatim insignita.

H

I Bilem flauam excipiens uesicula.

I Ventriculus suis uasis ac neruis, & deinstomacho & superiori membranæ omenti, & inferioris etiam humiliori portione ornatur.

K Superior omenti membrana.

L Inferioris membranæ omenti portio, quæ uelut à colo intestino initium ducit.

M Intestina ad unum omnia.

N,N Inferioris omenti membranæ portio uentriculo subdita, & colum intestinum qua uentriculo exporrigitur, dorso colligans: atq́ hic organorum per ipsam distributorum delineatur series, & uasorum distributio per mesenterium in intestina excurrens.

O Lien è caua ipsius facie potissimum expressus.

P Dexter ren.

Q Sinister ren.

R Vterus simul cum suis testibus uasísq́ delineatus.

S Mulieris uesica simul cum meatuum urinæ à renibus deferentium portione, ac dein cum umbilici uasis expressa. Verùm animum modò adhibe notis supra septum positis.

T Venæ caudex, quà inter cor & iecur consistit.

V,X Cordis basis, atq́ adeò uasa id coronantem uisu succingentia.

Y Cordis mucro.

Z Venæ sunt & arteriæ per cordis corpus digestæ.

a Sedes, qua caua caudex in cordis dextrum sinum dehiscit.

b Dextra cerebri auricula.

c Sinistra auriculæ apex.

d Venæ arterialis caudex. Venalis autem arteriæ initium quia in sinistro cordis latere: ut hic cauæ orificium in dextro consistit, conspici hac figura nequit. Notans tamen e & e uenalis arteriæ & uenæ arterialis in dextrum pulmonis partem progressū, nondum pulmonis substantia undique circundatos.

f Magnæ arteriæ caudex.

g Magnæ arteriæ truncus, partes cordi subditas petens.

h Superior & pectus magnæ arteriæ trunci portio, sinistro brachio potissimum obsita.

i Dicti modò trunci insignior portio, atque adeò ipsius in duos impares ramos distributio, quorum

k alter sinistra est soporalis k notata grandior ueró dextram formas soporalem l insignium, & arteriam potissimùm in dextrū brachium excurrentem, & m notatam.

m

n,n Hæc excurrens septi transuersi nerui, quorum initium in figura cuiusa cuius indicem prosequimur firmatur, P insignietur.

o Venæ paris destitutæ initium, ipsius uerò seriei in præsentis figuræ tergo sit conspicuæ.

p Cauæ in iugulo bipartitò, ac utrinque ad p latera exortus apparens uentriculo ad p latera proprium, ad eius umbilici usque regionem excurrentium. Harum altera simul cum comige sibi arteria, q & u insignia, in uno latere & notatur.

q

u Venæ superior aliquot costarum interualla & deuniens initium.

ſſ Vena per transuersos ceruicis uertebrarum processus caluarium petens, atque in secundum duæ membranæ sinum simul cum coniuge arteria absumpta.

t,t. Notatur enim primus sinus t, t. Secundus x,x-y. dus u, u.tertius x, x. quarti initium y.

u,u.

x,x-y.

v Axillam petens uena, quæ in sinistro latere humeraria à indicatam promit. In dextro autem latere illius inutili sit uelut à externa pendet iugulari.

q,q Hic abrruscæ propagnant illæ sunt, quæ ab axillam petenae uenæ in thoracis anteriora, posteriora & latera digeruntur.

ſſ.ſ Vena ab umbilico in iecur exporrecta.

ſſ.ſ Vmbilici portio.

ſſ.ſ Meatus urinam fœtus inter secundum ipsius inuolucrum & intimum deferens.

u,u,u,u Arteriæ fœtui peculiares.

x Vesicæ ceruix.

x Vesicæ ceruicis musculus.

a,a Superius uentriculi orificium, cui stomachus à tergo agglutinata figuræ continuatur, atque hic etiam notatur uena & arteriæ coronæ modoid orificium succingens.

β Stomachi initium cui consilile adhuc affirmatur.

ɣ Inflexus stomachi ad dextrum latus, illisíq́ peculiares glandes.

δ Neruorum sexti paris ad stomachum series.

ɛ Inferius uentriculi orificium, & neruus ab elatiori orificio uentriculi ad inferius excurrens. Verùm neruus ille iecur adiens, in iecoris cauo etiam ε in dicatur.

ʒ Inferius uentriculi orificium, & duodeni intestini initium.

η,η Venæ & arteriæ huc ab illis deductæ, quæ lienis cauo continuantur.

θ,θ Vasa dextram sedem fundi uentriculi implicantes.

ι,ι Vasa sinistram sedem fundi uentriculi inexpensia, & superiori membranæ omenti, ut & nuper dicta uasæ, surculos deprouentia.

λ,λ Musculus rectum intestinū orbiculatim ambis.

λ,λ Musculi rectum intestinum post egestionem sursum trahentes.

μ Sedes qua colum intestinum recto continuatur, atque ideo interuallum à μ ad μ rectum est intestinum.

ν,ν,ν Colum intestinum.

ξ,ξ,ξ Cæcum intestinum.

ο,ο,ο Omnes isti anfractus ilei seu uoluuli, intestini ieiuni censentur.

π,π À π usque ad π duodeni intestini maxima est portio.

ρ Glandium duodeno intestino, ut & ieiuni initio adnatum.

σ,σ Meatus bilis uesiculæ duodeno insertus.

τ Venæ portæ caudex.

υ Iecori insitæ arteriæ & neruus quoq́ illi exporrectus arteriæ.

φ Bilis uesiculam adiens arteria & neruus.

χ Venæ bilis uesiculam adeuntes.

ψ Venæ iter arteria posteriorem uentriculi sedem iuxta ipsius inferius orificium accedentes.

ω Venæ & arteriæ, dextram fundi uentriculi sedem implicantes.

b Minor portæ maximè distributionis truncus.

c Grandior truncus maximè partitionis uenæ portæ.

d Venæ & arteriæ duodeno intestino potissimùm exporrectæ, & ipsis astenso corpore glanduloso suffultæ.

e,e Venæ cum coniuge arteria dextram sedem adiens inferioris membranæ omenti.

ſſ Radix arteriæ in iecur, uentriculum, lienem & omentum, & b lis uesiculam digesta.

g Venæ cum coniuge arteria superius uentriculi orificium corona modo tandem cingens, atque in uentriculi figura inter ɣ & α occurrens.

h Venæ & arteriæ præcipuam inferioris membranæ omenti sedem petens, & colon qua uentriculo exporrigitur implicans.

k Glandulosum corpus uasorum distributioni hic præsidium.

k Inferioris omenti membranæ sinistram sedem accedens uena.

l,l Vasorum series ad lienem.

m,m Vasa ab illis quæ lieni inseruunt sinistram uentriculi sedem adeuntia. Verùm præcipua m indicantur, quæ sinistram sedem fundi uentriculi implicant.

o,o,o Series est uenarum & item arteriarum intestinis propriarum.

p Radix præcipuæ arteriæ intestina petentis.

q,q Minor arteriæ intestinis propria.

r,r Glandulæ in mesenterio positæ, & nuper narratos uasorum diductus corroborantes.

ſſ Foramen septi transuersi stomachum transmit

o Surculus communis internam manus adiens sedem, & hic alijs commixtus ramulis.

o Axillaris ramus ulnæ exporrectus, uariéq́ in cutem dissectus, & suo extremo cum quodam humerariæ ramo coiens, ubi η posuimus.

q,q Series uenarum internam cubiti cutem & uolam implicantium.

u Vmbilici portio.

Venæ per transuersos ceruicis uertebrarum *(column headings continue)*

teus, atq́ adeò sinus iecoris stomacho cedens.

I Iecoris ligamentum, quo sinistra ipsius pars septo nectitur.

M Magna arteria septum permeans, atq́ adeò ipsius ramus in dextram septi partem excurrens.

n Cauæ uenæ caudex.

y Venæ sinistri renis pinguem arteriam tunicam.

y Venæ & arteriæ reni dextro oblatæ.

y Venæ dextri renis pinguem tunicam arteriæ.

ς Sinistrum renem accedens uena & arteria.

τ Sinistra seminalis uena.

v Dextra seminalis uena.

ν., Arteriarum seminalium ortus.

χ. Sinistræ seminalis uenæ & arteriæ congressus.

ψ. Ramuli à uena & arteria in membranam excurrentes, quá peritonæo committuntur.

ω. Portio uenæ & arteriæ testem adeuntium, superiorem fundi uteri sedem petens.

λ Commixtio uenæ & arteriæ seminalium, quæ instar pyramidis est, & uaricибus assimilatur.

λ Testis sinister.

μ,μ Vas semen à teste in uterum deferens.

ν Obtusus uteri fundi angulus, in quem uas semen deferens inferiorem molitur.

ξ Hac sede fun.us uteri in ceruicem terminatur, bacq́ regione ipsius consistit orificium.

ο Vteri ceruix.

π Hic uesicæ ceruix in uteri ceruicem producitur ac desinit.

ρ Vasa sunt inferiorem uteri fundi sedem & ceruicem implicantia.

τ,τ Cutis uteri oris colliculi.

υ,υ Meatus urinam è renibus in uesicam deducentes.

χ Venæ & arteriæ lumborum uertebris ipsísq́ adnatis musculis, & abdominis lateribus exporrectæ.

ψ Venæ cauæ & arteriæ super os sacrum partitio.

c,c Arteriolæ sunt sacri ossi foramina petentes.

d Sinistri partitionis dictæ trunci diuisio.

f Interiorum rami dictæ diuisionis propago, nates & coxendicis ossi adnexæ petens.

f Dicti rami propago tandem uesicæ & utero digesta.

g Pars est arteriæ fœtui peculiaris, quam antea ad uesicæ latera u, ut & hic quoque in maiori figuræ u portione, notauimus.

h Portiuncula exterioris rami dictæ uenæ diuisionis ad reliquam accedens interioris rami.

i Reliquum interioris rami per pubis ossi forame in musculos interiorem uertebris ipsísq́ adnatis musculis, & abdominis lateribus exporrectæ.

k Sedes quæ soboles dicti reliqui alteri uenæ commiscetur. Verùm hic ex tabula promptè animaduertis, quando & arteriæ subdiuidendum est, quum scilicet uenæ arteriam attendi cernis.

l Exterioris rami propago, abdominis inferiorem sedem ab umbilico usq́ perrepens.

m,m Venæ fer femoris & tibiæ interiorem sub cute ad digitos usque pedis distributæ, & in progressu uarios lienes surculos.

n Coxendicis exteriora petens, sub cute tamen.

o Musculos in cutem femoris exteriorem sedem occupantes intertexens.

p Musculi anteriorem sedem femoris occupantibus digesta.

q Dictæ modo uenæ congressus cum ea quæ per pubis ossi foramen femur adit.

r Hac præcipua femur petens uena secundum femoris os reflectitur.

s,t Propagines musculos posteriorem femoris sedem occupantes, & cutem huius sedis ad suram usque accedentes.

x Diuisio in poplite, atque adeò rami in musculos à femoris capitibus hic pronascentes distributi.

z Maioris dictæ diuisionis trunci ramus, externam tibiæ cutem ad summum usq́ pedem implicans.

y Venæ & arteriæ quanquam ist non addituum op or tuis: fibulæ exporrectæ, ac inter musculos latitas.

z Maioris dictæ diuisionis trunci ramus, cutem internam tibiæ sedem integentem, ad digitos usque uarié subiens.

β Ramus dicti trunci seram ad calcem usq́ petens.

γ Propago grandioris trunci inter musculos tibiæ anteriorem sedem occupantes, ad pedís usq́ superiora & digitos digesta.

δ Trunci grandioris reliquum inter musculos posteriorem tibiæ sedem sibi continuatos deorsum repens, & inter x biam & calcem pedem subiens, ramulos digitorum inferiori sedis communicans.

VENARVM

VENARVM, ARTERIARVM, NERVORVMQVE OMNIVM INTEGRA DELINEATIO,

SIMVL CVM NVTRITIONIS QVAE CIBO POTVQVE FIT ORGANORVM, ET CORDIS PVLMONIS'QVE
ac demum muliebrium generationi subseruientium instrumento-
rum imaginibus.

FIGVRAE HVIC CHARTAE IMPRESSAE,
cuíq́; alia agglutinatur, ac quæ peculiariter neruis ostendendis parata est, characterum Index.

CEREBRVM uná cum cerebello cerebríq́; exoríbus eum in modum hic
delineauimus, quasi à caluaria enudatum in ipsius basita conspiceretur, ut appar-
ret si quis erectus caput in posteriora quàm maximè flecteret, sursúm retrorsúmq́;
oculos acturus. Cæterùm quoniam utríusq́; lateris eadem neruorum in præsenti figura est natos, suffecerit uni tantùm lateris characteres adhibere.

A,B,C Cerebri ex altero latere basis notatur, ac A indicat partem ipsius ad neruís sim
mùm prominulam, nonnullísq́; mamillarem processum nuncupatam. B uerò cerebri
partem insinuat, amplum caluariæ sinum subeuntem, qui ad latus sinus consistit, quo
glans cerebri pituitam excipiens reponitur. C autem maximè posti
cam cerebri sedem notat.

D,D Cerebellum.

E Sinister cerebri processus, organo olfactus subministrans.

F Nerui uisorij sinistri ortus.

G Neruorum uisoriorum coitus.

H Tunica, in quam uisorius neruus exoluitur, degenerat ue.

I Secundum neruorum cerebri par.

K,K Minor radix tertij paris.

L Crassior radix tertij paris.

M Quartum par.

N,O Quinti paris gracilior radix.

O Quinti paris insignior radix.

P Membrana, in quam quintum par in auditus organo præcipuè
exoluitur.

Q,R Maioris quinti paris nedicis propagines, quorum hæc per cæ
cum elabitur soramen, illa uerò per aliud sibi proprium.

S Sextum neruorum par.

T Sept:mum neruorum cerebri par. atq́; horum neruorú progressú
hic non delineari potuere, quamuis interim magna ex parte in alijs
huius compendij figuris passim, præcipuè uerò in huic superposita,
& tertia ad muscutos ostendendos præcipuè paratauí occurrant.

V Dorsalis medullæ ex cerebri basis medio initium.

O Dorsal:s medullæ sedes qua caluariam egreditur.

1,1,&c Numcri characteres septem ceruicis, duodecim thoracis,
quinq́; lumborum, & sex sacri ossis indicat uertebras, atq́; aceò uir-
ginea neruorum à dorsali medulla prosilientium paria, quorum se-
rient quàm potui accuratè stimé & simplicissimè in hac tabella meo
w.xrtè delineata expressi. Verùm quia hic locus exiguam characterum declarationem admitit, non omnes neruorum soboles literis
insignimus sum.

P Septi transtuersi, si, sinister neruus, quem citra aliam characterum
operam ex quarti, quinti & sexti parium propaginibus effomari
conspicis. promptum enim est delineationem intelligere, si prius de-
scripta neruorum series hic picturæ accommodetur.

Q Neruus à quinto pari cui summum humerum inuestienti, & dein
musculo brachium mouenti præcipuè distribuitur.

R Primus brachij neruus, ipsiúsq́; propagines hic in cute excurrétes.

S Secundus br.ch: neruus, ipsiúsq́; in anteriorem cubitum flectentium musculum soboles.

T Tertius brachij neruus, ipsíeq́; propago cuti anteriorem brachij
sedem induranti oblata.

V Tertij nerui propago à musculum posteriore cubiti flectenti.

X Secundí nerui portio se retum accedens.

Y Ramus secundi caput adiens longioris radium in pronum mouentis musculi.

Z Secundi distributio in duos impares ramos.

a Minor ramus secundum radium cuti & pollicé usq́; exporrectus.

b Crass:or ramus mox in duas propagines diuisus, quarum series in
conspicuo est.

c Tertij nerui soboles :n musculos internam cubiti sedem occupantes digestæ.

d Tertij ramus radio exporrectus, ac dein pollici & indici & medio
surculos offerens.

e,e Quartus brachij neruus-atq́; inferius & ramos notat musculis cu
brum extendentibus deprompstos.

f Qu.rti ramus internam brachij cutem adiens.

g Quarti ramus externam & posteriorem brachij accedens cutem.

h,b Qu:rti ramus cuti externæ cubiti digestus.

i Qu:rti præcipua distributio ad ingressum cubiti.

k,k Qu:rti ramus radio exporrectus, & externæ sedi pollicis, indicis,
& medij soboles offerens.

l,l Qu:rti nerui ulnæ exporrectus, & musculis atr externæ ipsius sede initium ducentibus ramulos exhibens, ac ante bruchiale cessans.

m Quintus brachij neruus.

n Quinti nerui series in musculos ab interno brachij ossis tubere pro
natos.

o,o Quinti nerui ramus ulnæ exporrectus, & internæ sedi parui digiti
& anularis, aliquando & medij ramusculos dispergens.

p Dicti modò rami soboles in externam manus sedem reflexæ, ac externæ parui digiti sedi & anularis & medij surculos dispersans.

M Sextus brachij neruus, ipsiúsq́; sub cute tantú duclá series . Quis
uerò brachij neruorum sit exortus, principiorum que plexus, ab :sq́;
notis promptè dignoscitur.

7,7,7 Nerui sunt intercostales, illic precisi, quà cum costis entror-
sum resleciuntur.

s,s Rami in posteriora deducti, hic etiam undiq́; obuij.

t,t Huiusmodi serie nerui musculos adeunt thoracis ossibus insertos.

u,u Propagines indicantur sexti paris neruorum cerebri ramum co-
statuum sacibus exporrectum augentes.

x,x Propagines neruorum ex lumborum uertebris exilientium, quæ ab
dominis & huius sedis musculis & cuti dispensantur.

y Neruulus restem frequenter petens, hicq́; resectus.

z Propagines sextum femur mouentium adeuntes musculum.

σ Primus femur petens neruus.

---

a Primi nerui propago cuti oblate.

β Primi nerui propago alijus inter musculos absumpta.

γ Secundus femur petens neruus.

Δ,Δ Secundi nerui soboles per internam femoris &
tibiæ sedem ad pedis usq́; superiora sub cute excurrentes.

e Secundi nerui propago musculus anteriorem fe
moris sedem occupantibus deprompta.

ʒ Tertius femoris neruus.

η Tertij propago, internam femoris cutem implicans.

θ Tertij propago musculos adiens.

ι,ι Quartus femoris neruus, cuius exortus æquè
atq́; trium superiorum est conspicuus.

κ,κ Series anteriorum propaginum inferiorum pa
rium à sacro ossé prodeuntium.

λ Dorsalis medullæ extremum.

μ Quarti femur petentis nerui propagines ad ca
pita musculorum à coxendicis ossis appendice
prodeuntium sparsæ.

ν Quarti nerui soboles in posteriorè femoris cuté
ad medium usq́; longitudinis femoris excurrés.

ξ Propago præcipua in quartam tibiam mouentium musculum, ac dein in reliquam posteriorem
femoris cutem iuxta genu digesta.

ο Soboles in musculos ab inferioribus femoris ca
pitibus pronatos.

π,π Quarti nerui in duos truncos distributio. ac m
quidem minorem, ϱ uerò insigniorem notat.

ς Minoris trunci propago, externæ tibiæ cuti
ad parui digiti usq́; extremum diffusa.

τ Propago fibulæ inter musculos exporrecta.

υ Ramulus anteriorem & cutem:implicans.

φ,φ Grandioris trunci ramus internæ cutis:tibiæ ad
pollicem usq́; digestus.

χ Grandioris trunci ramus, posteriori tibiæ seu
suræ cuti exporrectus.

ψ Grandioris trunci ramus, ligamenti penetrás
sibulam tibiæ quà hæc ossi inuicé dehiscunt cō-
mittens, ac dein ad digitorum usq́; superiora
excurrens.

ω Præcipua grandioris trunci portio, inter tibiæ
os & suram pedis inferiora petens, singulísq́;
digitis surculos offerens.

FINIS.

Prima columna in E, uersu 17. lege, promit 1 col. F, uersu 11. glandula nucis pineæ
instar effigiata 2 col. in G, uersu 9. perficiuntur.

SERIES CHARTARVM.

A B C D E F G H I K L M, præter duas chartas nullo
charactere insignitas: è quarum una figuram parare licebit, figuræ in pagina secunda folij G depictæ agglutinandæ. ex altera uerò, figura parabitur, ad figuram quæ huic:paginæ impressa est,
figenda . Reliqua uerò duodecim folia ex cuiusque arbitratu
sunt inuicem nectenda: quáuis magis conueniat A cum M, &
B cum L, & C cum K, & ita deinceps iungere, ut uniuersa Epi
tome quodammodo sexternione constituat, modò in
libri formam hæc concinnare lubeat.

BASILEAE, EX OFFICINA
Ioannis Oporini, Anno M D XLIII.
Mense Iunio.

M

SEXTA.

PRIMA.

DVODECIMA.

SEPTIMA.

SECVNDA.

OCTAVA.

TERTIA.

QVINTA.

QVARTA.

VNDECIMA.

NONA.

DECIMA.

DECIMA.

AD figuram neruorum seriem in ultima totius Epitomes charta proponentem, figuræ multis extructa partibus glutinatur, quæ præter uenarum arteriarumq; seriem, & nutritionis quæ cibo potuq; fit organorum, & corpartiumq; ipsi submisstrentium imagines, generationis in mulieribus instrumenta proponit. Verum quia uiri alicubi spectanda erant, præsentéq; chartam parauimus, quæ ab illa quæ figuram ultimæ chartæ committendam continet, nulla ex parte differt, præterquam in generationis organis. Licet itaque pleræque in hac charta impressæ figuræ illis respondeant quæ in nuperdicta proponuntur charta, neutiquam obsueit, ex his omnibus unam parare tabulam, quam quintæ musculorum figuræ affiges. Toti itaque chartæ membranam subglutinabis, omnesq; figuras a superflua papyro circumscindes, nisi quod in prima quæ cæterarum est præcipua, ac uelut aliarum basis, supra caput portiunculam seruari conuenit, a qua tota agglutinata pendeat. Dein u:næ ac arteriæ ad u:sicam & pudenda excurrientes, ab abundanti papyro non sunt resecandæ, ut QVARTA figuræ quæ intestina proponit ipsi conglutinari illic queat, ubi inscriptú habet nisi fortè illam SECVNDAE (quæ uentriculum, stomachum & o mext: superiorem membranam proponit) tergo iungere uelles, ut utriusque figuræ respondent. TERTIA humilioris membranæ, quæ sub coli intestini parte uentriculo exporrecta consistit, omensi posteriorem faciem ostendens, ad secundam ita nectetur, ut K opponatur L, ac sacculi imago consurgat. Nunc secundam ad primam nexuris, in septo transuersali occurrit, securaq; stomacho cedit, suramen molieris, per quod stomachum ita traijcies, ut essere arteria succumbat, nexusq; ad foraminis tergum fiat. QVINTA humiliorus membrane omensi portionem uentriculi posteriori sedi subditam cum liene & portæ uenæ illic que arterijs distributione commonstrans, cauæ iecoris sedi in prima figura glutinabit, ubi in ambabus figuris v, φ, & x occurrunt. SEXTA, quæ meatum urinam à renibus uesicam deferentili portionem exprimit, & seminalium uasorum cum testibesq; tsoruni inuolucris cõmonstrat, illic primæ est iungenda, ubi unæ & arteriæ seminales urinaevijs meatibus incumbere uidentur, aut ubi in sinistro latere in utraque figura x spectabitur.
SEPTIMA figura inferiorem penis corporú sedem & meatum urinæ seminisq; communem cum ipsum ambiente musculo ostendens, ex proportione sub octaua est conglut:náda, ut x, z, 4, u muicè respondeant. OCTAVA autem uesicam, umbilicum, cum ipsius uasis & glandulose corpore uesicæ ceruici adnato & pene commonstrans, ad sextam illic est committenda ubi φ spectatur, ut scilicet φ septimæ figuræ ad φ sextæ committatur, ac dein penem inslar 8 literæ complectis. NONA poruionem gibbæ sedis iecoris proponens, non muxisier ueluti ex puncto illic glutinabitur, ubi A inter φ & F maioris seu primæ figuræ consistit. DECIMA, quæ uenæ pari cauentis d:stributionem proponit, magnæ figuræ tergo illic uenit committenda, ubi cauæ caudex eam uenam promit, ac o in utrisq; figuris scriptum spectatur. VNDECIMA, ubi à redundanti papyro circumcisa erit, duas partes constituet, quarum superior uenam arteriamq; dextri lateris exprimit, sub pectoris osse superiorem abdominis sedem petentes. Huius itaque partis q ad magnæ figuræ q figitur, & x ad renum qui ad dextrum latus ç & m in magna figura occurrit. Cæterúm humilior pars uenam arteriamq; exprimens, quæ inferiorem abdominis sedem explicant, illic est iungende, ubi earum radices iuxta l in dextro latere spectatur.
Figuræ quæ DVODECIMA inscribitur, & si huic chartæ impressa sit, non ad primam figuram est committenda, ueram ad illam quæ quinta musculorum tabula uocatur. Hic enim pubis ossium anterior sedes cum cartilagine ossium illorum coalitum interuenientes, delineatur. Qui autem glutinanda sit, prompt:ssimè obseruabis, quum illam à superflua charta recisam, altera ex parte quintæ musculorum tabulæ committere studebis, ubi pubis ossa ab illa uides adempta.

OMNES figuræ hac charta impreſſæ ſimul ad unam ſpectas, quæ ex capite, aut uterm commodius duxeris, illi figuræ agglutinada uenit, quæ neruorû ſeriè proponit, ac in folio in inſcripto, ſeu omniû ultimo ſpectatur. Quod eos admonitos uoluimus, qui in imbutata incude exemplaria, ſuoq marte ac induſtria hæc ſibi concinnabunt: in quo opere tum in glutinando & ſingulis à ſuperflua papyro reſcindendis, tum coloribus ſi uſum erit adhibendis, quiſque quemuis uolet praeſtabit. Dein ut robori conſulatur, toti huic chartæ non inutiliter membrana ſubglutinabitur, priuſquam totæ charta in tot fruſta quot figuras complectitur, diuidatur, quibus numerum in hoc aſcribam, ut quo quæq loco committenda ſit, explicem, quantumq in me eſt ſtudioſorum labori conſulam.

PRIMAM ceterorum precibuam, ac uelut aliarum omniû baſim ex figure nudam muleriſ imaginem exprimentis proportione, ui & ceteras omnes hic obuias delineauimus, quæ primam umlecunq in amb tu proxime ad delineationem à re ligua chartæ eſt reſcindenda, interim latiuſcula reſeruata in capitis uertice portione, à qua poſtmodum glutinari queas, ſimilaſque reliquæ partes ipſ fuerint commiſſæ.

SECVNDAE figuræ ſtomachum & anteriorem uentriculi ſedem ſimul cum ſuperiori mē brana omenti, harumq partium uaſis & nerui proponent, aliquot aliæ. priuſquam primæ committatur, ueniunt agglutinandæ. TERTIA enim, quæ poſteriorem regonem exprimit, tot ut inferioris membranæ ſedis quæ ſub colo inteſtino conſiſtit, quâ id uentriculi exoritur tur, ita ex proportione ſuperiori membranæ omenti glutinanda eſt, ut omentum ſacculi imaginem referat.

QVARTA dein, quæ inteſtinorum imaginem ſpectandam offert, tertiæ figuræ tergo ea ſede eſt committenda, quâ inferius uentriculi orificium inteſtinorum principio continuatur. Sedem hanc im ſecunda figura et quarta poſiti indicant. Quum tamen quartæ committis, conduxerit utrinq ad latera chartæ portionem aſſeruare, illamq tertiæ figuræ, ut quarta ualidius hæreat, agglutinare.

Nunc ſecunda & prime nexurus, tranſuerſam ſectio në in binis imbit duces, ubi ſi n hum or lēget tranſuerſa ſede occurrit, iecoris ſinili indicans. quo id ſtomacho hac tranſeunti cede. Per hoc ſorius ſtomachum ita traſmittes, quæ aſperæ arteriæ ſubijciatur, uentriculuq ſuæ ſede conſiſtat. Nexum neruis ad prime figure tergum iuxta nuper dictum foramen molirus.

QVINTA figura inferioris omentimē branæ tot onem exp u mit, quæ poſteriori uentriculi ſubijciuri ſedi, ac uenæ portæ diſtributionem ſimul cum arterijs neruiiſq hac excurrentibus ſuſtinet. Inſuper prætereiuſmodi uaſa, hic etiā ſim cum uenis ac arterijs ſor meſenterū diffuſe ſpectatur, totaſq figura ad primam in iecoris cauo ita eſt glutinanda, ut ſ p tus in utriſq figuris occurrentia ad uicem reſpondeat.

SEXTA figura uterum cum teſtibus ſ minalibuſq uaſis proponens, hot figuram ceterarum modo circunciſa erit, primæ ſubi in dextro latere et ſiniſtro iungetur, ubi urna arteriæq ſeminales ſimul coeunt & in ſiniſtro latere in primæ figure & ſexta ſpectatur. Quum hanc iungis, etiam SEP TIMA, quæ ueſicam ac umbilici uaſa ſimul cum meatu um urinam è renibus deferentium portionë eaſdem ſedi ad primam ita eſt conglutinanda, ut meatus illi ſeminarij uaſis ſubglut nerueri, ipſa autem ueſica utroru incumbat, proportioneq quâ poſita optimam hic obſeruans, quam uertū delineatio ac cont nutas facilē commonſtrant.

OCTAVA iecoris gibbæ ſedis eam portionem neat am core nens, quæ in anteriori corporis reg one ſpectant occurrit, à iecoris fiſſura reſer t, cui uena ab umbilico ducta inſeritur. Hanc itaq uelut ex puncto tantum, illic iecor in prima fi gura committes, ubi A inter F & ſ ſpectatur.

NONA uenæ peri carentis ſeriem oſten dēs, ad primæ figure tergum eſt committenda, ubi caua caudex uenam illam ſine coniuge promit, atq idſ t è tromptæ, ſt ad o nambabus figuris animi adh baeris.

DECIMA, quæ duas partes, ubi à ſuperflua papyro reſecta erit, conſtituet, ſuperiori ſede urnam ac arteriam dextri lateris delineatas continet: quæ ſub pectoris oſſe deorſum uexentes, ſuperio rem a dominis ſedem beet s. Hæc ſuo charactere q m ingulo ad primæ figure q glutinabitur. H aut m ad remum primæ figure, qui ad dextrum latus & m reſectus conſiſtitur. Humilior decimæ figuræ pars uaſa oſtendit n inferiorem abdominis ſedm excurrentia, quæ in bi ad primem figuræ ſunt com ttenda, ubi in dextro latere l iuxta uaſa crus petentia obuii eſt, illorumq uaſorum apparentium à Nunc primam figuram charta committes, cuæ ner uorum ſeriem proponit, t, leu negoc o obſeruabis quo ſitu ſingula ſint locanda, ſi mod s characterem indicem partiumq deſcriptionem operi adhibueris.

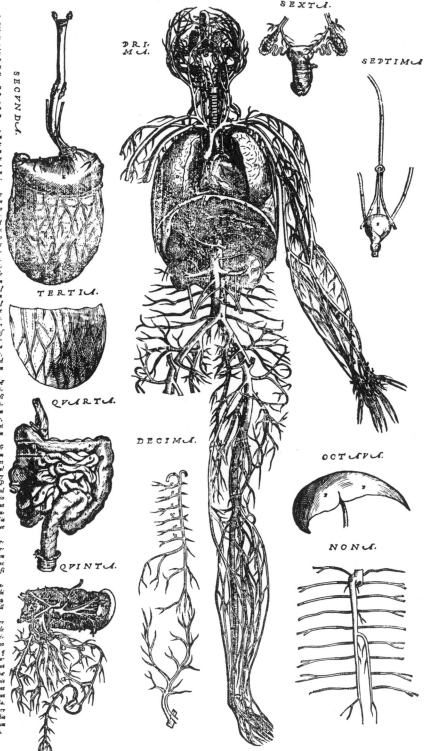